100

YEARS OF
'THE TRADE'

Edited by
Martin Edmonds

ISBN: 1-86220-106-4

First Published by CDISS, February 2001

Cover photographs with the kind permission of
BAE Systems

Cover designed by Vicky Bower
Text: 9.5pt on 10.5pt Palatino

Printed and bound by Pagefast Limited
4-6 Lansil Way · Caton Road · Lancaster LA1 3QY · UK
Telephone: 01524 841010
Fax: 01524 841578

Published by CDISS
Centre for Defence and International Security Studies

Cartmel College · Lancaster University
Lancaster LA1 4YL · United Kingdom

Telephone: 01524 594254
Fax: 01524 594258
Web site: http://www.cdiss.org

Contents

PART III: RN SUBMARINES & SUBMARINERS INTO THE 21ST CENTURY

PART IV: THE ROYAL NAVY & OVERSEAS SUBMARINE FORCES

PART V: SUBMARINE DESIGN, CONSTRUCTION & SUPPORT

PART VI: FUTURE SUBMARINE & UNDERWATER TECHNOLOGIES

Foreword

The Centenary of the Royal Navy Submarine Service in 2001 will provide a unique chance to celebrate 100 years of extraordinary technological advances together with the ingenuity, dedication and professional skill of Britain's submariners and the people who have designed, built and supported our submarines throughout the past century. Equally, it will offer an opportunity to commemorate the huge sacrifice made by submariners of all nations through two World Wars and 40 years of the Cold War.

I am therefore extremely grateful to the Centre for Defence and International Security Studies component of LYDRI, and to Professor Martin Edmonds in particular, for organising such a hugely successful conference at Lancaster University in September this year dedicated to the theme of the Royal Navy's Submarine Service and the submarine worldwide. Well attended by over 175 delegates from the academic, service and business communities of some 13 submarine operating nations, this landmark event with its wide ranging agenda, extending from the earliest days of "The Trade" through the present to our aspirations for the future, was clearly very well received.

What struck me in particular from the various pieces presented during the three days at Lancaster was the enduring determination of our submariners throughout the past 100 years to extend the broad utility of the submarine into all areas of warfare. It is clear that innovation, courage and huge personal commitment have always been and, I am glad to say, still remain the cornerstone of the Royal Navy Submarine Service and as an edited collection of Papers, this volume neatly captures both the spirit of the Conference and its sense of optimism for the future. As such, it is an important historical document; but it is more than that, it is also a fascinating read!

As we enter our Centenary Year, the Conference has provided an excellent springboard from which to go about setting the seal on the Submarine Service's first hundred years of achievement; and to start off our thinking about the next hundred years - a century in which I fully expect our submarines to remain where they have been almost continuously since their first inception: at the forefront of the Royal Navy's offensive power.

ADMIRAL SIR MICHAEL BOYCE GCB, OBE, ADC
Chief of Naval Staff and First Sea Lord

Preface

The origins of this book, and the conference on which it is based, go back to June 1999. The Centre for Defence and International Security Studies had just organised and hosted a conference on Maritime Contributions to Joint and Combined Operations (MJCO) when Captain Peter Hore RN, the Head of Defence Studies Royal Navy, asked if we would be prepared to take on a second assignment, the Royal Navy's Submarine Centennial Conference. Buoyed, possibly, by the success of the previous one, we immediately agreed, little thinking of the extent of the task, and responsibility, we had taken on.

The harsher reality became evident when Captain Hore came back a little later with a more specific brief: the conference, he said, had to be "authoritative, a celebration, and, because submariners say they never have any money, cheap". We wondered whether he had been taking his cue from the Smart Procurement Initiative ('faster, better, cheaper') but took him at his word. The three requirements proved initially to be somewhat contradictory: proper celebrations are expensive; and to get authoritative speakers would require generous support.

The solution was to seek generous sponsorship and in this respect the assistance afforded initially by GEC Marconi Marine and, subsequently, BAE SYSTEMS, enabled us to plan the conference and to allow some of our more extravagant ideas to develop. Not all our initiatives materialised. Regrettably, we were not able to bring to reality re-runs of the films 'Hunt for Red October', 'Das Boot', 'Above us the Waves', etc., authors, directors and film stars included, or secure contributions from the authors of such books as *HMS Unseen*, *Kilo Class*, or *Blind Man's Buff*, but we did try. Perhaps that was just as well, since the programme was a very full one, as the chapters of this volume bear testimony, and there would have been little time for literary 'diversions'. Those will likely happen during the Navy's Centennial Year, and in the many events that have been organised throughout 2001.

Identifying and securing the contributions of authoritative speakers soon proved to be no problem. Commander Jeff Tall, Director of the RN Submarine Museum, proved to be not only a mine of information, but also seemingly knew everyone who knew anything about submarines, past, present and future. Furthermore, and this says something about the sense of community and comradeship among submariners and those who study the submarine service, all those approached immediately agreed to participate. We were able, therefore, to assemble very quickly the very best and most authoritative submarine historians to start the conference.

The Office of Flag Officer Submarines (FOSM) gave the conference their full support and hence the part of the programme devoted to current defence naval policy, and the role of the Submarine Service in it, was soon covered. The conference industrial sponsors, (BAE SYSTEMS Marine, Rolls-Royce Marine, Strachan and Henshaw, and Devonport Management Limited) were each keen to explain how they were responding to the changed defence procurement environment and detail which new technologies, both with respect to the manufacture and construction of submarines and procurement processes, they were adopting and developing. With all that support, we knew that we could not go far wrong.

We were keen, however, that one hundred years of Royal Navy Submarine Service should not simply be a 'domestic' affair; for this reason, it was felt that representatives of submarine services overseas should be invited to join in the occasion and contribute. Again, the readiness of representatives from overseas Submarine Services to participate was very gratifying, and confirmed that the bond among submariners definitely transcends national boundaries.

This bond was manifest throughout the conference, but no more so than with the participation of Captain First Rank Igor Kurdin (standing in for Captain First Rank Igor Kosyr) from the St Petersburg Submariners Club in the Russian Federation. The conference took place some few weeks after the tragedy of the Russian submarine KURSK, so his participation gave an added poignancy to the occasion. The open way that he discussed the events surrounding the KURSK was deeply appreciated, and the genuine sympathy accorded by those present to him and, through him, to the families of the officers and men on board was evident.

Not included in the volume are other contributions that made the conference rather special. We have not been able to include the colourful submariners' "Dits from the back bar" from Commander Jeff Tall and Commodore Martin MacPherson (both of whom also contributed papers). Nor have we been able to add the speech after the conference banquet from Councillor Eric Thompson, former Commodore Clyde; his sensitively balanced speech combining rich entertainment with sober reflection of the sacrifices submariners have made over a century of courageous service could not have been bettered. Also absent are the generous comments of the First Sea Lord who gave time in a very busy schedule to preside at the conference banquet, though he has kindly contributed a foreword to this volume.

This book, however, is more than merely a repeat of the proceedings. Some new materials have been added and, in the light of the conference, its structure has been altered in several places to give it an overall coherence. I hope that those who read it will find its contents as moving, informing, fascinating, entertaining, enthralling and rewarding as did those of us fortunate enough to attend the conference.

MARTIN EDMONDS
Lancaster, November, 2000

Acknowledgements

This volume is the outcome of a conference entitled, "A Centennial Celebration of the Royal Navy's Submarine Service" held at the Lancaster University Conference Centre from September 27-29 2000. Those who helped make the conference possible, effectively have made this book possible, too. Each is gratefully acknowledged here.

The conference was primarily sponsored by BAE SYSTEMS Marine at Barrow-in-Furness with additional financial support from the Royal Navy Maritime Institute for Maritime Studies, Rolls-Royce Marine, Strachan and Henshaw, and Devonport Management Ltd. The banquet after-dinner speaker was generously sponsored by MITIE Lindsay of Glasgow. Neither the conference nor the book would have been possible without their generosity, for which grateful acknowledgement is accorded.

As a conference of that magnitude would not have been possible without financial backing, so also it would not have happened without the generous help, time and support of a number of people. Working closely with the sponsoring companies meant that the contributions of a number of individuals must be acknowledged. From BAE SYSTEMS, I would like to thank Peter Kenyon and Tony McGarry, for believing in the project at the start, Mike McIlroy for his graphics and exhibits, and most especially Marianne Buchanan for everything else, matters too numerous to mention here. Marie McFarlane of Rolls-Royce Marine, Tony Laker of Devonport Management Ltd and Jeff Owen from Strachan and Henshaw were our main, and always accommodating, contacts.

A special note of gratitude is due to Jeff Tall, Director of the Royal Navy Submarine Museum at Gosport. His unfailing optimism, unbounded enthusiasm, and encyclopaedic knowledge of all things to do with submarines and submariners was both a tonic to those of us unversed in these matters, a necessary reassurance, and a source of valuable information and contact. His contribution both to this volume and the conference should not be underestimated.

From the Navy, for whom and with whom the conference and this book were prepared, I must acknowledge first and foremost Captain Peter Hore for initiating the whole thing and for having confidence that we at Lancaster could do a decent job. Much of the planning, sound advice, and liaison with all other branches of the MoD and Navy was provided by Commander Paul Stanley RN. I regret that at the final count he was not able to participate and enjoy the fruits of his endeavours. Those, in fact, were left to Commander Mike Mason, his replacement at MISS, who gave essential and, at times, crucial assistance during the frenetic times before the day. Mrs Joyce Henderson on the Naval Defence Studies staff gave invaluable help throughout the year and especially with the detailed preparation immediately before the conference began.

From FOSM's Office, thanks also go to Commander Frank Worthington, who now has the additional task of preparing the Submarine Service's 2001 centennial year celebrations. The help of the Liverpool University Royal Naval Unit during the conference was extremely valuable, both in transporting delegates and hosting them on arrival. Our thanks go to their Commanding Officer, Lieutenant Rob Giles, RN.

During the conference, a number of people kindly allowed themselves to be persuaded to take the chair at the different sessions to whom our grateful thanks go for the commensurate and skilful way they managed the proceedings: Rear Admiral Rob Stevens, Captain Peter Wilkinson RN, Rear Admiral John Hervey, and Professor Bill Oliver.

Many people at Lancaster helped make the conference 'work': John Adams, Hilary Barraclough, Janet Clements, Neville Horner, John Stewart, Drew Wallace and Steve Watson. For a spectacular banquet, the services of Phil Rhodes of Karen Rhodes Catering Ltd have to go on record. It scarcely seems credible, however, but at Lancaster there was only a small core team of people who worked on the project. The person who carried the lion's share of the organisational, financial and bureaucratic burden throughout was Pauline Elliott, the Executive Secretary of CDISS, and on whom much of the sub-editorial and preparation of this book also fell. Without her nothing would have been possible; my thanks, and those of the sponsors, to her are boundless. She was ably assisted with many of the time-consuming, but necessary chores, by Stewart Fraser, Sandy Edwards, Jairo Lugo and Tim Ripley and to them also I extend my gratitude.

MARTIN EDMONDS
Co-Director, Lancaster and York Defence Research Institute

List of Illustrations

Introduction

Flag Officer Submarines, Rear Admiral Rob Stevens

This volume is based on the papers that were presented at the Conference to celebrate one hundred years of submarine service that was held at Lancaster University on September 27-29 2000. By way of introduction, my objective is the same as it was at the Conference itself, namely to provide a chart upon which it is possible to plot the course of the book. I want therefore to give an idea of where we in the Royal Navy Submarine Service are heading in the future. I want also to describe what we have been getting up to in the last twelve months and to give a flavour of modern submarine business from my perspective as Flag Officer Submarines (FOSM).

But, as with any attempt at Navigation, one needs a departure fix; so, I also intend to touch on our illustrious past. But before I do, I want to thank Professor Martin Edmonds and Mrs Pauline Elliott at the Centre for Defence and International Security Studies - as well as the key Sponsors BAE SYSTEMS Marine, Rolls Royce Naval Marine, Strachan and Henshaw, MITIE Lindsay, Devonport Management Limited and the Royal Navy - for putting together a fascinating and varied programme. The Conference was a wonderfully timely event and will serve as a valuable prelude to the 2001 Centenary Year; and this book that has emerged from the proceedings is a welcome contribution to the year's activities.

And what a first 100 years it has been. It is one that has witnessed the massive technological leap in underwater technology from the Sinn Fein-designed 'Holland' to the final 'Vanguard' Class SSBNs (HMS VENGEANCE) and the incredibly successful Trident missile firing in September 2000. For all of these impressive technological achievements, however, let nobody forget the sacrifices that underpin those successes.

The recent KURSK tragedy has again served to underline the danger of submarining. Equally though, it also highlights the enormous camaraderie and bond that exists between and among the world's submarine community. This camaraderie was evident during the disaster itself, but I have particularly noticed it in the aftermath. The unsolicited collections co-ordinated through the Royal Navy Submarine Museum for the families and relatives of those who died in the KURSK tragedy to the concerns expressed during the NATO Escape and Rescue exercise in September 2000, in Turkey, are all moving examples of the bond between us all. And I feel that international flavour of this conference is further evidence of that bond.

But enough of how special we are; I would now like to describe where we are all headed.

The Royal Navy's Submarine Service's past successes, unflinching courage and the bond between all of us could, if not properly harnessed, be the cause of our downfall as well. Our tactical and technological victory in the Cold War could lead us to think that the operational concept of covert independent operations was the only way to go. On this note, independent anti-submarine warfare (ASW) operations are but one part of our capability. The integrated operations with the carrier, the intelligence gathering Special Forces and the Tomahawk missile capability are all key ingredients in the maritime contribution to joint operations. If we do not improve on all our capabilities we could fall into the trap of complacency. This was a point made by Mr Richard Danzig, US Secretary of the Navy, when he drew the analogy that the submariners were like Narcissus; we are so busy admiring our own reflection in the water that we are in danger of failing to see the world developing around us and eventually we too could wither and die.

Of course, we must build on our proven skills of anti-submarine (AS) and anti surface ship (ASS) warfare; but we must also integrate these skills into joint and task group operations so effectively as to make the submarine indispensable to the Joint Commander. The key to this, of course, is discrete instant communications. This is an area in which we in the Royal Navy must really improve if we are to break away from the unsatisfactory twelve-hour delay that the submarine broadcast interval brings into any Joint Commander's calculations. Until we make this transition, we in the Submarine Service will not be able to take advantage of the information revolution and make the submarine truly 'joint'.

Healthy scepticism has always been a feature of submarine life; so, for those who doubt that I practise what I preach, the Royal Navy Submarine Service is already notching up a number of successes in the four areas of core submarine capability that are assuming increasing importance. Our third TLAM boat, HMS TRAFALGAR, is just completing work up; HMS TRIUMPH recently completed TLAM integrated with the US Fleets in the Gulf and the Mediterranean; and, of course, we all know of HMS SPLENDID's successes during the Kosovo crisis.

At the same time, during my two years as Flag Officer Submarines, (FOSM), we have conducted twelve operations of various kinds covering the whole spectrum of operations that I have already mentioned. Furthermore, we have integrated our SSBN force into a wider role than just SSBN duties. On the technological front, we are moving forward in our attempts to put commercial off-the-shelf processes into legacy systems. We are looking at some innovative techniques to ensure our 'S' and 'T' Classes remain as available as possible whilst attempting to reduce the through-life costs and bring a little rationality (without undermining our excellent safety record) into nuclear safety cases. The 'Astute' Class submarine is on track for delivery in 2005 and here is real hope of funding to improve our satellite communications systems.

This leads me very nicely to the final day of the conference the papers of which are concerned with submarine design construction and technology, and the future. Here there is an array of talent from the major industries and support areas who look ahead and consider how we might overcome some of today's technological limitations and harness the information revolution of tomorrow.

The Royal Navy Submarine Service has come a long way since Admiral of the Fleet, Lord Fisher, wrote to Winston Churchill in 1913 stating that "the submarine command cannot capture the merchant ship; she has no spare hands onboard to put a prize crew onboard; she cannot convoy her into harbour. There is nothing else the submarine can do except sink her capture. This is freely acknowledged to be an altogether barbarian method of warfare, (but) the essence of war is violence and moderation in war is imbecility". Neither Churchill nor his advisors were prepared to accept this vision and Fisher's successor as First Sea Lord said that the suggestion of such "barbarity" marred an otherwise brilliant paper. By 1917, though, Walter H Page, the US Ambassador to Britain, had already started to write that "the submarine was the most formidable thing that war has produced - by far". Looking at the Submarine Flotilla today from HMS VENGEANCE to HMS SPARTAN that vision of 'barbarity' has matured into the whole spectrum of deterrence, and the Royal Navy's Submarine Service is at the heart of it.

They had the right vision. It is my sincere hope that, as we approach a new century of submarine operations in the Royal Navy, we too have the vision to see the wider utility of the submarine. As we look forward to receiving the papers presented at this Conference on one of the most formidable things that war has produced - the submarine (and ultimately the SSBN) - we can also develop our vision for the future.

PART I

GENESIS & EARLY YEARS
OF 'THE TRADE'

1

For, 'tis Private – the Submarine Pioneers

Richard Compton-Hall

The submarine is an Irish invention. This is why we are celebrating the centenary of USS HOLLAND (SS-1) together with HM Submarine TORPEDO BOAT No1 (the 'Holland 1'), both named after its founding father from County Clare and, latterly, New Jersey, USA.

But there have been plenty of well-publicised underwater pioneers besides the quirky little quondam monk, of whom more later on; but was John Holland alone in getting it right? I used to think the early stories were vaguely credible until I put them under the harsh light of experience with midget submarines. You get a bit adjacent to submarine principles in those.

It turns out that pioneering theories were not far off the mark; but tales of early submersibles are mostly a load of old wives' tales.

In order of appearance, the first was William Bourne (1535-83), a 'poore gunner' in the Elizabethan navy. He described "...a Ship or Boate that may goe under the water unto the bottome" (to surprise hapless Spaniards) and redefined Archimedes's ablutionary discovery as follows:

> ...any body that is in the water, if that the quantity in bignesse, hauing alwaies but one weight, may bee made bigger or lesser, then it shall swimme when you would, and sinke when you list.

Although Bourne did nothing practical and apologised for writing a "rude and barbarous volume...the writer being most unlearned and simple", it was a quite extraordinary admission for a gunnery officer.

The next on stage was the Dutchman, Drebbel. This archetypal defence sales con-artist recognised James I as the perfect 'punter'. The King watched Drebbel's prototype war galley that was intended for sinking 'enemy ships lying safely at anchor' while twelve oarsmen rowed it down the Thames in about 1620. In 1662, 28 years after Drebbel died, Robert Boyle (of 'Boyle's Law') wrote glowingly about this "...vessel to go under water, of which trial was made...with admired success", but there is not a scrap of evidence to show that it submerged.

A leather-covered barge, however, may have been weighted until the crew was below the surface and sheltered from missiles. The chief marvel for Boyle was "to make men, unaccustomed, to continue underwater [as technically they were] for so long without suffocation". He extolled Drebbel's "chymicall liquor which...[would] speedily restore to the troubled air...vitall parts as would againe for a good while be fit for respiration". Liquor it may have been - distilled in Holland, no doubt - but oxygen it was not. Probably it emitted sufficiently strong fumes to overcome the stench of a dozen sweating London labourers, which leaves Drebbel an originator of the air freshener, not the submarine!

Meanwhile, in the 1630s a couple of French priests published their concept of a submarine gunboat: Abbé Borelli suggested goatskins for internal ballast tanks thereby changing weight rather than size; and Abbé de Hautefeuille set himself up as a submarine commentator. In 1648, Oliver Cromwell's brother-in-law, John Wilkins, a Doctor of Divinity and future Bishop of Chester, envisaged "... an Ark for submarine navigation" about which Wilkins, a founder of the Royal Society and prominent Freemason, was uncannily prescient:

> *"'Tis private 'tis safe from the uncertainty of Tides and the violence of Tempests [and] from Pirates and Robbers which do so infest other voyages; from ice and great frosts which do so much endanger the passages towards the Poles…" and "…a Navy of enemies…by this means may be undermined."*

Moreover, he foresaw "noisome and offensive things that must be thrust out", anticipating crucial underwater plumbing.

Clergymen have greatly influenced submarine development. This long association with the Church may well account for the quiet, devout, almost mystical demeanour that so clearly distinguishes submariners from, say, gunnery officers.

Yet Wilkins, for one, gave no thought to sea-pressure. John Day was the first to find out about that, but the hard way. Heavy bets were laid on his survival, or otherwise, when he went down in a wooden box aboard the sloop MARIA that was deliberately sunk in 22 fathoms outside Plymouth on 20 June, 1774. The gambling First Lord of the Admiralty, Lord Sandwich - he of the eponymous snack at a gaming table - wagered on a happy outcome. He lost, which boded ill for submarine support at head office.

Two years later, during the American War of Independence, the most enduring of all pioneering legends was created with David Bushnell as its hero. Bushnell discovered that a gunpowder charge was more effective exploded in water than in air and so he devised a one-man submersible, known as the TURTLE, to carry destruction to the enemy.

In the summer of 1776, a British armada anchored in the approaches to New York City, making life difficult for General Washington's forces. However, (according to received history) TURTLE was at hand to frighten off the foe.

This one-man midget submersible had (it says here) a brass conning tower with glass ports; muscle-powered propellers for horizontal and vertical propulsion; a valve for admitting ballast water to the bilge and a hand-pump for ejecting it; a luminescent depth gauge and compass; and an auger at the top, worked from inside the craft for screwing a back-pack explosive device into a wooden hull from below. This remarkable weapon system was reputedly completed in less than seven months by two farmers, working intermittently without boat-building facilities on an isolated beach of the Connecticut River.

At 11pm on 6 September 1776 (continuing the legend) a volunteer crewman, Sgt Ezra Lee, set off from Manhattan to attack Admiral 'Black Dick' Howe's flagship, HMS EAGLE, lying off Staten Island. But Lee was unable to screw home the auger. Copper sheathing was blamed, although Bushnell thought the sergeant had continually struck an iron rudder-strap and should have moved along to try again. Eventually, Lee called it a night and wended his way home. Nevertheless, Bushnell believers insist that TURTLE's attempt forced Howe's ships to cut their cables and retreat in cowardly fashion, depicted as typical British behaviour and recently portrayed in the historical film "The Patriot".

It is true that a 'water machine' was contemplated by some of the finest colonial minds among whom was Benjamin Franklin. Almost all were Freemasons, like

Brother George Washington, implying a mutual trust, confidentiality and access to technology in Europe. However, although submergible hardware may have been planned, the story handed down is the stuff of legend and, in fact, plain nonsense.

Apart from improbable construction claims:

- HMS EAGLE was anchored close to where the Statue of Liberty now stands and not off Staten Island where troop transports lay. Standing orders for Marines on guard were meticulous: no suspicious activity could have gone undetected. Entries in EAGLE's three official journals note 'Flatt boats', flags of truce, minor ship movements and the infliction on Samuel Kingston, Seaman, of twelve lashes for drunkenness at 12pm on the 6th - but nothing unusual.
- EAGLE was not coppered until 1782; and Lee would not have struck the same strap repeatedly in a tideway.
- Washington later said of Bushnell "He never did succeed…although it (the TURTLE) was an effort of genius". Lee kept quiet for forty years and by the end of that time he was understandably vague.
- TURTLE, with an unmeasured quantity of water sloshing around the bilge, could not have achieved neutral buoyancy. If, miraculously, Lee had been able to place his craft beneath the target, TURTLE would have been pushed *down* when the auger endeavoured to push *up*.
- Bushnell let loose 'infernal devices' or floating mines to 'annoy' the British off New London and down the Delaware River between 1778 and 1780 and then became an Army Engineer. He disappeared to the state of Georgia in the late 1780s and changed his name to Dr David Bush, an act that was hardly the action of a triumphant submarine constructor.

The chances are that the TURTLE, myth or bluff, originated in the New Haven Masonic Lodge where Craft Fellows hugged themselves with laughter at the thought of deterring the British by leaking word of a terrifying mini-monster. In the event, 'Black Dick' was not in the least deterred and he was soon sending ships up the Hudson River itself.

Another American, Robert Fulton (1765-1815), followed hard on Bushnell's elusive heels and, theoretically, improved on TURTLE which he did not recognise as fictional. Fulton was a brilliant engineer (he had some Irish blood) but his dramatic shifts of allegiance as a would-be arms supplier during the Napoleonic Wars to France, the Netherlands and Great Britain, before returning to the United States, earned him nothing but odium.

Fulton professed a concern for the freedom of the seas. He advocated getting rid of navies by the threat of 'plunging boats' and 'torpedoes', a policy that was welcomed by the United States, where warships were barely affordable, and by the French, who were perpetually confronted by a persistently more powerful Royal Navy.

Eventually, Fulton extracted money from the French Directory for his copper-skinned NAUTILUS, a vessel some 21ft long and 6ft broad, that was built in Paris and propelled by a two-bladed, hand-cranked propeller that Fulton called a 'flyer'. There was a collapsible sailing rig for when the boat was on the surface.

Launched in May 1800, NAUTILUS made her debut in the Seine. Like Drebbel, Fulton used the current to make it appear that the vessel had a fair turn of speed. His displays were always expertly spin-doctored, and onlookers cheered; but NAUTILUS was not fully submerged, even though Fulton might have dipped momentarily, having judiciously flooded the three ballast tanks to a pre-determined level and adjusted his three-position horizontal rudders aft (an undeniable first). Although these rudders would have had scant effect when maximum speed through the water was no more than one or two knots - and that only for so long as two musclemen held out - NAUTILUS did, nevertheless, sit safely on the bottom at 7 metres in the port of Brest, for one hour.

Armament was initially a spike attached to a magazine (similar to Bushnell's weapon system) but this was changed to a towed 'carcass' when the inventor realised that NAUTILUS would never be controllable under water and that attacks would have to be conducted on the surface. On 1 October 1801, preliminaries for a (short-lived) peace with England were agreed, whereupon Napoleon's advisers lost interest in underwater warfare, although France would invest heavily in *les sous-marins* towards the end of the century.

Meanwhile, Fulton had already sold NAUTILUS for scrap – so much for his faith in the submarine! Then, after a rejected pass at the Dutch government, he went to England under the name of Mr Francis and was quite successful in selling 'submarine bombs' and floating mines (still called 'torpedoes') to Prime Minster Pitt, before returning to America in late 1806 to badger President Jefferson into adopting torpedo tactics. However, he built no more submarines.

We can step quickly past the bad-tempered Bavarian NCO, Wilhelm Bauer (1822-75); although he made 134 dives in the SEETEUFEL ('Sea Devil') built for Russia, there is nothing to suggest that the boat did anything other than to go to the bottom and up again, quickly or slowly depending on the state of ballast. It could well be, however, that the convict-style treadmill propulsion enabled SEETEUFEL to slither across the seabed if in reasonable trim, something that other nineteenth-century inventors managed similarly.

Then came war, always a technological stimulus. The American Civil War (1861-65) found a Federal fleet blockading Charleston, a principal port for supplying the South. Striving gallantly to break the blockade, a tiny steam launch, very low in the water and bearing a lance-like 20ft spar torpedo, severely damaged the 3,486-ton USS IRONSIDES on 5 October 1863. The 'David' escaped to tell the tale even though the captain and fireman were hurled overboard when backwash poured down the funnel. Thirteen bullet holes were found in the superstructure, but none was below the waterline. The idea of putting the vitals of a boat under water – Drebbel's idea originally – was thus proved sound in action.

All the same, a boat with very low freeboard was at risk of being flooded unless the entire hull was sealed, so one might as well build a proper submersible. Accordingly, the 'diving machine', CSS HUNLEY, took shape in 1863. The thirty-foot cylindrical pressure hull (created from a boiler) had a squat conning tower at each end for the captain and his first officer, and a bench for eight crewmen who rotated a longitudinal crank to turn the propeller. The initial method of attack, feasible in still waters, was to tow a horned torpedo mine under an enemy keel. If the open-topped ballast-cum-compensating tanks forward and aft, each with a flood valve and pump, were filled to precisely the right level, the craft could dive at up to 2.5 knots. Presumably, by setting the forward 'side-fins' first to 'down' and then, after a calculated interval, to 'up', it seems that HUNLEY could glide down to about twenty feet before returning to the surface. There is no record, however, of her maintaining a particular depth and she had no periscope. Instead, a catenary sufficed for the tactic envisaged.

Two disasters ensued. One resulted, when coming alongside, from the captain treading on the hydroplane lever whilst leaning over to grab a mooring rope and tilting both open hatches under water. Salvage, sixteen days later, called for "a half box of soap... and six brushes for scrubbing" to be requisitioned from Army stores.

On 1 October 1863, Lt George E Dixon of the Alabama Infantry was appointed to command what was becoming known as 'The Murdering Machine' or, more pointedly, 'The Peripatetic Coffin'. He soon got the hang of it, but on 15 October, the rich, but inexperienced, Horace L Hunley, after whom the craft was named, took the submarine out himself, probably to instil confidence in the second crew. Alas, he fumbled the drill: the boat plunged up to its side fins in the clinging mud of the Cooper River 50ft below the surface.

The iron hull was again raised rather more than three weeks later. Inside, "the spectacle was indescribably ghastly". The forward flooding valve was wide open and the wrench that turned it was lying in the bilge. The after tank had been pumped dry, presumably by the first officer breathing in an air pocket at one-and-a-half atmospheres until carbon dioxide poisoning and lack of oxygen killed him. It had not, of course, been possible to open the hatch against four tons of water.

This time, it took ten black slaves with scrubbing brushes, soap and a barrel of lime to clean out the boat. Dixon had to recruit a third crew; but the rewards offered by Charleston merchants for destroying Union blockade vessels were so great that men came forward willingly. On the evening of 17 February 1864, Dixon stealthily steered for the wooden steam sloop-of-war HOUSATONIC two-and-a-half miles offshore. It is fair to suppose that he promised the replacement crew that he would not dive unless forced to do so. In any case, the towed charge had been replaced by a spar torpedo. There was no need, therefore, to attack whilst submerged, and circumstantial evidence suggests that HUNLEY did not do so.

At 8.45pm, a lookout on HOUSATONIC sighted something on the starboard beam; then, almost immediately, there was a violent explosion. The jinxed assailant and her victim sank together. The HUNLEY, tomb of her brave Confederate crew, was found in 1995 and raised, for restoration, in the summer of 2000.

Next in line is Commander the Reverend George W Garrett, Pasha BA (1852-1902), the supreme master of Victorian hype. Garrett was ordained curate to his father, the Anglican vicar of Moss Side Church, Manchester, in 1877 when the latter needed a low-paid assistant. However, Deacon George's parochial attention was focused on enabling people to breathe under water (preferably with his own 'Pneumatophore' invention) and/or sinking ships by means of torpedoes carried on 'subaqueous vessels'.

Garrett Senior did not demur. Backed by the Rev. Norman Mcleod, Chaplain to Her Majesty, he explained that "as to [submarines] being for murdering people - this is all nonsense…..". He had no clerical qualms about becoming Chairman of the Garrett Submarine Navigation and Pneumatophore Co. Ltd and incorporated by five trusting Mancunian businessmen with a capital of £10,000.

George promptly built a 4-ton experimental ovoid (the 'Curate's Egg', of course) and expanded, in 1879, to his 30-ton RESURGAM, optimistically meaning 'I shall rise again'. Maybe one day she will, because the wreck was located in 1997 off the coast of North Wales.

RESURGAM, which was lost in February 1880 whilst under tow to Portsmouth for naval evaluation, had a "Lamm's fireless locomotive" power-plant that could propel her at 2 or 3 knots for about 4 hours without air. Apart from being watertight and having 'side rudders' amidships, however, she had no submarine attributes and, practically speaking, she could never have dived deliberately.

Garrett was later financed by the armament tycoon, Thorsten Nordenfelt, for ambitious all-steam submarine deals with Greece, Turkey and Russia. None succeeded, not least because the long, thin vessels, with downhaul propellers for clawing them under water were terrifyingly unstable longitudinally.

Late nineteenth-century French inventors, reviving the challenge to *la perfide Albion* at sea, also favoured steam, but sensibly installed electric motors for short-haul trips and submergence. Significant contributions to subsequent development were Maxime Laubeuf's double hull, which eventually led to saddle tanks for main ballast and hydroplanes forward as well as aft. By 1901, the respected *Engineer*

7

journal, however, was remarking "…those who most favour the submarine boat…do not pin their faith on France".

Why, despite courage and determination, did all these early pioneers fail? First, because they did not go fast enough for submerged control; and, second, because (except for Bauer who was defeated by lack of speed) they tried to dive, surface and change depth on a level keel instead of pitching down or up.

Simple; but it was going to need an Irishman to get it right!

2

British Submarine Policy from St Vincent to Arthur Wilson

Peter Hore

Robert Fulton came to London to study as an artist under Benjamin West. Gradually, he turned to mechanics and engineering and, by 1800, we find him trying to interest the French government in a submarine to sink the blockading British fleet. The vessel he demonstrated, the NAUTILUS, folded its mast and sail flat and, with a three-man crew cranking a screw, submerged, allegedly, to about 25ft. The French were sceptical and Fulton returned to London in 1803 to try to sell his ideas there. The grosser history books will claim that the British showed no interest either. The truth is that the American, Fulton, collaborated with the British for at least three years and the British participated enthusiastically in his experiments and operations.

In one experiment, Fulton successfully demonstrated his submarine weapons by blowing up a captured 200 ton Danish brig, DORETHEA, thoughtfully provided by the Admiralty, a demonstration witnessed by "...the major of the officers of the fleet under the command of Lord Keath (sic)...", including three of the more inquisitive minds of their age, Home Popham,[1] Sidney Smith[2] and William Congreve - famous for his rockets. The ungrateful Fulton, however, alleged that, when interviewed by Earl St Vincent,[3] the great man had said that, "...Pitt was the greatest fool that ever existed, to encourage a mode of war which they who commanded the seas did not want, and which, if successful, would deprive them of it..."[4]

Quite remarkably, these alleged words, or rather a close approximation of them, were quoted in an Admiralty board minute nearly a hundred years later:[5] Arthur Wilson,[6] it is alleged, said that submarines were underhand, unfair and damned un-English, and that submariners should be hanged as pirates.

Some commentators generally found British attitudes - and especially the British Navy's - towards submarines and, indeed, all innovations reflected in these two doubtful statements. What I hope to demonstrate in this chapter is that the history of the introduction of the submarine into service with the British Navy is an exemplary case history of a pragmatic and successful policy towards new technology. The Navy, in fact, had a 'wait-and-see' policy towards technology, with two distinct strands to it.

First, (thought his quotation refers to 'Ironclads') there was a clear understanding that:

> "...it is not in the interest of Great Britain possessing as she does so large a navy to adopt any important change in the construction of ships of war which might have the effect of rendering necessary the introduction of a new class of very costly vessels until such a course is forced upon her... it then becomes a matter not only of expediency but of absolute necessity..."[7]

Second, as 'Jacky' Fisher[8] made clear, when the moment of necessity had arrived, "...[Britain] cannot afford any foreign power to possess any type of war vessel superior to her own...". This policy was remarkably effective in the case of the submarine. Starting with a policy of 'wait-and-see' during all of the 19th Century when the technology was unready, by 1914 Britain had 3,000 submariners in an all-volunteer force, 16 depot ships at six bases, and the largest and most modern fleet of submarines, 72 in all.[9]

The Navy achieved this by keeping itself spectacularly well informed of what was happening in the world of submarine invention. This started with Robert Fulton, who after his rejection by the French, came to Britain in 1803 and met both Lord Melville,[10] First Lord of the Admiralty, and Pitt, the Prime Minister. The three men signed a secret agreement under which Fulton was paid £200 a month for the exclusive right to his inventions.[11] He was given £7,000 to finance his experiments and he was to be rewarded £40,000 for sinking his first French line of battle ship, and half the value of each ship thereafter. In the agreement, Fulton was described as "...citizen of the United states of America and inventor of a plan of attacking fleets by submarine Bombs..." In one clause, Fulton claimed to have deposited plans with a confidential agent, plans that would be released to the United States in the event of his death. However, in the agreement with Pitt and Melville, Fulton agreed not to disclose his plans for fourteen years.

Home Popham was nominated to be the Admiralty's representative to whom Fulton was to disclose his ideas. In fact, apparently in breach of his agreement, Fulton's own account of his second stay in Britain, called *Torpedo War and Submarine Explosions*, was published in America in 1810. Perhaps it is not surprising that, in the rising tide of anti-British feeling leading to the War of 1812, Fulton chose to emphasise the deterrent effect which knowledge of his weapons would have on the Royal Navy. He also played down somewhat his own enthusiastic collaboration with a foreign government.[12]

Ten years later, the Second Lord Melville,[13] like his father before him and also First Lord of the Admiralty, reached another secret agreement, this time with Captain Thos Johnson. The agreement is very reminiscent in its terms and payment by results of that which had been struck between Melville's father and Robert Fulton. Johnson proposed to destroy the French fleet by submarine attack using a boat which he had built "... of wrought iron and capable of containing three men... that I can plunge her to any depth I like under water and remain there for twelve hours..." [14] However, once the war was over, Melville dropped his support of Johnson including Johnson's claims for recompense (sic) for his personal outlay on his invention.

Between the end of the war in 1815 and 1900, the Admiralty examined over 300 submarine inventions, each of which was carefully considered for its various merits.[15] Watch was kept on the submarine achievements of principal rivals, such as France, Turkey and Russia, and some less likely navies such as those of Sweden and even Bavaria. The Navy knew, for instance, that the French had used a submarine, or bell, on the construction of the breakwater at Cherbourg in 1846.[16] During the Russian War of 1854-56, there were British trials of a primitive bottom-crawling, man-powered submarine conducted by John Scott Russell. Russell was using ideas he had derived from Wilhelm Bauer, while Bauer himself tried to interest the Russians in his own ideas.[17] Another typical example was the stream of high grade intelligence sent home between 1860 and 1871 by Captain Edward George Hore, the naval attaché in Paris (in those days he was the only attaché anywhere and was supposed to cover the whole of Europe). These reports included eyewitness reports of the trials of the French submarine LE PLONGEUR off Rochefort in 1862.[18]

Two noteworthy episodes of intelligence gathering concern the United States of America. In the Civil War, the Confederate States Navy had built at least four submarines, one of which, the HUNLEY, sank the USS HOUSATONIC off Charleston, South Carolina on the night of 17 February 1864. At least one Confederate submarine was subsequently captured by the Federal government and taken to the New York Navy Yard. There, it was allowed to rust away but not before Rear Admiral Inglefield, the British naval attaché in Washington, had gone to New York to inspect the vessel. In March 1872, Inglefield took the Superintendent of the Navy Yard and his deputy out to lunch and later returned to the yard and gained entry "...by a process it is unnecessary (to embarrass their Lordships) to describe..."[19] Later that day, Inglefield frantically wrote up his report and sketches of the boat invented by Mr McClintock of Mobile he had seen, but these do not appear to have survived.

However, McClintock himself was smuggled to Halifax, Nova Scotia, in October 1872 and there he was debriefed by onboard HMS ROYAL ALFRED, the flagship of the North America Station. The flag captain, Nicholson, and the Chief Engineer of the Fleet, Ellis, recorded that "...we are of the opinion that Mr McClintock's boat is capable of performing all that he promises for her..." The drawings which McClintock made are now in the Public Record Office, though recent research shows that the submarine he sketched was an idealised design which drew on his experience of previous boats.[20] McClintock was paid £50 for his pains from secret service money by the British Consul in Mobile, but a scheme to bring McClintock to London in1873 fell through because he could not afford to travel and the Foreign Office – which controlled the secret fund - refused to pay!

Nevertheless, the Admiralty's watch on submarine developments continued. In 1886, Captain Samuel Long proposed that a committee be formed to assess developments in the submarine boat.[21] Characteristically, Charles Beresford, as fourth Naval Lord, put himself in charge of an impromptu committee and went to investigate the capability of another submarine, also called NAUTILUS, a private venture which was being built on the Thames. For the public trials of this vessel, Captain Lord Charles Beresford, a junior Naval Lord, Sir William White, the Director of Naval Construction, and Captain Eardley-Wilmot embarked in the West India Dock, "..before a party of about 130 ladies and gentlemen...who [had been] conveyed in special train to witness further trials in the deep-water dock..."[22] The descent was not only into the darkness but also into chaos. The NAUTILUS stuck in the glutinous mud at the bottom of the dock, and the captain of the craft suffered a heart attack.

For about 15mintues, three senior naval officers, who to say the least were unfamiliar with the working of any submarine, considered what to do, until Beresford, the Fourth Naval Lord, and White, the Director of Naval Construction, took off their coats and ordered Eardley-Wilmot, the Director on Naval Operations, to join them in flinging themselves from side to side of the NAUTILUS. It worked, and the NAUTILUS bobbed to surface to the applause of the ladies and gentlemen who were unaware that they had nearly witnessed the death of one of the British Navy's more flamboyant characters. Not surprisingly, when invited the following year to witness the diving trials of the NORDENFELT IV in Southampton Water, Beresford expressed himself much interested but otherwise engaged in London.[23] Incidentally, the NORDENFELT IV was built at Barrow and her arrival at Spithead and trials in May 1887 were witnessed by one Captain Arthur Wilson, then Assistant Director of Torpedoes.[24] White was no more impressed by the NORDENFELT IV than he had been by the NAUTILUS, and the Admiralty rejected Long's proposal on the grounds that "...the development of submarine boats had not reached a stage to render a (special committee) necessary..."[25]

Once, however, the French had perfected the GUSTAVE ZEDE, and the Americans had built several 'Holland' boats, the first Lord of the Admiralty, Goschen remarked, "... I have read the whole of these papers most carefully, they are not pleasant for clearly great strides are being made in the submarine boat..."[26] but "...our want is a design."[27] France had taken six years to perfect the hydroplanes of the GUSTAVE ZEDE and was unlikely to sell her designs. But America was another matter. The American Navy was actually unenthusiastic about the submarine and their commercial rivalries ruled. [28]

Although the Holland boats had some defects, they were not so great, as reported Captain Ottley the Naval Attaché in Washington, that they could not easily be rectified by British naval expertise.[29] Thus, the purchase of the first Holland boats had a clear intention:"...it would give substantial advantage in point of assured and immediate success, since we [will] profit by all the [25] years of work and experiments on actual vessels which Mr Holland has performed...".[30] Five boats were ordered[31] and the Admiralty felt confident that it could rely on superior industrial capacity to out-design and "...the pluck and resource of the British Sailor..." to out-build and out-perform all rivals...".

It was given out that the purchase was to enable the fleet to gain experience of operating against submarines; having purchased the boats, however, and gained the technical advantage, this purpose soon changed. The submarine building programme was pursued in some secrecy until about 1908 with few details appearing in the press whose readers were otherwise fascinated by details of the design, armour and armament of battleships. British designs soon outstripped French and American submarines. The improvements to the 'Holland' boats, drawing from many sources such as the Italian designs of Laurenti, included the double hull that did away with cumbersome and ineffective saddle-tanks and the early adoption of the diesel engine that gave the British 'A' and 'B' Class submarines after 1903 substantial autonomous range. The 'wait-and-see policy' was well vindicated.

Meanwhile, Britain's naval rivals were losing interest in the possibilities of submarine war. The French were enthusiastic submariners but did not develop their ideas consistently: starting in 1885, France had experimented with 28 different types of submersible and submarine vessels and 19 of these were in service in 1914. Only two types had been produced in series: 20 tiny diesel driven NAIADES for harbour defence and 34 steam-powered PLUMAIRES, perhaps intended to dominate the South China Sea. France at one stage actually cancelled her submarine programme in favour of semi-submersible vessels.[32]

In Germany, Admiral Tirpitz denounced submarines in 1904 as only local and secondary weapons and refused to take part in what he described as a museum of experiments. Germany did not build her first submarine until 1906 and no more until 1908.[33] As late as 1914, various officers felt Tirpitz's wrath for supporting what he dismissed as *kleinkreig* (little war).[34] His subsequent statements after the First World War would appear to contain a great deal of post-rationalisation and self-justification: "I refused," he claimed, "To throw away money on submarines so long as they could only cruise in home waters. As soon as sea-going boats were built, however, I was the first to encourage them on a large scale."[35] Germany even preferred the paraffin engine for submarines until 1910, the sparks making German submarines more visible by night than by day.[36] Eventually, the German submarines which might have helped Germany win the First World War were built from a design by a Spaniard who adapted French ideas to a Russian specification.[37]

Most notably, by the outbreak of the First World War, there had been no strategic development whatsoever in Germany. Submarines might be strung out in a line across the North Sea as a defence against the British Grand Fleet, but the descent by Keyes's British submarines on the German coast was totally unforeseen. The Japanese, who had built seven boats for the Russo-Japanese War, acquired no more until 1907-8. And the Americans, who had failed to develop their lead in submarine technology for want of a strategic and tactical concept for the submarine, banished their small submarine fleet to the Pacific Ocean.

By contrast, the submarine was introduced into wargames at Greenwich in 1901[38] , and Roger Keyes had formed a committee of junior officers to develop and advise upon the use of submarines…[39] By 1906, the Royal Navy had 20 submarines and was building new boats at the rate of 6 per year. Production, which had been confined to the remote Vickers yard at Barrow-in-Furness, was expanded into the Royal Dockyard at Chatham. The submarine building programme, 84 'A', 'B' and 'C' Class boats in all between 1901 and 1914, is reminiscent of similar efforts that Britain made in its gunboat-building programme in the previous century. A squadron of three 'C' Class submarines had shown their capability for worldwide use by deploying to Hong Kong in 1911.[40] Perhaps one failure was not to see earlier the possibility of offensive submarine warfare, a fact that is all the more remarkable because Holland himself, in a hand-written note preserved in the archives, had described in detail how submarines could be used to attack the enemy in his home ports, and just as the Navy had used Fulton's submarines to attack the French at Boulogne.

The Admiralty had patiently maintained a policy of 'wait-and-see' for nearly a hundred years; when the technology was ready and the long hundred years peace ended, it was ready with 3,000 all-volunteer submariners, 16 depot ships at six bases, and 72 of the largest and most modern submarines in the world.

What then of those two quotations so often used to characterise British attitudes towards advances in technology and to submarines? Of the first, allegedly by St Vincent, we have only Fulton's evidence. He may well be accurate; in which case it is only an illustration of the British 'wait-and-see' policy, though the words themselves cannot be used as evidence of British attitudes against submarines for the important reason that the vocabulary has changed. Just as when Farragut in the American Civil War said, "Damn the torpedoes!" Fulton, St Vincent and Farragut were not talking about submersible vessels but about what today are called mines.

Of the second quotation, there is simply no record that Arthur Wilson ever said anything about pirates and hanging. He did say that the development of submarine warfare would be detrimental to a nation dependent on trade by sea for its supplies, but he went on to say that we cannot stop invention in this direction.[41] He also predicted that submarines would be used for a *guerre de course* that by the standards of his time would be considered illegal. He suggested that the Admiralty should announce that "…certain foreign nations… having shown their intention to make use of thus underhand method of attack…[and] if submarines are used against us, the [British] Government will have to make use of every available means for their destruction…" Neither 'unfair' nor 'unEnglish' was mentioned, but the deterrent intention of his words was clear: they have a very modern ring to them. The rest of Wilson's board broadly agreed with him. H. O. Arnold Forster, Financial and Parliamentary Secretary, whose son would soon command one of these first operational British submarines, concurred that "…we should have the best type (of submarines) and that we should have at our disposal the latest scientific knowledge with respect to them…"

As Wilson himself wrote, "…our policy has been consistent since Lord St Vincent…" Indeed, British naval policy had been consistent from St Vincent speaking to Fulton in the panelled rooms of the Admiralty in 1805 to ink drying on Wilson's page in 1901.

NOTES

1. Hugh Popham, *A Damned Cunning Fellow: the eventful life of Rear Admiral Sir Home Popham KCB KCH KM FRS 1762-1820* Tywardheath: Old Ferry Press, 1991 pp112-124. Although the "secret and unethical weapons" described here appear to be Captain Johnson's plunger, a submersible or semi-submersible rowboat. The name plunger for a submarine was to persist in English and French for most of the 19th Century.

2. Tom Pocock, *A Thirst for Glory: the life of Admiral Sir Sidney Smith* London: Pimlico, 1998 p. 175-7. Barham, Castlereagh and Smith planned to use 'Mr Francis's' submarine weaponry to destroy the combined fleet at Cadiz, or drive it out to sea. Nelson, as ever in this matter, was sniffy.

3. John Jervis, Earl of St Vincent (1735-1823), First Lord of the Admiralty 1801-04.

4. Robert Fulton, *Torpedo War and Submarine Explosions* (Chicago: Swallow Press, 1971). Facsimile print of 1810 edition.

5. ADM 1/7515. Memoranda and minute by Rear Admiral Sir Arthur Wilson dated 21st January 1901 "Holland Type Submarines - Offer by US Firm Holland Torpedo Boat Co to build for Admiralty".

6. Admiral of the Fleet Sir Arthur Knyvet Wilson, Controller of the Navy 1897-1901 and First Sea Lord 1910-11. Wilson was been the RN's pioneering underwater specialist, who in two spells in HMS VERNON, the Navy's underwater school, invented inter alia a system of underwater mining and counter mining and the submerged torpedo tube. Though he could write well, he was not good in debate. For an evaluation of Wilson's brief period of office as First Sea Lord see Nicholas A Lambert's chapter in Malcolm H. Murfett, ed., The First Sea Lords: from Fisher to Mountbatten (Westport: Praeger, 1995) pp35-53.

7. Captain Sir Baldwin Wake Walker (1802-76), Surveyor of the Navy 1848-60. On 22 June 1858, in response to news of the French ironclad *La Gloire*, cited in Robert Gardiner, and Andrew D. Lambert, eds., *Steam, Steel, and Shellfire: the Steam Warship 1815-1905* London: Conway Maritime Press, 1992. The British response to LA GLOIRE was to build HMS WARRIOR, a ship superior in every respect, including iron rather than wooden frames, the largest marine steam engines yet built, she was longer, finer, faster, more stable as a gun-platform and more heavily armed.

8. Admiral of the Fleet Lord Fisher of Kilverstone (18.-1920), Controller of the Navy 1892-97 and First Sea Lord 1904-10 and 1914-15.

9. Adm 116/1122.

10. Henry Dundas, first Viscount Melville (1742-1811), First Lord of the Admiralty 1801-05.

11. Adm 1/5121/22.

12. The British took these experiments seriously. In addition to Home Popham, four of the leading scientists and engineers of the age were appointed to a committee of supervision: Sir Joseph Banks, Henry Cavendish, William Congreve and John Rennie.

13. Robert Saunders Dundas, second Viscount Melville (1721-1851), First Lord of the Admiralty 1812-1827 and 1828-30.

14. SRO GD51 1/2/5 and SRO GD51 1/2/477/1-5.

15. Adm 12/1241 and Adm 12/897 "Projects for annoying the enemy (Torpedoes, etc)".

16. M. W. Dash, *British Submarine Policy 1853-1918* Unpublished PhD Thesis, King's College, London, 1990 p. 40.

17. Richard Compton-Hall, *The Submarine Pioneers* Stroud, Glos: Sutton Publishing, 1999 pp 60-64.

18. Adm 1/5901.

19. Adm 1/636 Inglefield's report dated 4th March 1872 in "Report on a boat invented by Mr McClintock of Mobile U.S. of America".

20. Rich Wills, *The H.L. HUNLEY in Historical Context* Washington, Navy Historical Center 1999.

21. Adm 12/1154.

22. 6236 box II.

23. *The Times* 21 December 1887 p 6 col a Adm 12/1170.

24. Adm 1154 and Adm 12/1170. Wilson reported "...the vessel would prove of little value in time of war..." He was commenting on the NORDENFELT IV's particular operating ability rather than the potential of the submarine in general.

25. Adm 12/1154.

26. Fisher to Selbourne 18 Dec 1900 FP56.

27. Adm 1/7462.

28. Dash p153.

29. Adm 1/7471.

30. Adm 1/7516.

31. Adm 1/762.

32. Adm 231/48.

33. Adm 271/48.

34. Herwig H H, *'Luxury' Fleet: the Imperial German Navy 1888-1918* London, George Allen & Unwin, 1980.

35. Tirptiz, *My Memoirs* London 1917 p138.

36. Herwig *op cit* p.87.

37. Dash *op cit* p.211.

38. *ibid*, pp. 231-5.

39. Adm 1/8374/93.

40. Adm 1/8213.

41. Adm 1/7515 Minute by Wilson dated 21st January 1901 "Holland Type Submarines - Offer by US Firm Holland Torpedo Boat co. to build for Admiralty".

3

Submarines in the First World War

Lee Willett

'*If ever there was a case in which a service staff should have accepted historical experience as a guide it was in the application of a convoy strategy to the conditions produced by the unrestricted U-boat campaign.*'

CAPTAIN SW ROSKILL RN

By the time the Great War broke out in 1914, the submarine was a largely untested warfighting concept. Its size, shape, speed, armament, method of employment and very nature were all practically experimental.[1] Moreover, it was a concept that had few supporters in navies as a whole as its prospectively revolutionary capabilities potentially rivalled the fiscal and military grounding of more established naval assets. However, submarines were developing into efficient warfighting machines. Although still somewhat limited in terms of firepower, their raw principle of covert operations and their flexibility quickly would prove to have a significant impact on naval and grand strategy in the First World War.

Admiral of the Fleet Sir Jackie Fisher, First Sea Lord in 1914, believed that to prevail in any conflict Britain could not allow for any foreign power to obtain technological superiority in any type of naval vessel, and that Britain had to produce a 'two power Navy' – a Navy stronger than *any* potential combination from two other naval powers. This benchmark certainly was applicable to the development of the Royal Navy's submarine force. As a result, by 1914 the Royal Navy possessed the world's largest and most technologically advanced submarine force with 72 boats. At the Armistice in 1918, this number had reached 142.[2]

Set against this force was a German Navy and submarine force with one primary grand strategic aim – to knock Britain out of the war before the United States arrived. Certainly, with this aim in mind, the German forces possessed a notably more clear cut strategic aim than Britain. German submarines were to play a critical role here.

History notes that the submarine campaigns of the First World War played a decisive and unexpected role in its outcome. What history notes less is the critical impact of revolutionary changes in both the British *and* German submarine doctrines and strategic, operational and tactical concepts of operations that guided these campaigns. This chapter will not provide a history of submarine operations in the Great War. Instead, it will assess the impact of the submarine on naval strategy. Notably, the fractious debates in the Royal Navy caused in striking a balance between exploiting new technology while developing an appropriate naval strategy saw the post of First Sea Lord change hands no less than six times between 1910 and 1918.

Moreover, the submarine demonstrated its ability to change fundamentally the nature of warfare. Here, for example, battlefleets no longer could guarantee to achieve their strategic aim of sea control and could no longer guarantee decisive victory in fleet-on-fleet engagements – the possible presence of a single submarine in any situation had seen to this. The advent of the submarine also helped sway the contemporary balance between two schools of naval strategic thought – Alfred Thayer Mahan's belief in decisive fleet engagement and the Sir Julian Corbett model of combined operations and trade protection, as set out in his 1911 *Principles of Maritime Strategy*. Perhaps the most unexpected developments were: the use of submarines in roles other than fleet defence, primarily to conduct devastatingly effective campaigns against merchant shipping; and the resultant Allied decision to employ a convoy strategy to protect this shipping.

FISHER'S REVOLUTION

It has been perceived that, at the dawn of the 1900s, there was within the Admiralty an aversion towards submarines. Initially, the submarine was sometimes regarded as "a weapon of the weak".[3] Some analysts argue that the Admiralty treated American developments in this field "with a mixture of scepticism and disdain".[4] Other reports suggest that Britain sought to outlaw submarines, moves driven by a refusal to accept such boats as a "lawful weapon of maritime warfare."[5] In January 1914, Winston Churchill, as First Lord of the Admiralty, wrote that he did not believe that submarines could ever be used by a civilised power to sink a merchant ship.[6] Most importantly, it was believed in some circles that submersible ships would have little military value and would threaten the strategic primacy of other programmes. Intra-service rivalry did not promote the submarine's cause.

However, the Admiralty's interest in the submarine as an instrument of war was tangible. Technical blueprints of Confederate submarines – employed effectively to sink Federal warships in the US Civil War - can be found in British naval archives.[7] With Britain's Naval policy-makers maintaining a watching brief on evolving submersible technologies the Victorian Navy, for example, "generally kept itself well informed about submarine development."[8] Because much about the combat capabilities of a submarine remained unknown, it can suffice to say that the Admiralty simply had been adopting a policy of 'wait-and-see' towards submarine developments. Once the technological possibilities had been realised, Britain went to war with the largest and technologically most capable submarine fleet in the world.

One of the first British naval officers to see the potential of the submarine was Jackie Fisher.[9] Fisher was responsible for a revolution in British grand strategic naval thought. This revolution was based largely on a threat re-assessment. Here, in a dramatic and controversial move at the turn of the century, Fisher had shifted the emphasis from using the Navy for Empire defence to its employment to offset the German threat in home waters. Furthermore, in diverging from an emphasis on traditional battlefleet units, Fisher's revolution also placed fleet submarines more centrally in British naval strategy. As Steven Roskill notes, "the fleet which fought the 1914-18 war was to a very great extent Fisher's creation."[10] Submarines were a key component of Fisher's strategic revolution: along with destroyers, they would represent a highly mobile and less expensive form of flotilla defence. Fisher saw submarines as "the weapon of the strong".[11] As early as 1904, Fisher argued that, "I don't think it is even faintly realised – the immense impending revolution which the submarines will effect as offensive weapons of war."[12] In 1912, he added that, "this submarine menace is a truly terrible one for Great Britain and British commerce alike".[13] Fisher's foresight that submarines would play a highly influential role, including in an unrestricted *guerre de course*, proved to be "uncannily accurate".[14]

At the time, however, although Fisher had argued widely for the use of convoys to guard against the potential threat of rogue submarines to merchantmen and although a decision was taken in 1913 to arm merchant vessels with anti-submarine guns, the official view remained that the German surface fleet would continue to provide the principal threat in fleet-on-fleet engagement. Thus, given the sheer strategic dominance of the British Navy there was a lesser need for sea denial assets such as submarines than for sea control capabilities. As a result of Fisher's building of a navy and a maritime strategy around the need for sea control, submarines – which were and continue to be the quintessential sea denial weapon – were regarded as less important than aircraft carriers, cruisers, destroyers and escort vessels.

THE BRITISH CAMPAIGN

Although Britain was moving ahead in submarine technology, it was not evident that Britain's strategic thinking on the submarine's contribution to contemporary warfare was similarly maturing. As noted above, initially Britain remained wedded to the ideas of the Grand Fleet and of defeating the German High Seas Fleet head-to-head as the principal method for facilitating victory on land. Yet the potential impact of submarines had not gone unnoticed. In the early stages of the war, Commander-in-Chief of the Grand Fleet, Admiral Jellicoe, chose to keep Britain's battleships out of harm's way for fear of pre-war predictions of their vulnerability to submarines. Jellicoe did not wish to risk the breaking of the English Channel as a notional line of strategic defence. The submarine threat here fundamentally weakened the foundations of the 'Blue Water School' theory – that as long as the Royal Navy remained intact and in control of the North Sea and the English Channel, invasion was impractical. Thus, Britain accumulated a large submarine fleet because of the perceived need for flotilla defence, to deter and prevent invasion.

From the British perspective, submarines could not win the war at sea: they could only assist the surface flotilla in achieving this goal. British submarines played a central role in the blockade of German ports, in ambushing German vessels and, thus, in cutting off German supply lines. Despite the success of her own submarines in targeting German sea lines of communication, Britain herself continued to perceive convoys as impractical because they risked providing the U-boats with more plentiful targets and that offensive anti-submarine warfare – as opposed to convoys - was the best method for halting the U-boats' success. Moreover, while Britain continued to support a strategy of fleet-on-fleet engagement, the impact of Britain's own submarines in such engagements remained limited, not least because the High Seas Fleet chose not to engage in such confrontations. A J Balfour argued that the North Sea was controlled by neither the British nor the German Navies: it was under "joint occupation by the submarines of both countries."[15] Simply, the advent of the submarine brought the naval campaign to a strategic stalemate.

Britain's success with submarines in World War One may have been limited more by the fact that contemporary British strategy did not serve to maximise a submarine's unique capabilities and because Britain preferred to pursue technological rather than strategic solutions. Technological innovation can sometimes spark a sudden increase in military capabilities and broadening of military roles.[16] The Royal Navy exercised notable imagination in the development and employment of its emerging submarine programme. Yet British policy tended to look for a technological solution to any challenges which arose in the submarine field, filling new roles with new classes of submarine. For example, the 'K' Class submarine was designed to have greater speed in order that it could play a greater role in fleet operations as a whole. Moreover, to counter the threat of the German submarines themselves, the 'R' Class was built as an anti-submarine warfare platform. Perhaps an exception to this rule was the 'M' Class 'battleship sub'. In 1915, Fisher floated the idea of attaching a 12" battleship gun to a submarine. The concept was simple, and worked remarkably well in practice. The submarine would approach by stealth, surfacing briefly to blast its target before disappearing. This helped overcome one particular problem for the embryonic Submarine Service – that of finding sufficient appropriate targets. It also built on the success of submarine land attack operations in the Dardanelles, when a Royal Navy submarine bombarded targets ashore in Constantinople with torpedo and naval gun fire, prompting Sir Winston Churchill later to comment that British naval history contained "no page more wonderful than that which records the prowess of her submarines at the Dardanelles."[17] However, the ultimate failure of Britain's Dardanelles campaign showed that submarines were not yet proving decisive as instruments of war – at least, the available technology did not yet permit submarines to have a ground-breaking role when employed in traditional fleet-on-fleet engagement strategies. As Fisher is reported to have said, the submarine was not governed by accepted laws of strategy and tactics.[18] The impact of the German submarines, however, may be perceived to have been greater simply because the strategy they were employing, that of rogue operations to counter enemy fleet and commerce units, was more radical in itself.

THE GERMAN CAMPAIGN

It was not until later in the conflict that both sides came to recognise the strategic advantage of 'commerce raiding' merchant vessels that broadened what was a rather limited submarine target package. It was here that German strategy in submarine warfare almost decided the outcome of the war.

The German employment strategy for submarines in World War One was largely asymmetric to that of the Royal Navy. Whereas the Royal Navy used superior numbers of technologically more capable boats to enforce a wide-ranging blockade of German waters, to conduct anti-submarine warfare, and to reconnoitre the High Seas Fleet, the German Navy was forced – by numerical inferiority in both submarines and in the fleet as a whole – to employ its submarines to raid Allied units in 'rogue' operations. When so employed, the German submarines proved to have a near-decisive impact. As a result, submarines largely were more important to the German Navy than to their British counterparts.

At the turn of the century Alfred von Tirpitz, when Secretary of State of the Imperial Marine Office, faced the task of building from scratch a navy which could offset the influence of the most powerful navy in the world - the Royal Navy.[19] In the long-term, submarines would prove to be fundamental to this cause. Initially, however, Tirpitz did not support the idea of *kleinkreig* (little war), and had seen submarines as only local and secondary weapons; the available technology seemed to suggest little potential for submersible vessels other than in coastal defence.[20] As a result, the first German submarine was built only in 1906 and by the outbreak of hostilities there was no evident change in German strategic thinking on the role of the submarine. Moreover, it was not until much later in the war – too late – that Germany came to realise the potential strategic value of its U boat fleet and instigated a vigorous submarine building programme.

Yet it became apparent very quickly to the German Navy that the strategic, technological and numerical advantage held by the Royal Navy required Germany to use sea denial as its strategy for countering Britain's naval superiority. Simply,

Germany did not have enough submarines to be employed as a blockade force or in support of the High Seas Fleet (where, as with the British Grand Fleet, the limits of submarine capabilities in terms of poor communications, slow speed and limited firepower meant that their contribution was relatively small). This drove the German Navy to use submarines as rogue force elements. As Vice-Admiral Reinhard Scheer, commander of the Third Fleet and later commander of the entire High Seas Fleet, later noted, the German Navy was convinced that the numerically-superior British Fleet would attack the German Fleet as soon as it appeared and, thus, the German Navy would not be able to risk engagement until a state of equality had been achieved and/or unless the High Seas Fleet had adequate protection from submarines.[21] In the only Fleet-on-Fleet engagement at Jutland – one in which submarines played very little part - the Royal Navy's Grand Fleet forced the German Navy's High Seas Fleet back into home waters from where it rarely strayed subsequently. Here, the German U-boats would play a primary role. Also, the vulnerability of surface ships to a single shot from a torpedo suggested that submarines would be better operated independently in search of individual targets which they could sink before fleeing. This was the principle on which the German U-boat campaign was founded.

Mahan had argued that the battlefleet should be cited at the fulcrum of naval strategy and that an enemy's commerce routes could be cut off by blockade. This thesis supported British strategy in the Great War. Mahan also argued that weaker naval powers would be forced into the role of commerce raiding, or *guerre de course*. Here submarines, with their inherent ability to attack by stealth, were instrumental.

The U-boats would attain a primary place as the strategic strike force of the High Seas Fleet through the campaign against British merchant shipping.[22] Submarines were essential to the German strategic cause, as wresting control of the sea was a key to sinking the wider Allied campaign. Unable to risk confrontation with the Grand Fleet, despite the on-going desire for what James Goldrick refers to as 'prize warfare', the Germans chose to use their new asset to target the Allies' lifelines to the land campaign – the merchant convoys.[23] Initially, Scheer refused to sanction an unrestricted U-boat campaign while he saw a continued strategic need to destroy the British fleet and while neutral opinion decried such 'underhand' tactics. However, an unrestricted campaign was first implemented on 4 February 1915, with Germany declaring that it would sink any ship, no matter under which flag it sailed, entering or leaving Allied ports. Scheer's predecessor, Admiral Hugo von Pohl, wrote in the *Imperial Gazette* on 4 February the same year that the,

> "*waters around Great Britain and Ireland, including the whole of the English Channel, are hereby declared to be a War Zone.... Neutral vessels also will run a risk in the War Zone... [as]... it may not always be possible to prevent attacks on enemy ships from harming neutral ships*".

US protests, to the point even of threatening war, following the sinkings in the summer of 1915 of several surface vessels carrying American citizens, saw this strategy rescinded in September of the same year. However, on 1st February 1917, the campaign was once again unleashed. The decision, approved by the Kaiser on 8th January, was based on a careful, but critical, calculation by the German Naval Staff that the campaign would inflict within five months shipping losses on Britain that would be too much for it to bear, both in terms of the psychological and economic impact upon the nation as a whole and in terms of its ability to re-build its merchant fleet.[24] More importantly, it was hoped that Britain could be coerced out of the war before the US would become involved. Moreover, British shipping lines needed to be cut as the German land campaign was proving to be a greater drain on resources than had been anticipated, with the British using strategic mobility to outflank the stalemate of battlefields such as Verdun to link up with Russian forces to the east.

The importance of submarines to the German Navy is highlighted by Sir James Cable. Cable argued that, in a war where "naval performance... [had]... disappointed the pre-war expectations that had triggered the Anglo-German naval race... [,]... German submarines nevertheless came closer to defeating Britain than even the German Army."[25] The unrestricted U-boat campaign was sinking British merchant ships three times faster than they could be built.[26] Indeed, by April 1917, the sheer tonnage of Allied merchant shipping being sunk – almost a dozen ships per day - led the then First Sea Lord Jellicoe to remark that "it is impossible for us to go on with the war if losses like this continue".[27] The U-boat campaign was a 'revolution in strategic affairs': for the first time, a continental power was able to wage a near-decisive *guerre de course* at sea.

RETURN TO CONVOY

Britain managed to offset the effectiveness of the German *guerre de course* – but only just. As late as January 1917, despite two years' of pressure from those stressing the submarine threat, the Admiralty told the War Council that:

> *a system of several ships sailing in company as a convoy is not recommended in any area where submarine attack is a possibility... It is evident that the larger the number of ships forming a convoy, the greater the chance of a submarine being able to attack successfully or of the escort in preventing such an attack.*[28]

The Admiralty wasted much time and tonnage awaiting a technological solution to the U-boat problem. Moreover, the Royal Navy favoured the pursuit of offensive, rather than defensive, measures to offset challenges – in this case, the development of ASW campaigns. Yet the introduction at the eleventh hour of the classic convoy and escort strategy for merchant shipping stopped the haemorrhaging.[29] Following the loss of 354 ships in April 1917 and after a considerable amount of covert political negotiation in Whitehall, Prime Minister Lloyd George imposed upon the Admiralty the directive that a convoy system should be put in place. The first convoy sailed from Gibraltar in May and got through with no losses. By August the strategy was being widely applied, with losses being halved between April and September.[30]

The Royal Navy also began to have more success in U-boat hunting. This was caused by two factors. First, the Royal Navy was developing better ASW capabilities; and, second, by concentrating the merchant vessels they would also have concentrated the areas of U-Boat operations, thus making the U-boats easier to find. Moreover, a U-boat attacking a convoy with what was rather limited firepower was then highly vulnerable to the escorts protecting the convoy. Indeed, more than two-thirds of the U-boats lost were sunk once the convoy strategy was implemented.[31] The wider use of mines may also have been a contributory factor (although the success of such minelaying has been widely questioned). Allied submarines also proved to be very effective in halting German U-boat operations; although only 19 U-boats were sunk by Allied submarines, German submariners were reported to be psychologically affected by the growing threat from them.[32] Moreover, although trying to force Britain out of the war before the US chose to become embroiled, targeting merchant shipping in an unrestricted U-boat campaign served only to hasten the Americans' entry.

CONCLUSION

Wayne Hughes has argued that Mahan "missed the point that strategy would also be affected by new weapons".[33] Mahan's logic, that superior battlefleet power would prevail, was proved correct – but only just. However, what the arrival of the submarine had helped to achieve was the torpedoing of Mahan's argument supporting the on-going utility of a decisive Fleet-on-Fleet engagement. Instead, the harsh realities of warfare, coupled with key emerging technologies, saw that Corbett's ideas - that naval influence on the land battle revolved around combined operations and the protection of trade at the expense of actions between opposing fleets - were proving to have greater durability. As Cable wrote, "nobody's battleships played a decisive, or even a significant part".[34] Indeed, because of their relative lack of speed and firepower, submarines played very little part in traditional naval engagements during the war. Instead, their employment in wider roles was part of the maritime contribution to what was by definition a joint operation ashore.

The emergence of the submarine in the Great War taught navies a lesson that continues to stand the test of time – a vessel hidden below the surface is an asymmetric threat against which there has yet to be developed an effective countermeasure. As has been noted, submarines have since developed to become the capital ships of the modern world.[35] Indeed:

> *World War I was ultimately to justify every fear that the British Naval Establishment had expressed over the value of submarines to an inferior naval power. The new weapon of war was to bring the world's premier maritime nation to its knees.*[36]

The RN has an unbroken 400 year tradition of being a strategically decisive instrument of national policy.'[37] The effect of sea power in making a decisive contribution to the outcome of World War One has been the subject of much debate. What was unquestionable was the significant impact of the submarine. Paul Kennedy argued that the "greatest effect upon the British side had been wrought by the advent of the submarine".[38] Yet perhaps the decisive impact of submarines was perhaps not so much the role of Britain's own submarines but that of the German U-boats, whose *guerre de course* forced the Allies to make the ultimately key strategic decision to employ convoys to protect merchant shipping supporting the war on land. Here, it was the defeat of the German submarines, as opposed to the success of their British counterparts that brought about the successful conclusion of hostilities for the Allies. As Kennedy notes, "there is no doubt but that this new weapon almost brought the British Empire to its knees: only the belated decision to re-institute the old convoy system saved its seaborne trade".[39] Yet, Britain's ability to take sequential strategic decisions – such as to switch to a convoy strategy at critical times as the sequence of events required - was a political strength that the German cumulative grand strategy was unable to match.

NOTES

1 Whitehouse, A.. *Subs and Submariners*. London: Frederick Muller Ltd., 1963, p. 77.
2 A. Harrison, *The Development of HM Submarines*. Unpublished Master's thesis. Gosport the RN Submarine Museum, 1979, p. 12.1. Cited in Eric Grove, "British Submarine Policy in the Inter-War Period 1918-1939". Chapter four in this volume.
3 The quotation is that of Hugh Oakeley Arnold-Forster, cited in: D. van der Vat, *Stealth at Sea: the History of the Submarine*. London: the Orion Publishing Group, 1994, p. 33.
4 Miller, D. & Jordan, J. *Modern Submarine Warfare*. London, Salamander Books, 1987, p. 15. See also Capt J.E. Moore, RN, and Cdr R. Compton-Hall, *Submarine Warfare: Today and Tomorrow*, London: Michael Joseph Ltd, 1986, p. 14.
5 H. Sprout, & M. Sprout, *Towards a New Order of Sea Power: American Naval Policy and the World Scene, 1918-1922*, New York, NY, Greenwood Press, Publishers (first published by Princeton University press in 1940: reprinted by Greenwood between 1969 & 1976, p.198 (incl. n19 & 20).
6 Churchill. Quoted in J. Crane, *Submarine*. London: British Broadcasting Corporation, 1984, p.125.
7 See: N. Lambert, Draft volume on the Royal Naval Submarine Service. Royal Navy: Navy Records Society. (Forthcoming, 2001); Also E. B. Potter, (ed.), *Sea Power: a Naval History*. Second Edition. Annapolis, MD: Naval Institute Press, 1981, p. 129.
8 N. Lambert. Draft volume, *op cit*.
9 Some analysts argue that Fisher foresaw also "the decisive importance of airpower". See, van der Vat. 'Stealth at Sea', *op cit.*, p.34).
10 Captain S. W. Roskill, *The Strategy of Sea Power: Its Development and Application*. Aylesbury, John Goodchild Publishers,1986, p. 102.
11 J.E. Moore & R. Compton-Hall. 'Submarine Warfare', *op cit*, p.64.
12 Quoted in: D. Everitt, *The K Boats*. London: George G. Harrap & Co. Ltd., 1963, p. 16; also, van der Vat. 'Stealth at Sea', *op cit* p. 34.
13 J. Crane. 'Submarine', *op cit* p. 125.
14 *Ibid.*, p. 102.
15 Quoted in H.R. Moon, *The Invasion of the United Kingdom: Public Controversy and Official Planning 1888-1918*. Doctoral thesis, London, 1968, pp. 503-512.
16 Rear Admiral John Hervey, CB OBE, *Submarines*. London, Brassey's Sea Power: Naval Vessels, Weapons Systems and Technology Series; Vol.7, London, Brassey's, 1994, p. 6.
17 See: E. Gray, *The Underwater War: Submarines 1914-1918*. New York, NY: Scribner's Sons, 1917, p. 145; Cdr K. Peppe, USN. "Re-Thinking Tomorrow's Attack Submarine Force", in The Submarine Review, January 1995, Naval Submarine League, p. 56 (incl. n 3).
18 Noted in: Everitt. 'The K Boats', *op cit*, p. 18.
19 A. Gordon, *The Rules of the Game: Jutland and British Naval Command*, London: John Murray, 1996, p. 395.
20 Adm 271/48 and H. Herwig, *'Luxury' Fleet: the Imperial German Navy 1888-1918*, London: George Allen & Unwin, 1980. Both cited in Peter Hore, "British Submarine Policy from St Vincent to Arthur Wilson". Chapter Two of this volume.
21 Admiral Scheer. *Germany's High Seas Fleet in the World War*, London: Cassell, 1920, pp. 10-11 & 25.
22 See: van der Vat. Stealth at Sea, op cit, pp. 27 & 81; E. B. Potter, (ed.), *Sea Power: a Naval History*. Second Edition. Annapolis, MD: Naval Institute Press, 1981, p. 197; Miller & Jordan. *Modern Submarine Warfare*, pp.16-17; F. Uhlig, *How Navies Fight: the U.S. Navy and Its Allies*. Annapolis, MD: USNI, 1994, pp. 84 -5; D. Nelson, & S. Truver, *Submarines in the RMA: Heralds of the Revolution*. Critical Issues Paper. Center for Security Strategies and Operations, Techmatics Inc., 28 May 1997, p.3 (incl. n4).
23 Captain James Goldrick, RAN. "The Battleship Fleet: the Test of War 1895-1919", in J. R. Hill, J.R. (ed.), *The Oxford Illustrated History of the Royal Navy*. Oxford: Oxford University Press, 1995, p. 307. See also Eric Grove, *Vanguard to Trident: British Naval Policy since World War Two*. Annapolis, MD: Naval Institute Press, 1987, p. 2.
24 See: Memorandum from Chief of Naval Staff Admiral von Holtzendorff, 22 December 1916. Quoted in Scheer, 'Germany's High Seas Fleet', *op. cit.*, pp. 248-252; E.B. Potter. 'Sea Power', *op cit*, p. 224. Also, Fred Ikle, *Every War Must End*. New York, Columbia University Press, 1971, p. 43 (incl. n 3-5).
25 Sir James Cable, *The Political Influence of Naval Force in History*. Basingstoke: The MacMillan Press Ltd., 1998, p. 166.
26 A. Gordon. 'The Rules of the Game', *op cit*, p.531.
27 P. Padfield, *War Beneath the Sea: Submarine Conflict during World War II*. New York: John Wiley & Sons, Inc., 1995, p. *9 n 1*. See also A. Gordon, *op cit*, p. 531.
28 Winston Churchill. *The World Crisis*, vol. IV, Part II, p.364, cited in Roskill, 'The Strategy of Sea Power', *op cit*, p. 130 n 1.
29 *Ibid.*, pp. 9-10 (see also p. 25).
30 Captain S.W. Roskill, 'The Strategy of Sea Power', *op cit*, p. 131.
31 E.B. Potter. 'Sea Power: a Naval History', *op cit*, p.230.
32 See, for example: E.B. Potter, *ibid*, p. 228.
33 Captain W. P. Hughes, USN. *Fleet Tactics: Theory and Practice*. Annapolis, MD: Naval Institute Press, 1986, p. 2.
34 Sir James Cable, 'The Political Influence of Naval Force in History' *op cit*, p. 112.
35 Dr D. Owen, *The Politics of Defence*. London: Jonathan Cape Ltd.. 1972, p. 131; also Colin S. Gray, *The Leverage of Sea Power: the Strategic Advantage of Navies in War*. New York, The Free Press, 1992, p. 26.
36 J. Crane. Submarine, *op cit*, p. 126.
37 Admiral of the Fleet Sir Benjamin Bathurst KCB (former First Sea Lord), "The Royal Navy - Taking Maritime Power into the New Millennium", in *RUSI Journal*, August 1995, p. 10.
38 Paul Kennedy, *The Rise and Fall of British Naval Mastery*. London: the Ashfield Press, 1976, p. 244.
39 *Ibid.*, p. 249.

4

Two Committees, Three Submarine Classes and 31 Hulls: the 'R', 'K' and 'M' Class Submarines

Jock Gardner

It would be very easy to produce a brief history of what appeared to have been three, not very successful classes of submarine. Indeed, two out of three seem not merely to have been undistinguished in service but also tragedy-ridden. But rather than concentrate on the specification, building and operational performance of these submarines it is perhaps better to place them into the contexts of two exercises in attempting to define the submarine fleet. One of these preceded their building and one happened after most of the experience of their operation had passed, even though a few of the submarines themselves remained in service at that point. As a brief coda, it is instructive to make some forward comparisons of these classes with the present-day flotilla.

That said, it is necessary to give some idea of the nature of these submarines before attempting to place them into the context of their times. Treated chronologically, the 'K' Class submarine came first, its requirement having been specified in 1915 for a submarine designed to operate in close co-operation with the Grand Fleet. This was a very large submarine for its day, some 2,500 tons, well armed, and used steam propulsion to meet the necessary speed requirement.[1] The 'M' Class was conceived in 1916 and was called a 'Monitor' submarine. The main characteristic of this boat was a 12-inch gun.[2] The requirement for the 'R' Class was not stated until 1917 and it was a much smaller anti-submarine boat, the first designed for this purpose in the world.

'R', 'K' and 'M' Class Submarines: Leading Characteristics			
Class Characteristics	**'R'**	**'K'**	**'M'**
Role	Anti-submarine	Fleet	Monitor
No completed	10	18	3
Displacement	503	2566	1946

None of these designs sprang from a vacuum. They all had their origins in the needs of the World War then raging. The experience, thus far, of a relatively young Submarine Service was of the bureaucratic structures of the Admiralty and Royal Navy. In particular, some perspective on these can be gained through considering the general procurement environment in which these submarines came into service. It has since become commonplace that the pace of contemporary change is as great, or indeed greater, than it ever has been, but an historical perspective would cast some doubt on this judgement. Naval warfare in the early 20th Century was, arguably, undergoing changes at least as fast as any now evident.

Battleships were reaching the peak of their development, rapidly increasing in size, gun power, speed, and armour protection. Their eclipse as capital ships, totally complete by mid-century, scarcely seemed credible. A marked, if hardly sturdy at this point, naval technology was becoming evident in the shape of aviation at sea. The mine, having been a more salient feature of the second half of the 19th Century, was still much in evidence and was to have a marked, if low profile, influence on naval operations in World War II. But what was probably the fastest growing area was that of submarine warfare.

Most advanced nations, including the USA, France, Italy, Japan, Austro-Hungary and Russia, all had submarines but the leading operators of submarines by the First World War were Germany and the United Kingdom.[3] It has to be said that the German operations almost certainly made the greatest impact on the war as a whole by means of their series of campaigns against Allied merchant vessels. This provided the principal impetus for the 'R' Class submarines, a point that will be returned to later.

The British probably operated their submarines in a wider range of roles; this was often done through a multiplicity of submarine classes, reflecting a tendency both to advance the technical state of the art by building new classes and also a high degree of role specialisation. This was probably never more marked than with the three classes that are the subject of this paper. There tended to be a multiplicity of sources for these requirements, either from within the Submarine Service itself, the Admiralty, or other bodies, such as the Grand Fleet. Clearly such a system could lead to very varied and, in the absence of a Naval Staff as we would now understand the term, disparate requirements. Nevertheless, attempts were made from time to time to harmonise the process. One of these was the Submarine Development Committee of 1915 which identified several different generic types of submarine.[4]

At this point, the ones of greatest interest were the Fleet submarine, the 'Cruiser', and the 'Monitor' submarine.[5] Although the former was not proceeded with, at least not during the war, there was a view that there was a confluence between this and the 'Monitor', always provided that the gun size selected for the 'Monitor' was consistent with the cruiser submarine concept.[6] It is helpful at this point to highlight one linguistic difficulty with the word 'Monitor', currently not in the naval vocabulary. The term is normally taken to mean a low freeboard, shallow draft ship with one or two large guns for coastal bombardment purposes.[7] But it is clear from the outset that action against surface ships was also contemplated, although the only wartime potential use made of one of these submarines lay in preparing to bombard Constantinople (now Istanbul). This was a task that was probably best not attempted in reality because of the extensive mine defences in the long approaches to the Turkish city.[8]

What perhaps was most noteworthy in the deliberations of the Submarine Development Committee was its principal omission - the anti-submarine submarine. To be fair, at this point, the German submarine problem had not built up to any great extent, at least not to the high peaks of crisis that were going to occur in 1917.[9] The difficulties, however, of carrying out an attack on a surfaced submarine from a submerged one were well recognised. Even before the outbreak of war, these had been summarised as: limited battery power; the performance of periscope and compass; low speed (both on the surface and submerged); limited range periscope vision; and difficulty in determining fire control data via the periscope.[10] So, the

24

combination of lack of requirement and the difficulty of carrying out the task made this role unnecessary in 1915.[11]

Turning to the fleet submarine, it would only be right to note that this was the greatest leap forward in the concept of submarine operational employment and also represented the greatest technical challenges. Nevertheless, of the two most innovative types principally explored by the committee - monitor and fleet - the latter was the most advanced chronologically, although even here, the committee urged caution in further developing either concept or future designs before the results of the trials of K-3 were known.[12] In the light of the various difficulties that were to be encountered by the Class in both trials and service, this was a good, level-headed decision.

The concept and design of the 'K' Class was an interesting one. Historians have often been misled by the name 'Grand Fleet', assuming merely that this was a re-titling of a pre-war formation but, as Nicholas Lambert has ably demonstrated, this was actually a much more sophisticated and complex concept, attempting to co-ordinate the activity of large numbers of battleships, battlecruisers, cruisers and destroyers.[13] To this were to be added the relatively new innovations of submarine and aircraft. The problem of integrating the existing elements was already a formidable one without the later additions.

An interesting comparison might be made, for example, between Nelson's forces at Trafalgar and Jellicoe's at Jutland. Nelson's ships were relatively slow and had limitations imposed on what directions they could steer by the wind.[14] Their fire power and protection were several orders of magnitude less than that of Jellicoe's fleet. On the other hand, Nelson probably deployed a rather more homogenous force. But the very much greater offensive and dynamic power of Jellicoe's fleet was not matched by a corresponding increase in two vital fields: communications and reconnaissance.[15] The Classes of submarine actually available in the summer of 1916 did not fit particularly well into this scenario, being speed limited in comparison with the Grand Fleet and usually being even more limited in their ability to communicate.

Nevertheless, the prospect of submarines being able to operate in conjunction with the Grand Fleet was a powerful and attractive one, and this greatly conditioned the characteristic of the 'K' Class. The concept of a flotilla of submarines able not only to scout but also to position themselves ahead of the main battle fleet was an attractive one. They could then submerge on the approach of the German fleet and deliver a very powerful torpedo attack with even less warning than a formation of destroyers, the normal tactic of the period.[16]

The manoeuvring requirement imposed a demand for surface speed that could not be met by diesel engines of the period and thus a steam turbine plant was fitted. This imposed a very important constraint on diving as the steam plant had to be shut down adding to the time taken and also introducing a degree of complexity into the control of openings which was hardly conducive to safe operations.

The 'M' Class design had a lesser requirement for surface speed than the 'K's, so reverted to diesel propulsion for surface use. Some accounts say that the 'M's were constructed from the hulls of the uncompleted K-18-21, but dimensional differences indicate that the there was only a limited utilisation of 'K' material.[17]

The requirement for the 'R' Class submarine was not to be stated until 1917 and there were three strands to the genesis of this revolutionary development. The first was that submarine skills and techniques had developed considerably since the period of the problems of 1914 previously noted in this paper, and that such problems were less salient. The second was that, by now, German submarines were wreaking enormous mayhem on the Allied stock of merchant shipping. Further, at least at the beginning of that year, there was little clear conception as to how the problem could be contained, far less dealt with by any conceivable methods.[18]

A third, totally new, factor was that the British submarine force had by then experienced a number of attacks against German U-boats. This was almost certainly a reflection of the crowded nature of the North Sea in particular and the littoral nature of the maritime war in general. By the middle of 1917, an analysis of no less than 124 shots could be made and this had gone up to 165 by November.[19] Such a degree of relatively chance encounters suggested an expectation of further significant numbers of such actions, but it also highlighted that the performance in attacks was not especially good. Nevertheless, it indicated the potential of such attacks and highlighted the necessity of measures to improve the success rate.[20]

Such factors had a considerable influence on the design of the new anti-submarine submarine, the 'R' Class, but her most distinctive feature was to be the strong emphasis placed on underwater, as distinct from surfaced, performance. This was done by the fitting of relatively large batteries, an unusually powerful electric motor and paying great attention to underwater smoothness. Care was also lavished on such details as periscopes and although there was much discussion on fitting a powerful gun armament, possibly two 4-inch guns, none of the Class was ever equipped with guns.[21]

In operation, these submarines had a somewhat mixed record. The 'K's, advanced concept that they were, were never really able to operate as had been intended and, somewhat sadly, their main impact on posterity was almost certainly the so-called 'Battle of May Island'.[22] Nevertheless, the idea of operating submarines in relatively close proximity to, and co-operation with, the fleet was a powerful one which would be returned in later decades.

The 'M' Class, limited to three boats, were to undergo a series of fates. Firstly, they were to suffer a high casualty rate; both M1 and M2 were lost in peacetime mishaps. Secondly, and unusually amongst the three Classes considered, they were heavily converted; M1 alone retained its original form, but M2 was converted into a seaplane carrier in 1928 whilst M3 was converted into a submarine minelayer at about the same time. Although she was the last to be sold in 1932, she probably won the prize as the ugliest British submarine ever.[23]

The 'R' Class, which started to enter service in the summer of 1918, really came along too late to demonstrate its true potential. By that time, the German submarine problem had been largely contained, principally due to the introduction and spread of the convoy system. No 'R' boat, of which only six were in service by the armistice, ever completed an attack against a U-boat.[24] Ironically, the 'K' Class managed to get rather closer to a submarine kill through K7's attack on U95 in June 1917. This resulted in a hit, but no sinking, due to a malfunctioning weapon.[25] Some of the 'K' Class were also fitted with depth charge throwers and post-war consideration was given to the fitting of Asdic.[26]

By 1934, not one of these submarines remained in service. It would be difficult to suggest that their operational careers were illustrious; but were they total failures? Some perspective is provided on their collective experience by an Admiralty committee of 1925, which, rather like the Submarine Development Committee of 1915, pondered the future of the submarine in the Royal Navy.[27] The comments of various authorities prepared for the committee produce an interesting and, on the whole, consensual view of future submarine types.

Six different types of submarine were considered by the area Commanders-in Chief (Atlantic Fleet, Mediterranean, China and East Indies), as well as Rear Admiral (Submarines) and Captain S4: an 'overseas patrol'; fleet; cruiser; minelaying; antisubmarine; and monitor submarine. There was scant enthusiasm for the cruiser and little more for the antisubmarine boat, whilst the minelaying submarine, as a specific type, attracted few adherents. The monitor was only promoted by C-in-C China, who saw its value as mobile artillery. On the other hand, the overseas patrol boat was universally accepted and the only significant discussion concerned the specific requirements of the design.

Opinion was rather split over the fleet submarine. At one end of the spectrum stood C-in-C East Indies, who deemed it a luxury, whereas the two 'home' C-in-Cs, Atlantic and Mediterranean, were proponents, the former laying down specific characteristics and the latter taking the view that their development was necessary as a step towards the general development of submarines. C-in-C China was positioned somewhere in the middle, agreeing the role but considering that the work could be done "by GS type", presumably the overseas patrol boat. Interestingly, professional submarine opinion was split, RA(S) noting them as required, but Captain S4 thinking them "not worth the cost". RA(S) went even further, suggesting a proportion of two 'fleet' submarines for every one 'reconnaissance patrol' submarine.

What can be seen, some ten years after the 1915 Submarine Development Committee recommendations, is that the Submarine Service had entered into its second age when the initial rush of development had slowed to some extent and the vast proliferation of types was neither needed nor desired. Care, too, was taken over the prolifgate extension of roles. To be fair, the stimulus of a war in progress was no longer present and the considerable constraint of economy was much in evidence. What remained was the clear conviction of the importance of the submarine and its wide scope in modern warfare.

Leaping forward to the present time, some interesting comparisons with the 'R', 'K' and 'M' Class submarines can be made. These are best dealt with under two headings: features and roles. The first feature to note is generic and not specific. The main thrust of this paper is concerned with three classes of submarine at what might be thought to be at the margins of the flotilla of their day. Today, three classes make up the flotilla. Further, there are now only 16 hulls, as against the 31 aggregate of the 'R', 'K' and 'M' at their, admittedly, artificial peak.[28]

However, all of the current flotilla utilise steam propulsion (like the 'K's) and, similarly, are all capable of high speed, even if this property is not always used operationally. These speeds are all realisable underwater, as in the case of the 'R' Class. Further, all current submarines have very long ranges, as was specified for the admittedly unprocured cruiser submarine.[29] When it comes to armament, the reach of the 'M' Class is echoed in several of today's weapons systems.

Turning to roles, it is notable that all those envisaged for the three early classes are also represented in the modern era. Anti-submarine capability is built into all modern British submarines and it is surely the case that the SSN is the best single-platform ASW system there is; such is the legacy of the 'R' Class. All the SSNs are used to operate in direct support of surface fleets, albeit not in the style envisaged in the First World War with close formations of submarines deployed initially on the surface. However, there can be little doubt that there is a line of descent from the requirements and aspirations that resulted in the 'K' Class.

It is arguable that the greatest vindication of the 1915 requirements lies in the idea of the Monitor submarine, then represented by the 'M' Class. Despite the confusion evident in 1915 about targets for these submarines - surface ships or land targets - it is clear that the modern submarine covers both of these very well indeed. Against surface ships both the torpedo and Harpoon are very potent. Perhaps, however, the demand of the C-in-C China in 1925 makes the best reading 75 years on, with his plea for "mobile artillery". Deployable over a great part of the globe, Tomahawk and Trident are certainly 'mobile' and probably just about describable as artillery.

The aspirations of Admiralty and Flotilla of 1915, and even 1925, may have been severely circumscribed by the available technology. But with the hindsight of at least 75 years, it would be very difficult to make a charge stick of lacking imagination.

APPENDIX: 'R', 'K' AND 'M' CLASSES - CHARACTERISTICS

R, K and M Class Submarines Leading Characteristics			
	R	**K**	**M**
Characteristic			
Role	Antisubmarine	Fleet	Monitor
Requirement	1917	1915	1916
In service	1918-1934	1916-1931	1918-1932
Number in Class	10	18	3
Submerged Displacement	503	2566	1946
Surfaced speed	9.5	23.5	15
Submerged speed	15	8+	9
Endurance	2000 surface, 15@15, 240@4	960@24 surface, 13.5@9	4000@11 surface, 10@10, 80@2
Weapons	6 18-inch TT	4+4+2 18-inch TT, 2 4-inch guns, 1 3-inch HA	4 18-inch TT, 1 12-inch gun, 1 3-inch gun
Complement	22	58/65	68
Features	High underwater speed	Steam propulsion, speed	Large gun
Failures	None	Communications	Role ambiguity
Remarks	4-inch gun planned (but not fitted)		Conversions to seaplane-carrier (M2), Minelayer (M3)

NOTES

1   Full details of the Class can be found in the relevant ship covers at the National Maritime Museum, as it can for the other two Classes. The relevant entries in Paul Akerman; *Encyclopaedia of British Submarines 1901-1955*; Chippenham, Wiltshire; Maritime Books, 1989 are also useful, as is an unpublished item in the Royal Navy Submarine Museum; A N Harrison; *The Development of HM Submarines from Holland No. 1 (1901) to Porpoise (1930).* The' K' Class has a book-length account of its history: Don Everitt; *The K Boats*; London, Harrap, 1963. On the 'R' Class, see J D Brown; "The 'R' Class Anti-Submarine Submarine, 1917-1934" a paper presented at "Un Siècle de Construction Sous-marine", Cherbourg 25 October 1999 and David Miller; "The First Hunter-Killers: British 'R' Class Submarines of 1917" in Robert Gardiner (editor); *Warship 1993*; London, Conway Maritime Press, 1993 pp. 65-76.
2   There is a monograph on the M-Class; Martin H Brice; *M-Class Submarines*; London, Outline Publications, 1983.
3   *Jane's Fighting Ships 1914* (facsimile edition).
4   *Technical History*, p. xx.
5   Other categories were coastal, patrol and minelaying.
6   The cruiser submarine concept was eventually realised in the single 'X' Class submarine of 1925-1936, a 3,600 ton boat with four 5.2-inch guns as well as a torpedo armament. For convergence of this with the monitor submarine, see TH xx post-meeting (8 October 1915) note by Commodore (S) noting convergence of cruiser and monitor designs if the 7.5" gun is adopted.
7   Kemp, Peter (editor); *Oxford Companion to Ships and the Sea*; London, Oxford University Press, 1976; pp. 555-6 also notes the origin as the American Civil War vessel, Monitor which, paradoxically, was most famous for a ship-to-ship duel.
8   Brice, *op cit* p.8.
9   For a good illustration of this, see Vice Admiral Sir Arthur Hezlet; *The Submarine and Sea Power*; London, Peter Davies, 1967; p. 102.
10   PRO ADM137/1926 - *H.S.A. 128 Grand Fleet Secret Packs* Vol XLVI Pack 0022. Operations; Submarine Committee, Admiralty to Secretary to the Admiralty, No. 54 dated 5 May 1914, 460.
11   There were, however, very early deployments in September 1914 of six submarines between the Bass Rock and Heligoland "to search for, stalk and if possible attack the enemy's submarines." ADM137/1926 - *H.S.A. 128 Grand Fleet Secret Packs* Vol XLVI.
12   She was the only one of the Class to be completed before the end of 1916.
13   Nicholas A Lambert; *Sir John Fisher's Naval Revolution*; Columbia, South Carolina; University of South Carolina Press; 1999, p. 11.
14   Ships of that era could only manoeuvre for about 240 out of 360 degrees, always assuming that there was wind.
15   Although radio was widely fitted in ships, it was rarely used or usable for tactical manoeuvring and its longer-haul capabilities were under-utilised not because of lack of confidence in them but because the extensive British exploitation of comparable German communications imbued the British with a keen sense of their vulnerability.
16   However, most of the destroyers at Jutland would have been able to deploy the larger 21 inch torpedo as opposed to the 18 inch variety generally in use in submarines at the time. The element of surprise remains.
17   See also Richard Compton-Hall; *Submarine Warfare: Monsters and Midgets*; Poole, Dorset; Blandford Press; 1985; p. 31.
18   For instance in April 1917, submarines claimed 835 thousand out of 869 thousand tons sunk. *Statistical Review of the War against Merchant Shipping* London, Director of Statistics, Admiralty, 1918 p. 22.
19   PRO ADM 137/1926, 559-565 HMS VERNON to Director of Torpedoes and Mining, Admiralty No. W/3838/1 dated 29 August 1917.
20   Oddly, the earlier analysis noted that attacks carried out at ranges in excess of 3,000 yards were more successful than those in the bracket 1,000-3,000 yards. This was attributed to those at longer range being more deliberate.
21   Miller *op cit* p. 70.
22   A combination of unfortunate events in January 1918 in the Firth of Forth when a series of initially unrelated mishaps led to the sinking of two K boats, three more and a light cruiser being seriously damaged, as well as the loss of over 100 lives. Akerman, *op cit* p.204 and Everitt, *op cit* Chapter 5.
23   A recently published reference work shows a photograph of M3 saying that she is flying the ensign from the jackstaff. She wasn't, she really looked like that.
24   Four more were completed post-war and two were cancelled.
25   Naval Historical Branch; *Technical History* pp. 1, 14.
26   Ackerman *op cit* p. 201; RN Submarine Museum, A1928/2.
27   PRO ADM 116/3164 Case 1353; M01855/25 and P.D. 02152/25.
28   *Jane's Fighting Ships* London, Jane's Defence Publishers, 2000-2001 edition.
29   One example of the 'X'-Class cruiser submarine was built after the First World War.

PART II

WORLD WAR II & POST-WAR RN SUBMARINES

5

British Submarine Policy in the Inter-War Period, 1918-1939

Eric Grove

At the Armistice in 1918, the British Empire's submarine fleet consisted of 142 boats of 14 different Classes.[1] These varied: from the 37 small (200-525 ton)[2] pre-war flotilla defence boats of the 'B', 'C', 'V' and 'F' Classes; the 21 small wartime built American coastals of the 'H' and 'H 21' Classes; the 6 small (503 ton) anti-submarine submarines of the 'K' Class; the 57 medium sized (595-1080 ton) seagoing patrol Classes of the 'D', 'E', 'C' and 'L' Classes; the 20 large (1820-2566 ton) fleet submarines of the 'J' and 'K' Classes; and the 1,946 ton 12-in gun submarine M1.[3] By the end of 1920, all the old flotilla defence craft had gone, as had the 'D' and 'C' Classes. They were replaced, in part, by those boats of the wartime programmes that were completed by 1925: M2-3; H31-34/42-44 and H47-52; L18-27 and L33; R2-4 and R10; K26 of the improved 'K' design; and L52-6 and L69 and 70 of the 1,150 ton L50 Class. One of the latter, L55, was lost in the anti-Bolshevik intervention in 1919 and was raised and later used by the Soviet Navy.[4] By May 1920, there were 51 submarines left, although not all were operational; about half were post-war completions.[5]

In 1921, thinking began about future submarine policy. Plans Division identified six types of submarine:- fleet; overseas patrol and reconnaissance; cruiser; local defence; mining and anti-submarine.[6] The main matter for consideration was whether the large fleet submarine be perpetuated. The value of the existing steam powered 'K's was clearly limited and they were something of a luxury in the contemporary atmosphere of financial stringency. A policy was suggested of only keeping the three 'M's as fleet boats and expediting completion of K-26 for training and further tactical experience (in the event she was not commissioned until June 1923 being towed from Vickers to Chatham for completion). The meeting did not take place as the very month it was planned, October 1921, the Naval Staff proposed at least the consideration of the complete abolition of the submarine at the forthcoming Washington Conference.[7]

British submarine policy at this time was apparently contradictory. The month after the Naval Staff officially suggested the abolition of the submarine the biggest (3600 ton) British submarine yet, the cruiser submarine X-1 was laid down.[8] In fact, the two stances were not quite as contradictory as they seemed. There was little or no chance that abolition would be agreed and the real aim was limitations on the activities of submarines to prevent their unrestricted use against merchantmen. Although X-1 could be used for commerce raiding, the Admiralty were afraid of foreign emulation in this role and not much was made of this aspect of her capabilities.[9] Her anti-warship role was stressed, notably against anti-submarine forces in support of forward deployed reconnaissance submarines.[10] Her displacement would however eat substantially into any agreed limit on submarine forces, designed to encourage smaller, "defensive" submarines.[11]

In the end, because of French policy, no specific quantitative or qualitative limits on submarines were agreed, although the desired limitations on submarines' conduct, drawn up by the American Elihu Root, were signed up to by Britain - albeit not ratified by France.[12] The Admiralty felt themselves constrained by the Root Resolutions, although perhaps not that much. In 1926, it was remarked that "if in a naval war we were forced to sink ships as a reprisal we might have to suspend or abrogate this provision".[13] French non-ratification would have given the perfect excuse.

With Washington safely out of the way, Chatfield, the able Assistant Chief of Naval Staff who had masterminded the Naval delegation at the American capital, was able to hold the key meeting at the Admiralty on 2 May, 1922 to decide on submarine policy. It was agreed to make top priority the building of a larger overseas patrol type boat for work in distant waters. Such a boat could carry out most tasks and be of most general utility. Surface displacement would be in the region of 1200 tons (as against 960 for an 'L-50') and endurance at economical speed 10,000 miles. Habitability and internal arrangements were to be of a standard required for operations in the tropics.

With the Anglo-Japanese alliance now killed by Washington, arrangements for possible war with the erstwhile ally had to be made. Already by 1920, a dozen of the twenty 'L' Class boats had been based on the China station.[14] The new patrol submarine would have a maximum surfaced speed of fifteen knots with a cruising speed of twelve and a maximum underwater speed of nine. The required radio range would be at least 500 miles, preferably 1000, and the main armament of the new boat would six 21-in torpedo tubes in the bow, as in the L-50s.[15]

There was initial support for other types. It was calculated that in addition to ten overseas patrol submarines, there was a need for four minelayers, four more cruisers and seven fleet boats.[16] It was decided not to proceed with further cruisers and fleet boats until experience had been gained with X-l and K-26 respectively although work might continue on a specialist mine-layer. The requirement for a cruiser boat was also dependent on cruiser policy in general following Washington. The representative of C-in-C Atlantic Fleet made his Admiral's case for a fast (18-knot) boat to accompany the fleet, carry out torpedo attacks, and for reconnaissance; the conference, however, was "generally of the opinion" that constructing such submarines was "of secondary importance at the present time". Such boats might, however, have to be developed "at a later date".[17] No special submarines were to be built for local defence or anti-submarine duties; these roles were to pass to "normal type submarines no longer suitable for their primary duties. 'A/S' boats were a definite type to be borne in mind". It was concluded that it was unnecessary to develop a special design because of requirements of greater priority and the utility of other types of submarine in the ASW role.[18]

In his comments on the conclusions of the conference, that persistent submarine enthusiast, Roger Keyes, then DCNS, said that he thought submarines would be required for reconnaissance duties in a future war even more than they had been in the Great War. In the Spring manoeuvres 'EA', M-2 had shadowed a convoy for 48 hours and then carried out a simulated attack on the escorting battleship, HMS QUEEN ELIZABETH, in heavy weather. He agreed, however, that economy dictated concentration on an overseas patrol type with improved habitability; fleet submarines could be kept 'in abeyance' until trials had been completed with K-26 and X-l. By then, Keyes saw the latter as having primarily a fleet role as the Washington Treaty had ruled out its original role of commerce destruction. Ordering further boats of the type was inadvisable in the current financial climate.[19] Beatty,

1   The 'Holland', HM Submarine TORPEDO BOAT No1 (1901-1903)

courtesy BAe Systems

2   The 'A' Class Home waters Patrol Submarine, HMS A-5 (1903-1904)

courtesy BAe Systems

3   The 'C' Class Sea-going Patrol Submarine, HMS C-17 (1909)

courtesy BAe Systems

4   The 'D' Class HMS D-4 the first submarine to be fitted with a gun (1911)

courtesy BAe Systems

5   The experimental submarine, HMS NAUTILUS (1914)

courtesy BAe Systems

6   The 'E' Class Sea-going Patrol Submarine, HMS E-20 (1915)

courtesy BAe Systems

however, sounded a note of caution. He said that "the question of the Fleet Submarine must not be overlooked and when funds permit we must hope to develop this type".[20]

The result of the meeting was a proposal for a programme of ten reconnaissance and patrol submarines, two fleet boats, two minelayers and two cruisers. By September 1922, the existing submarine flotilla stood at 44 boats in commission and 11 in reserve, a small increase since 1920.[21] Recognition of the "extreme desirability" of a replacement programme led to the Board of Admiralty decision on 15 February 1923 to build the new 'O'; (for 'Overseas') Class patrol submarine. The Board recognised that the 'L' Class was unsuitable for operations in large areas of the world. A new prototype was necessary to produce a standard design so that suitable vessels could be produced in an emergency. [22]

The 'O' Class, "a reconnaissance submarine, which has superior offensive qualities, suitable for service in Far Eastern waters", was regarded by both the Naval Staff and the Submarine Service as "essential so it may serve as a pattern for immediate replacement".[23] O-1, later named HMS OBERON, was put into the 1923 Programme and laid down on 22 March 1924. She was commissioned on 24 August 1927 and displaced 1831 tons submerged and 1311 on the basis of the new treaty 'standard' displacement. Disappointingly, she was not as fast as intended with maximum speeds of 13, 7.5 and 7.8 knots afloat and submerged, but speed had not been a priority in her design, compared to range and habitability. Compared to earlier boats, she had greater endurance, increased diving depth and increased wireless range.[24] OBERON was built at the Chatham Royal Dockyard.

It was hoped to lay down three more 'O' boats in 1924-5, four in 1925-6 and seven each in the three successive financial years, but Churchill's Treasury would not allow such extravagance (after all the formidable Chancellor saw no chance of war with Japan in his lifetime). No more submarines were laid down in the 1924 and 1925 Programmes, a result of the battle between Churchill and the Admiralty over Naval expenditure. In 1925, the Admiralty presented the Cabinet Naval Programme Committee with proposals for a total force of eighty submarines, with eight boats being built annually. Churchill continued to oppose these figures, although he preferred submarines to other types, due to their relative cheapness, but only on the basis of three to four boats a year. In the event, a compromise was agreed. The 1925 Programme was only made up of cruisers, a defeat for the Chancellor, but it was decided to build six submarines a year from 1926 onwards. Beatty grumbled that this would make Britain inferior in numbers of modern submarines to the other naval powers but, in the circumstances, it was quite a substantial programme.[25]

With serious concerns about retention of submarine building capacity it was especially welcome that Australia ordered two 'O' Class boats from British yards. The Dominion had formed a powerful submarine flotilla of all six surviving 1820 ton 'J' Class boats in 1919. These large 1820 ton boats had obvious relevance, adding to the initial defensive phase of a Far Eastern war while contributing to Fleet operations once the main forces arrived. Financial problems saw the flotilla steadily reduce, but it was decided to replace it with two slightly improved and faster 'O' boats built at Vickers in Barrow. Named HMS OTWAY and OXLEY they were laid down in 1925 and commissioned in 1927. The two Australian 'O's were taken over by the Royal Navy in 1931 as the Depression forced emergency retrenchment in Australian Naval policy.

A significant factor in the development of novel thinking on submarines at this time was Captain Max Horton, Captain of the First Submarine Flotilla. One of his suggestions, the building of ten ton 1-2 man 'Devastator' type high speed midget submarines for deployment by surface ship or modified 'M' Class submarine for use against enemy capital ships at sea or in harbour was considered, but came to nothing.[26] More successful was his idea to use aircraft from submarines. This chimed in with the Naval Staff's reconnaissance priority for submarines. Horton argued that aircraft could make up for the submarines greatest defect in the reconnaissance role, its "lack of vision".[27] He suggested the conversion of the 'M' Class to this role, an idea communicated through C-in-C Atlantic Fleet at the end of July 1923. The Air Ministry said it could provide a suitable aircraft of new design, the Parnall Peto, and conversion of M2 to carry it was approved in September 1925. She was commissioned in her new role two years later.[28]

By the time conversion of M-2 began, a further conference to consider "the necessity for and uses of various types of submarine" had been held at the Admiralty on 19 February 1925.[29] The various views expressed by the various fleet, submarine and anti-submarine commands revealed a challenge to the submarine perhaps even more serious than abolition, the threat from asdic (sonar). The Naval Staff consensus was by now most pessimistic about the chances of a traditional torpedo attack against a defended fleet or convoy. The only chance for a torpedo attack was as large a torpedo salvo as possible at long range or attack against distracted enemy fleet units at or just after a fleet action.

The mutual possession of asdics also undermined the ASW potential of submarines; surface vessels were better for this role (although Rear Admiral (S), perhaps understandably, disagreed on this point). Submarines were therefore best employed for distant reconnaissance and mine-laying in hostile waters and local defence of bases against surface ships. The main scenario was war against Japan.

M-2 fitted well into the reconnaissance priority, as did the building of more new overseas patrol boats. In the five-year programme adopted in 1925, the Admiralty accepted six overseas patrol boats a year and an extended life of twelve years per boat. A force of 72 submarines was the objective, 60 of them overseas patrol types. Six 'O's were duly included in 1926 and laid down in the following year. These were of a larger (2038 ton/ 1475 ton standard) design with higher speed (17.5/8 knots). The 1925 Conference had insisted on a surface speed of seventeen knots and there was some controversy in design trade-offs before the legend and drawings were approved by the Board on 12 August 1926. Six generally similar 'Parthian' Class followed on 1927-8 and six 'Rainbows' were intended for 1928-9, although two of these were cancelled.[30] Under the replacement plan of 5 August 1927, the 'Odins' and the 'Parthians' were intended for the China Fleet, while the 'Rainbows' were to go to the Mediterranean.[31]

A specialist mine-laying submarine was also commissioned at last, albeit by conversion. Investigations of such had begun in July 1920 and an Admiralty meeting on 22 June 1923 drew up requirements for a 2500 ton minelayer with a capacity of 36-40 mines to be laid surfaced or submerged. Surfaced speed was to be the same as the new patrol submarine, with a range of 7-10,000 miles. The boat was also to be suitable for use in the tropics and be able to carry the communications, sensors and forward torpedo armament of a patrol submarine. The Conference concluded that a design with an internal amidships mining compartment should be prepared for laying down in the 1924-25 financial year. 'Oberon' had priority, however, and the 1925 Conference decided not to put a new minelayer into the next year's programme. Horton had however suggested conversion of an 'M' Class boat to this role and Rear Admiral (Submarines) preferred such a boat carrying a larger number of mines externally. This was eventually agreed and the surviving 'M' Class boat M3 (Ml had been tragically lost in collision on exercise experimenting with submarines screening a troop convoy off Start Point on 12 November 1925) was taken in hand for conversion in June 1927. She carried up to 100 standard contact mines in a superstructure on her pressure hull and was back in service in her new role by the end of 1928.[32]

The next major naval arms control conference was held in Geneva in 1927. Britain still officially held out for abolition of submarines, but again this was not seriously on the agenda. More realistic were proposals that within overall tonnage limitations there should be two types, Class 'A' (1600-2000 tons) and 'B' (under 600 tons) with the age limit set at fifteen years. Agreement was reached with Japan and the United States on a maximum of 1,800 tons and on a definition of 'standard' tonnage (hereafter 'Geneva' tonnage) but the attempt to limit American and British submarine tonnage to 90,000 and Japanese to 60,000 was unsuccessful. Submarine negotiations were still in progress when the Conference broke down on the cruiser question.[33]

One of the few occasions when it was agreed that a submarine could make a successful torpedo attack was in the confusion of a fleet action when the requirement and desire for a fleet submarine remained. The 1925 Conference had delayed the question of a new fleet boat until improvements in internal combustion engine performance had been obtained to provide sufficient speed. Oil fired steam was too problematical and unpopular. De Robeck, C-in-C Atlantic Fleet, had summed it up well for the 1925 Conference. The boilers made the living and working spaces too hot, ventilation was inadequate and it took too long to dive.[34] All the five surviving original 'K's had been removed from the active list by early 1926, leaving only the modified K-26. However, the prognosis for this boat was not bright. A Staff Paper of the end of 1926 regarded any reversion to steam to be a retrograde step, especially for long range operations in tropical waters. Possible future fleet boats might be modified X-ls without guns.[35]

In early 1928, Rear Admiral (Submarines) pressed the case for a faster version of the 'O'/'P'-design, perhaps for the 1928-9 batch, and certainly for the five or more follow-on boats planned for 1929-30. A maximum speed of 21 knots would allow a practical operational speed of 18-19 knots, a speed that would allow such boats to operate with the fleet which would be "considerably strengthened" as a result.[36] The endurance required for such a fleet boat was the same as that of a contemporary 'Nelson' Class battleship, 8500 miles at 12 knots. This was far and way beyond the capabilities of K-26 that had a maximum surfaced speed of 23.5 knots but could only do 2560 miles at 12 knots.

In a lecture to the contemporary Senior Officers War Course, the Naval Construction Department set out its views on a fleet submarine question. A fleet boat was required for:-

" 1) *Tactical co-operation with the Fleet by torpedo attack of the enemy Battle Fleet.*
2) *Torpedo attack on disabled ships, aircraft carriers or other detached units.*
3) *Offensive patrol of the enemy's line of retreat or advance.*
4) *Look-out duties, shadowing and reconnaissance".*[37]

The requirements were a certain speed of 21 knots under reasonable weather conditions, six bow tubes (plus possibly additional external tubes) and 'Nelson' endurance. In the context of possible arms control limitations 'Geneva' displacement should be no greater than 1,800 tons. The two existing boats considered to be 'fleet submarines', K-26 and X-l, were considered. The former, as RA(S) had pointed out, while fast was too short legged; X-l, while long ranged (14,500 miles at 8 knots), could only make 19.5-20 knots. It might have been added that they were also too big, respectively 2140 and 2425 tons standard. The lecture repeated the defects of steam; the extra risks and delays caused by the many openings in the hull, the steam boats, being "less flexible off the mark" after diving and the problems of habitability. Steam's disadvantages were considered to outweigh the advantages and the future of the fleet submarine depended on the development of the internal combustion engine in which great progress was being made.[38]

The 1928 submarines remained standard overseas patrol types but policy was being reconsidered. At a Staff Meeting on 18 June of that year, it was decided that a smaller or 'S' Class boat was required to replace the 'H', 'L' and 'L-50' Classes for training, nearer patrols in the vicinity of bases and operations in confined waters such as the Baltic.[39] To maintain numbers at twelve boats under the twelve year age limit would require six 'S' Class submarines in the 1929 to 1931 programmes and another six in 1933-35. The Fleet commanders were also consulted about their submarine requirements. The latter stated that they were no longer looking for a "battle submarine" but a boat that was fast enough "to accompany the fleet".[40] Both C-in-Cs were "of the opinion that it was unsound to differentiate between the type of submarine required for patrol work".[41]

Dudley Pound, the ACNS, said that now this had "cleared the air", the way was open to the adoption of the 'G' Class, a big 1800 'Geneva' ton, 21-knot version of the patrol type with the same wireless fit.[42] It was proposed to build twelve of these boats, each larger than an existing 'M' Class, four per year in Programmes 1929-31. W. W. Fisher, the DCNS, had been dubious about the capabilities of the 'G'. His view was that "unless the 'G' Type has got a reasonable chance of success of attacking the enemy's Battle Fleet in a day action, its *raison d'être* largely disappears". However, he thought that it now had this possibility, and he was thus in favour of altering the programme over the next three years to four 'G's and two 'S' Class submarines per year. This would cost less than the previous policy of six overseas patrol submarines annually, £2,240,000, as opposed to £2,352,000.[43] This would lead to a fleet by 1 April 1932 of thirteen older under-age small boats (ten 'L-50s', one 'H' and two new 'S' Class) and twenty eight under-age larger craft (21 'O'–'P' (including the Australian pair), four 'C' and one each of 'X', 'K' and the mine-laying 'M'). In addition, there would be 23 over age boats – (twelve 'L/L50', nine 'H', one 'K' and one aircraft operating 'M'). This would give a total fleet of 64 submarines completed and twelve (four 'S' and eight 'G') under construction.

In early 1929, work went on to define the characteristics of the 'S' Class. In a letter of 16 February to the Admiralty Rear Admiral (S), Edgar Grace, set out his requirements. While the 'O' and 'G' Classes were the most suitable for a Far Eastern war, "these vessels would be too large in terms of minimum diving depth and visibility to be used to the greatest advantage in the Baltic unless the conditions obtaining denied the operating submarines the use of a base at a distance of not greater than say 500 miles."[44] The 'O' Class was also too large for local patrols. His requirement was a boat with sufficient fuel to position itself 500 miles from base and remain there for ten days charging its batteries before returning. Armament should be six bow tubes with six spare torpedoes. Radio range was to be 500 miles covering the area Copenhagen to the Gulf of Finland and Mudros to Sebastopol - the USSR seems to have been the major target of these boats. He wanted the smallest tonnage advisable but he would settle for the 760 tons standard displacement of an 'L'.[45]

As staff discussions went on, the "main considerations" in deciding on the displacement of the small boats was the compromise between the maximum size required to enter the Baltic on an opposed passage and sufficient habitability and sea keeping. Another factor was the suggested maximum displacement of 600 tons proposed at Geneva; it was considered undesirable to exceed this figure. Two designs were considered: one of 600 tons and the other of 760 tons, the latter being considered the largest capable of operation in narrow waters. The endurance requirements were slightly altered to twelve days at nine knots plus eight days on patrol to allow operations 1200 miles from base. In the middle of 1929, a compromise 635-650 'Geneva' ton design was settled upon which met all the requirements of Rear Admiral (S). It cost £210, 000 against £392,000 for an 'O'.[46]

The cheapness of the 'S' Class was attractive and the 1929 Programme was eventually settled at two 'G' and four 'S' Class boats. This was not put into effect as international negotiations on naval limitation now began once more, this time in London. The resulting London Treaty of 22 April 1930 directly affected submarines much more than had Washington. Abolition was suggested by the British, but again to no avail, which surprised no one. Instead, the Treaty limited individual submarines to 2,000 tons 'Geneva' displacement and 5.1in guns except for three boats of up to 2,800 tons 'Geneva' with up to 6.1in guns. A thirteen-year age was decided on for replacement and replacement boats were not to be begun more than three years in advance. The completed 'Geneva' tonnage of submarines of each of the three major naval powers was to be no more than 52,700 tons by 31 December 1936.[47] The Treaty also repeated in revised form the rules for submarine warfare with the usual French reservations.

The initial reaction was to reduce the 1929 programme to one 'G' and two 'S' Class boats. HMS THAMES was duly laid down at Barrow and HMS SWORDFISH and STURGEON at Chatham. M-3 had been a qualified success in the minelaying role although her slow diving time made her unsuitable for wartime operations. Pressure for a more useful production minelayer was strong. Any larger boat than 1500 'Geneva' tons was ruled out post-London, and the resulting 'Porpoise' design (based on the existing overseas patrol design but with less powerful engines) was ordered together with two more 'S' Class boats, HMS SEAHORSE and STARFISH in the 1930 Programme. HMS PORPOISE could carry 50 mines externally, but the casing and mine arrangements were better designed than M-3s that allowed faster diving and greater controllability.[48]

At this time the eventual force envisaged by the mid-1940s was 20 'C's, six minelayers and a dozen 'S' Class which would add up to 52, 630 'Geneva' tons. The 1931 and 1932 programmes, therefore, were made up of each one slightly larger 'G' (HMS SEVERN and HMS CLYDE) and two slightly modified 670 'Geneva' ton 'S' types of the 'Shark' Class (HMS SHARK, HMS SEALION, HMS SALMON and HMS SNAPPER).[49] Submerged displacements of the these boats were HM Submarines THAMES 2,680 tons, SEVERN and CLYDE, 2723 tons, SWORDFISH, 927 tons, PORPOISE, 2053 tons, and SHARK, 960 tons.[50]

1932 saw the beginning of the World Disarmament Conference under the auspices of the League of Nations.[51] The British returned to proposing abolition of submarines or, at least, a limitation of submarines to 250 tons. More realistic were President Hoover's proposals to limit submarines to 1,200 tons. In this context of great pressure for smaller displacements and limited numbers - the British supported American proposals for only forty boats in total - the Naval Staff again reviewed policy. This was:-

> "a force of the larger patrol submarines sufficient for a Far Eastern war, with a number of smaller patrol type sufficient for training both submariners and anti-submarine personnel, and for operations in European waters. In addition we require a unit of minelayers, the composition of which is calculated to our Far Eastern requirements."[52]

To reduce total tonnage the large 'G' type boats would have to be dispensed with as would the submarines with limited or specialist functions such as 'X', 'K', 'M-2' and 'R' Classes.[53] K-26 had gone to the scrap yard in 1931 and was effectively replaced by 'Thames'. M-2 sank by accident at the beginning of 1932 and M-3 went for scrap shortly afterwards to be replaced by 'Porpoise'. X-l was laid up at the end of 1933 but, still being under age by London Treaty standards and therefore unreplaceable, was kept in reserve until 1937 when she was scrapped.[54] The last 'R', R-4, went for scrap in 1934, by the end of which year the other older Classes were down to twelve 'H', ten 'Ls' and six 'L-50'.[54] 'G' Class construction was suspended and the 1933 programme was two slightly modified 'Porpoise' type minelayers, HMS GRAMPUS and HMS NARWHAL, together with a fifth 'Shark', HMS SEAWOLF.

At the beginning of 1934, Rear Admiral N. F. Lawrence, Rear Admiral (Submarines), transmitted to the Admiralty his ideas on policy in the context of thinking in the Naval Staff in favour of smaller submarines. He defined the chief role of submarines in a future war as operations in enemy waters both for reconnaissance and to attack enemy vessels. The requirements of these roles were "good wireless and a good torpedo armament".[55] The presence of submarines would soon become known if they began to sink enemy shipping which would lead to hunting and escort operations by the enemy. Penetrating through a screen would be difficult so submarines would have to fire at greater ranges. If submarines were "to have as reasonable a chance of success as in former days they will require to fire bigger numbers of torpedoes".[56] This necessitated at least six tubes internally, supplemented by external tubes, if practical. A submarine operating in enemy waters would be subject to heavy anti-submarine attack; keeping submarines as small as possible gave better powers of manoeuvrability and evasion. In wartime, demand for submarines would outstrip supply and this, added to the London limit, would strengthen the argument for keeping submarines as small as possible.[57]

Lawrence doubted if the 'Thames' Class boats could be kept tied down with the Fleet as losses mounted in forward deployed boats. A C-in-C "would almost certainly use these larger vessels to supplement the smaller ones on patrol, for which work owing to their great size they are not suitable." He agreed therefore that instead of building more 'Thames' Class boats the tonnage should be used for a larger number of smaller boats. He thought of an 800-900 standard ton (1200 tons submerged) enlargement of the 'S' with enhanced armament and the radio fit of a fleet boat. Maximum speed should be 14.5 knots with an endurance of l0,000 miles at 8 knots.

Lawrence also pressed the case for a smaller submarine than the 'S' to provide targets for anti-submarine training. The demand for such boats would probably amount to eleven or more and the 'S' Class was "unnecessarily highly developed for anti-submarine training" being too expensive and requiring an unduly large crew. He suggested, therefore, that "in view of the great importance of anti-submarine training in peace and war, consideration might be given to the production of a small, simple and cheap submarine for this purpose". The old 'H' Class was almost ideal for this task and an even simpler and cheaper repeat of the 'H' should "be designed for the primary purpose of anti-submarine training, but carrying a good torpedo armament and therefore of considerable value in war for short distance patrols, if required." [58]

In February 1934, therefore, the Naval Staff set its sights at twenty patrol and six mine-laying submarines for a Far Eastern war, not less than twelve 'S' Class smaller patrol type boats for European war requirements and training amid six simple submarines preferably no larger than the 'H' Class for anti-submarine training.[59] The fleet, for Treaty calculations, would therefore be based on new construction larger patrol submarines being no larger than 1,000 tons standard displacement, only two thirds the displacement of the existing overseas patrol type. This would provide an eventual replacement fleet of 44 boats, six minelayers, twenty of the new 1,000 ton patrol type, twelve 'S' Class boats and six 400 ton Replacement 'H' Class. This came to 39,800 tons, within a 40,000 ton limit.

In reality, however, given the three 'G's and the 'O' Class not requiring replacement until the 1937 Programme, the likely fleet by 1945 would be 45 boats of 44,695 tons: six minelayers, three 'G's, fifteen 1,000 tonners, three remaining 'Rainbows', twelve 'S' Class and six replacement 'H' Class. This meant that Britain could not reduce below 45,000 tons in the near term although 40,000 tons might eventually be possible.[60] In the event, the London Treaty of 1936 placed no overall limits on submarines. It merely reiterated the 2,000 ton limit on individual boats. The related London Submarine Agreement also reiterated the limitations on the conduct of submarines as commerce raiders in war.[61]

Thus the 'T' Class submarine was born. Its displacement was kept to a minimum, Rear Admiral (S) minuting that, "It is desired to emphasise that every increase in size increases the submarine's vulnerability to anti-submarine measures, and hence decreases her efficiency".[62] Eventually, HMS TRITON of the 1935 Programme displaced 1,095 tons standard (1585 tons submerged) but later boats were reduced by a further ten tons. Speed was reduced slightly to 15.25 knots surfaced but the 'T' Class was a little faster than the older overseas patrol boats under water. The boats carried four external tubes to give the required heavy forward armament of ten 21in tubes.[63] The 1934 Programme had contained a fourth minelayer, HMS RORQUAL, and two more 'Sharks', HMS SPEARFISH and HMS SUNFISH, while the 1935 programme, as well as HMS TRITON, contained a fifth mine-layer, HMS CACHALOT, and the last of the 'S' Class, HMS STERLET.[64]

The replacement 'H' Class grew a little despite Director of Plans' injunction that as it was required primarily for training; it should therefore be "small and simple".[65] It had to be able to carry out short distance patrols and therefore to have a good torpedo armament. These patrols would be of up to ten days at a distance of 500 miles from base "which should meet any requirements that can be foreseen in a European war outside the Mediterranean".[66] Rear Admiral (S) saw the boat as very much a replacement 'H' with lighter engine, asdic, strengthened main ballast tanks and higher periscopes. He saw the boat as being no more than 450 tons.[67]

The Naval Staff, however, then broadened the boat's role to operations in defence of harbours and bases in the Far East before the arrival of the main fleet. The 'S' Class had insufficient habitability for operations in the tropics.[68] The new small boat would also require excellent underwater performance to deal with intense hostile ASW when engaging in offensive patrols in a European war. The type was thus developed into what the Controller called a "useful offensive submarine" with a displacement of 540 tons standard (730 tons submerged).[69] Two were put into the 1936 Programme (along with the minelayer HMS SEAL and the second 'T') and another in the Supplementary Re-armament Programme of that year. They became the 'U' Class.

Although in its request for a long term rearmament programme in 1935 the Admiralty had called for the construction of 24 submarines over the period 1936 to 1942, the Defence Requirements Committee in its November report called merely for a continuation of the building of three boats per year after the four in 1936.[70] Retention of the older overseas patrol boats would however allow the maintenance of the 55 submarines required by the so called 'DRC Standard'.[71] The latter was, however, still only a version of a 'one power standard' that had been made obsolete by German re-armament". A new two power standard of naval strength was therefore defined against both Japan and Germany.[72]

The Government, though reluctant to accept such an expensive new initiative, was prepared to sanction the 'acceleration' of certain programmes. This led to the approval of four more submarines in each of the 1936, 1937, 1938 and 1939 programmes a total of eight for 1936 and seven in each of the successive years. Another 'U' and three more 'T's were duly ordered in 1936 with the entire programme the following year being taken up by seven 'T' Class boats.[73]

1937 saw the Admiralty present its proposals for the 'New Standard of Naval Strength'. This called for a total fleet of 82 submarines.[74] The Government could not afford such ambitions and postponed a decision. Indeed, in 1938 the submarine programme was cut back to three boats, again all 'T's, in the general reduction in the naval programme forced on the Admiralty that year. It was decided, as Inskip the Minister for the Co-ordination of Defence put it, "having regard to the extent of the demands to be made on our available resources and in particular to the increased demands likely to be made by the Air, which at the present time is of the utmost importance, the proposed New Standard of Naval Strength is impossible of attainment and that we must rest content with something substantially less".[75] No more submarines were ordered before the outbreak of war.

On September 3 1939, the Royal Navy's submarine fleet exceeded the DRC Standard with 57 boats. It was indeed half way towards the New Standard with a dozen new 'T's, either building or on trials. Eight 'S' Class boats, HMS OXLEY and three 'T's were with the Second Flotilla at Dundee; the three new 'U's, two old 'L's and H32 were with the Sixth Flotilla at Blyth; the Fifth Training Flotilla had three 'H's at Portland and four more, plus HMS OBERON, at Portsmouth; the 1st Flotilla at Malta had three minelayers, four 'S' Class and three 'O's; HMS SEVERN and HMS CLYDE were at Gibraltar on passage to Freetown; and the China Station's Fourth Flotilla had four 'O's, five 'P's,, four 'Rainbows' plus three minelayers. Under refit at home were HMS THAMES, an 'L' and two 'H's.

This was about the same number of submarines as possessed by Germany and the British flotilla comprised a force of much larger displacement and reach, a reflection of the British Empire's very different strategic situation. Given all the other pressing requirements of naval policy, and the asdic threat to the submarine's future viability, the Royal Navy's Submarine Service had not done at all badly. The Royal Navy needed capital ships, aircraft carriers, cruisers, destroyers and escort vessels more than it needed submarines. The Royal Navy was about sea control; the submarine was about sea denial.

The relative decline of British naval power meant that, in comparison to the previous war, there would be more opportunities for British submarines to come into their own in hostile waters, notably in the Far East until the fleet arrived. This advised significant investment in submarines. Yet submarines could only enable surface forces to win any maritime campaign, they could not do it themselves. It is a sign of the perception of the trident slipping from Britannia's fingers that the Submarine Service was as welll equipped as it was.

British submarines suffered – although at times and only up to a point – from having been designed for the wrong war. Inevitably, the pre-war Royal Navy was built primarily to fight the Empire's greatest naval threat, Japan. The larger boats intended for that theatre suffered heavy casualties when used in waters for which they had not been designed. Larger quantities of 'S' Class submarines would have been built if inter-war Naval planners had been equipped with a crystal ball to foresee the priority being Germany and Italy. In January 1940, at a meeting at Britain's submarine HQ at Aberdour, ".....it was stated that the 'T' Class are too big and the 'U' Class too small for North Sea work and it would be very desirable, if possible, to repeat 'S' Class submarines".

It was therefore decided to replace five planned 'T' Class boats by the smaller type, that was then mass produced alongside later batches of the 'T' and 'U' Classes during the war. Yet the 'S' Class suffered as much, if not more, heavily than the other Classes, all but three of the original twelve being lost. Submarine losses were more due to the difficult conditions in which British boats operated and the effectiveness of their enemies than defects in the boats themselves. The three standard 'S', 'T' and 'U' Classes were good designs that together suited all the environments in which British submariners had to operate, including Far Eastern waters.

British inter-war submarine policy seems at this distance entirely logical and sensible. That it lacked consistency and was based sometimes on slightly spurious logic is part and parcel of the difficulties in policy-making in an environment where personalities are changing, technology is evolving, real operational experience is lacking, and money is tight. There are clear lessons for today, both in what was got wrong and what was got right.

NOTES

1   A. N. Harrison *The Development of HM Submarines*, unpublished Ms.(1979) Submarine Museum, Gosport, p.12.1.
2   Displacements are submerged unless otherwise stated.
3   Harrison, *ibid*. Also, Conway's *All the World's Fighting Ships 1906-21*. London, Conway, 1985, pp. 86-94.
4   *Ibid*. See also the Chapter by Igor Kosyn in this volume in which the details of the raising of the L-55 by the Soviet Navy in 1928 are described.
5   BR1736(52) (1)
6   Ship's Cover 424, *Oberon*, Agenda for Staff Conference, 8/10/21 (not held). See also Submarine Policy paper 29/S.92 in ADM 116/3164.
7   Naval Staff Memorandum of 5 October 1921 in CAB4/7.
8   X1 was laid down the following month. For Xl see R. Compton-Hall, *Submarine Warfare: Monsters and Midgets* Poole, Blandford Press, 1985.
9   Compton-Hall, *ibid*, p.48.
10 Paper on Submarine Policy,17/1/24, ADM ll6/3164
11 For negotiating strategy reference submarines see S. Roskill, *Naval Policy Between The Wars*, Vol 1, Chapter VIII London, Collins, 1968 and M.G.Fry, "The Pacific Dominions and the Washington Conference" in E. Goldstein and J. Maurer, *The Washington Conference 1921-2* London, Frank Cass, 1994.
12 T.H Buckley, *The United States and the Washington Conference 1921-1922*, Knoxville, University of Tennessee Press, 1970.
13 ADM1/8622 quoted Roskill, *ibid*, p.328
14 BR1736(52)(1)
15 Chatfield paper of 19 May 1922 in Cover 424.
16 'Agenda Notes', *ibid*.
17 Chatfield paper, *ibid*.
18 *Ibid*. See also 29/S.92 in ADM116/3164
19 DCNS, 30/5/22 in Cover 424.
20 1/6/22,.
21 BR1736(52)(1)
22 Board minute in *Ibid*.
23 29/S.92, ADM 116/3164
24 Conways *All The World's Fighting Ships 1922-1946* London, Conways,1980 p.47, see also Cover 424 and Harrison, *op. cit*, Chapter 14.
25 A. Henry, "British Submarine Policy 1918-39" in B. Ranft (Ed.) *Technical Change and British Naval Policy* London, Hodder and Stoughton, 1977, pp. 88-9
26 Compton-Hall, *op.cit* pp. 100-103.
27 Horton, memo. to Rear Admiral (S) quoted in *ibid*. p. 59.
28 *Ibid*.
29 Its papers are in ADM 116/3164.
30 Harrison, *op. cit*., 12.7-12.9; also, Conways l922-46, p.48.
31 RA(S) paper of 8/2/28 in Ship's Cover 458 Thames Class
32 Harrison *op cit* pp. 12-4-12.5. Compton-Hall, *op. cit*., pp. 42, 85-6.
33 Henry, *Op. Cit*., pp.90-1
34 ADM 116/3164
35 D of TD 27/11/26, Ship's Cover 458. *'Thames' Class*.
36 Paper of 8/2/28 in Cover 458.
37 Folio 5 in *ibid*
38 *Ibid*
39 "Submarine Building Programme" in Ship's Cover 458, and Folio 1 in Cover 510 *Submarines 'S' Class of 1931*.
40 Remarks by ACNS,16/3/29, Cover 458.
41 "Submarine Building Programme", Cover 458
42 Paper of 16/3/29, Folio 6, Ship's Cover 458.
43 Paper of 7/3/29 in *ibid*.
44 Folio 1 in Ship's Cover 510.
45 *Ibid*.
46 Folios 3 and 17, *Ibid*.
47 Harrison, *op.cit*. pp. 12.2-3.
48 Henry, *op. cit*., p. 94
49 Harrison, *op. cit*. p.12.10.
50 SC Conways, 1922-46, pp 48-49.
51 Henry, *op. cit*., pp.96-7.
52 Plans Division paper quoted in Folio 1 of Ships Cover 542, 'Triton' Class.

53 *Ibid.*
54 Compton-Hall, *op. cit.* pp.50, 64-5 and 86.
55 Conways 1922-46, p.13
56 Folio 1 of Cover 542, *'Triton' Class*
57 *Ibid.*
58 *Ibid.*
59 "Proposed Submarine Policy for the 1935 Naval Conference", Folio 1, Ship's Cover 542.
60 *Ibid.*
61 Henry, *op cit.*,p.101.
62 Ship's Cover 542.
63 *Ibid* 542
64 Harrison, *op. cit.*, p. 12.10
65 5 May 1934 in Ship's Cover 548, New 'H' Class Submarine
66 *Ibid,*
67 5 March 1935 in *Ibid.*
68 12/12/34, Folio 13,lbid.
69 Folio 31 *Ibid.*
70 S.Roskill, *Naval Policy Between the Wars*, Volume 2 London Collins, 1976 pp. 217-8
71 For the 'DRC Standard' see N.H. Gibbs, *Grand Strategy Volume 1, Rearmament Policy* London, HMSO, 1976 p.334.
72 *Ibid.* pp. 336-7.
73 P Ackerman, *Encyclopaedia of British Submarines* Liskeard, Maritime Books, 1989 p. 363
74 Roskill, *op cit.*, p.327.
75 Quoted in Gibbs, *op cit.* pp. 353-4.

6

The Development of Torpedo Fire Control Computers in the Royal Navy

Terry D. Lindell

INTRODUCTION

The development of Torpedo Fire Control Computers in the Royal Navy can be viewed as a simultaneous evolution of torpedo range, submarine technology, and the ability to compute. Increasing torpedo range and the introduction of gyro stabilized steering made accurate aiming essential. Improving submarine technology included the integration of control and sensor systems into a weapons platform that operated independently for extended periods of time. Finally, the development of the ability to compute mechanically reduced the overall error and dealt with more and more variables automatically.

It is the development of mechanical computers that finally created torpedo control systems that could represent and solve the physical problem accurately. Targeting a torpedo successfully requires a solution of the equations of motion for both the target and the submarine. It also requires accurate values for position, speed, and range for both. It requires accurate tactical values for the torpedoes. As torpedo fire control developed, more of these variables were integrated into the system. As the system became more complete, the accuracy improved. This paper examines the steps by which the Royal Navy went from aiming by eye to a completely integrated system after World War II.

DEFLECTION SIGHT TORPEDO DIRECTORS

The Royal Navy, just like all navies, first aimed torpedoes by eye. To get hits, they had to be close. The Royal Navy observed one of the first Whitehead torpedoes hit and sink the coal barge AIGLE in late August 1870, at a range of only 136 yards. Even at this close range, the event was amazing to everyone present. Soon afterwards, the torpedo operating range quickly increased, and, just as quickly, the need for a torpedo director became apparent.

The first torpedo directors were Deflection Sights Mk I and II. They were invented in about 1901 and were used during World War I. The Mk I Torpedo director was nothing more than a gun sight modified to work with torpedoes. To create the Mk I, the Admiralty Gunnery Branch dismantled a line-of-sight gun director. The top compass rose was replaced with 'deflection' bars that both sighted the target and computed the 'Director Angle' or 'DA' (at some times interchangeably referred to as the 'Deflection Angle'). In this way, a 'torpedo triangle' was represented and solved on the director.

To use the Mk I Torpedo Director, the type and speed of the torpedo was set up, and then a sliding bar with a locking nut and spring was used to set the estimated offset for speed of the target into the device. Next, the angle on the bow was set into the director, based on a reading obtained from a telescope. This angle was set into the director and the result lined up on the target pointer. This was the Director Angle, or alteration of course required to get a 'hit'. Setting this course into the torpedo was then accomplished by either training the torpedo tube, changing the ships own course, or off-setting the gyro of the torpedo.

By way of comparison, the Mk II director was contemporary with the Mk I and used as a line-of-sight director, with a small notch sight added to the top of the device. The Mk II could be used to directly measure the angle on the bow, thereby removing the error in transferring this reading from the telescope. With these directors, the DA angle was solved with simple triangulation. No adjustments were made for any other variables. Different torpedo speeds were handled by changing the entire top ring of the director.

The special problems of launching torpedoes from a submarine were accommodated by the introduction of the Mk. III Universal Sight in 1917. It came in two models: one for cruisers with a telescope sight and the other designed for use with periscopes on submarines. The advantage of this director was the adaptation of its own optics.

As torpedo targeting became more complicated, additional equipment was invented to handle other parts of the problem. The 'Torpedo Control Disc', was invented to adjust for the speed and range of the torpedo. A Range-finder was built into the periscope and a special Torpedo Plot for the chart table was invented. Tables were developed for estimating target speed. Even with all of these improvements, the top compass rose of the Mk III 'Universal Sight' still had to be changed for each different type of torpedo, making the sight not all that universal. As all of this associated equipment added to the job of getting a torpedo on target, torpedo firing became a complex project requiring several people working as a team.

THE NASMITH 'IS – WAS"

Then Lieutenant Commander Martin Nasmith, Royal Navy, invented the ubiquitous 'Is – Was' circular slide rule in 1917. It was first used in combat in March 1918. The popularity of the device was universal, for it was quickly copied in one form or another by all other submarine services. Its beauty lay in its simplicity. It collapsed the calculations being done by most all of the variation in deflection torpedo directors into one simple lightweight device that was typically hung from a lanyard and worn around the neck.

The 'Is – Was' got its name from the key problem in computing the DA. Because the submarine and target both moved, computing the DA for where the target 'Is' right now only identified where the target 'Was' a moment ago. Because the target moved, it 'Is' somewhere else in the next moment of time, and because of this the DA had changed.

This did not prevent the 'Is – Was' from giving important results. Quite to the contrary, the 'Is – Was' was found to be very useful in checking the results derived from other equipment. In addition, it was useful for computing where the target would be in the future if some constant course and speed were assumed. The 'Is – Was' brought solving the torpedo targeting triangle down to its simplest terms.

THE SUBMARINE TORPEDO DIRECTOR (MK I AND MK II)

Hugh Clausen was the chief designer of the STD, the first Royal Navy calculating torpedo director. Known as 'The Fruit Machine' because its appearance resembled candy fruit gum dispensers, the machine was entirely Clausen's design. However, prior to this success, Clausen worked closely with, and learned much from, both Harold Isherwood and D.H. Landstad.

During the 1920s, Harold Isherwood and D.H. Landstad were the chief designers of the computer that was to become the Admiralty Fire Control Table (AFCT) Mk I for the big guns on the battle ships. The device in service prior to this invention was known as the 'Dryer Fire Control Table'. Isherwood had been the chief designer from the Argo Clock Company, the builder of the 'Argo Clock', a competitive system to the 'Dryer Table'. For a number of reasons, some of them political, the 'Argo Clock' lost out to the 'Dryer Table', even though some argued that it was the better system. It was quite ironic that Isherwood went on to design a replacement for the very Admiralty that had turned him down before.

As chief engineer in the electrical mechanical department of the Admiralty's ordnance design bureau, Clausen had a large responsibility for the success of the new AFCT. The work on the AFCT Mk I was late and over budget. The first AFCT was installed just in the nick of time for the commissioning of HMS NELSON in August 1927 and the HMS RODNEY in the following November. The rush was so great that it took an entire year to produce a handbook for AFCT, dated 1928.

During this time, Clausen was working very hard trying to create further simplifications of the AFCT to get costs down. The cruiser version of the AFCT, called the Mk II, was put into service in 1930. He and his department came up with a succession of upgrades and modifications for the AFCT while at the same time he was trying to work on a submarine fire control system. Because of the stress level from doing all projects at the same time, and likely due to the collapse of the naval budget in the 1932 – 1933 year, Clausen had a nervous breakdown in 1932. Because of these health problems, the submarine fire control project was suspended. The STD Mk I re-started development when Clausen returned to work very late in 1933. There are no patents for the STD in the name of Hugh Clausen, which is not too surprising considering that they were highly secret.

It was to take five more years before Clausen had the time to complete the Royal Navy's Submarine Torpedo Director Mk I (STD). It was first delivered in May 1938. Two new machines per month were then delivered. It was not until well after 1939, however, before the entire submarine fleet would be equipped with the new director. The STD Mk I machine was installed in all 'U' and 'T' Class submarines during World War II.

It was a very compact angle solver that predicted a future firing point. The machine automatically updated the submarine's course into the calculation by driving a follow-up system from the gyrocompass. It solved the problem of getting the angles off the bow wrong by introducing a 'red' and 'green' system for keeping straight the starboard and port DA. For the first time in the Royal Navy, nearly all of the variables and calculations were embodied in one device. This is not to say that the STD's results were not checked against other information sources.

There was always an 'Is – Was' or two hanging around necks in the control room used to work out the current problem, future scenarios, and always as a check as if everyone's life depended on it. In fact, they did. In the end, however, it was still believed in the Submarine Service that nothing replaced having a talent for mental approximation. Over the eyepiece of the periscope on the Rothesay attack teacher at Port Bannatyne in Bute Scotland, there was a brass plaque engraved with the following words: "Remember, the DA is always 10 degrees."

This was generally true for a 7-knot merchantman during a normal approach; but it was not true when the rules of the game changed radically, or the submarine found its self in less than ideal conditions. The Mk II STD was developed in 1942 and was first installed in the 'A' Class submarines. The differences between the

Mk I and the Mk II were slight. They had the same mechanical layout, the same inputs, and even the same basic appearance, but the new Mk II STD was able to handle longer-range torpedoes and larger target sizes. The Mk II STD could set the torpedo speed without a conversion chart and had a slightly different face that measured the DA in increments of ten degrees.

Even with the improvements, the STD did not automatically track the position of the target and submarine, or set the gyro angle computed into the torpedoes in the tubes. At about the same time that the STD Mk II came into service, the Royal Navy was told about the American TDC Mk III used in the US fleet submarine.

THE AMERICAN TDC AND THE ROYAL NAVY

On October 22, 1942 Commander A.S. Conway RN, a British naval attaché to Washington, D.C. forwarded a report by the Admiralty on the American TDC system. This was the first time that the Royal Navy became aware of the American TDC and its capabilities. Overall, the Royal Navy was in the process of defining its own new director system with goals very similar to the functions found in the American TDC. The Royal Navy examined the American TDC Mk III, and several letters and reports were written looking at the possibility of adopting it as the new computer. The reports also examined the possibility of using the American TDC Mk III as an upgrade to the 'T' Class submarines.

The discussions with the US Navy and the contractor (ARMA), who built and designed the American, TDC progressed at a high rate. At one point, the Ordnance Department nearly cancelled development of it own new STD. Instead, at the last minute, it decided to continue the project on a very low priority while studies about how to adopt the American TDC continued. At one point, several of the older TDC Mk 1 machines were ordered as attack trainers and 24 sets were ordered from the ARMA Corporation.

There were a number of serious technical difficulties to overcome, but none proved an impossible task. In a paper written in 1945, the Royal Navy went through every value and variable in the American TDC and compared it to the specifications contained in the project for the completely integrated STD that was still only making slow progress.

A few of the new TDC's were delivered, but they could not be made to work. There was a problem with the shorter length from the control room to the torpedo tubes that could not be accommodated in the existing TDC. This, however, could be fixed with a modification that ARMA had already done to some other machines. In addition, there were engineering problems in gearing the American GISR (Gyro Indicating Setting Regulator) into the 'A' and 'T' Class submarine's torpedo tubes. For example, the ARMA TDC Mk III used a 110 Volt time motor whereas British submarines used 240 Volts. The 110 Volt 60 cycle AC power on the American submarine had to be replaced with 220 Volt 50 cycle AC on the British submarine.

All of these problems were fixed, but there was one big problem that could not. This was money. The TDC Mk III was very expensive. An American Torpedo Data Computer, with its angle setters, cost just over $100,000. For an American fleet submarine, with a total construction price of $10,000,000, this figure represented about 1% of the price of the entire boat. For a British submarine, with a price tag considerably less, this percentage of cost relative to the entire boat for just the fire control system was far too high.

During one of the many conferences and meetings that were held during that time, the British were looking for a way to eliminate the mechanical American angle setter with something that would set the torpedoes electrically. The TDC project engineer, Dr. Don Gittens at ARMA, had come up with an ingenious method for solving one problem by making contact between the outside circuits going to the computer and the torpedo, using a brush contact in the torpedo tube that would connect with buttons on the outside of the torpedo. It was pointed out that the brush contacts in the tube were made out of gold so that they would not corrode in the harsh salt-water environment. One of the attending British Commanders, upon hearing this, commented that there was only one problem with the design. The surprised ARMA engineer inquired what that problem might be, to which the Commander then replied, "the problem that we have is that you have all of the gold!"

POST WAR TCC MK III

In 1953, the Admiralty at Bath announced the completion of the prototype of the next generation of Torpedo Control Computer. It had developed its own experimental version of the American TDC Mk III system, with enhancements. The development of this machine had taken a tremendous amount of work and had to resolve a large number of problems.

In fact, the first version of the new machine was brought to Port Bannatyne in Bute. Captain John Coote, who at that time was in charge of the attack teacher, closely examined it. The machine pulled up in a plain un-marked white van, along with the project engineer. After a short conversation, "it quickly became apparent that the machine had been built without the designer having grasped the basic need to generate and utilise the target's rate of change of bearing. So it went back to Bath the very next day."

It was back to the drawing board until five years later when the Royal Navy finally got it right, emerging with the Torpedo Control Computer System for Submarines Mk 3. This system incorporated, for the first time, all of the specifications laid out when the Royal Navy was looking at purchasing the American TDC Mk III. It had the ability to track the target and the submarine; automatically set the Gyro Angle and the running depth; compute spreads; and take input from the ship's sensors. Indeed, the complete system exceeded the capabilities of the American TDC Mk IV that was, at the time, installed as an in-place upgrading kit to the TDC Mk III.

The TCC finally solved the entire torpedo-targeting problem. The integrated system provided submarine captains with the best available system in 1959. Both the TDC and the TCC were in service for a surprising number of years. The American TDC Mk III and IV operated in the fleet for forty years between 1936 and 1976. The Royal Navy TCC was in operational boats for thirty years from 1959 until at least 1979. These were the last mechanical analog computer systems developed for torpedo fire control and, quite possibly, nearly the last computers of their type in any system. All systems that succeeded both the American TDC Mk IV and the Royal Navy's TCC Mk 3 were electronic representations of these finely-made mechanical computers.

As the electronics started to take over the torpedoes' fire control and demonstrate their own special problems of cooling, lack of shock resistance, and frequent breakdowns, many submarine captains remembered fondly both the TDC and the TCC. To be sure, the problems with the electronics were all solved in time. However, no one can argue that the TDC and TCC were not very solid devices that always worked, no matter what other damage was on the boat. They completely represented the problem and presented a graphical solution. In short, the mechanical analog computers were a very successful, stable, and long-term solution to the Torpedo Fire Control problem.

7

RN Submarines in World War II

Jeff Tall

In the mid-summer of 1939, immediately prior to the outbreak of the Second World War, the Royal Navy possessed fifty-seven submarines. Twelve of these were of First World War vintage; the rest were of what was known at the time as 'new construction', designed and built in the period between the wars. They were broadly of six different types. The most numerous and oldest group was the eighteen boats of the 'O', 'P' and 'R' Classes that were large patrol submarines intended for operations in the Far East. They were of long endurance and had, for a submarine, good accommodation, but had external fuel tanks that tended to leak.

The three very large 'River' Class boats which, chronologically, came next were designed with a surface speed high enough to accompany the fleet. They suffered, however, from the same defects as the 'O', 'P' and 'R' Classes and proved too slow for the purpose. The 'Rivers' were followed by a Class of six new minelayers of the same size as the 'O' Class that could carry many more mines than earlier types of minelaying submarines. All these types of submarine were large, but in the early thirties it was decided to produce a smaller patrol submarine for use in home waters and the Mediterranean. Twelve of the 'S' Class of the same size as the successful First World War 'E' Class were built. The 'S' Class were not of high performance, but had internal fuel tanks and were handy and reliable. The latest designs were the 'T' and the 'U' Classes, the leading units of which had just come into service.

The 'T' had the same endurance as the 'O' Class, but was smaller, and, like the 'S' Class, carried its fuel internally. It also had a more powerful torpedo armament so that it could attack at longer ranges. Otherwise, its performance was only that which the 'O', 'P' and 'R' Classes achieved in service but they were, above all, reliable. Three 'T' Class had been completed and were doing their trials and another twelve were in various stages of construction. The original intention in the 'U' Class was to produce an unarmed training submarine to replace the rest of the ageing 'H' Class. With the gathering war clouds, however, the final design that emerged was of a small patrol submarine that was also suitable for training.

British submarines were designed primarily for attack on warships. All were armed with the 21-inch torpedo: the 'new construction' submarines carried a warhead of 750 lbs of high explosive and the older boats with a warhead of 500 lbs. All of the 'new construction' submarines could fire a bow salvo of six torpedoes. All, except the dozen submarines of First World War vintage, were therefore capable of sinking the most powerful warships afloat. The six minelaying submarines carried fifty moored contact mines as well as a salvo of six bow torpedo tubes. However, these torpedoes were straight runners without gyro angling, which made their effective use, particularly in a fast moving situation, all the more challenging for the submarine CO and his team.

The larger Classes of submarine mounted a four-inch gun in a rotating breastwork with quick manning hatches. The 'S' Class mounted a three-inch gun on the fore casing and the 'U' Class could also do so if they sacrificed two reload torpedoes. The elderly 'H' Class had no gun.

An asdic set was fitted in all submarines except eight boats of the 'H' Class. This instrument was mainly used as a hydrophone for listening but could also be used for communication between submerged submarines or for echo detection of another submerged submarine. All submarines had a wireless loop aerial which could receive low frequency signals from the Rugby wireless station when totally submerged in home waters, or the Mediterranean. New construction submarines could send messages by high frequency wireless from anywhere in the world to the Admiralty's shore network of receiving stations.

The larger submarines could remain at sea for a period of some six weeks, operating at about two thousand miles from their base. The medium-sized submarines of the 'S' and 'L' Classes could keep at sea for a month or so and operate at about a thousand miles from their base; for the smaller submarines of the 'H' and 'U' Classes, the figures were a fortnight and five hundred miles.

In all classes of submarine, the electric storage batteries had the capacity to drive the submarine at slow speed (two knots or so) for a period of twenty-four hours with a margin for making an attack or two or taking evasive action. It was then necessary to re-charge the batteries on the surface for a period of some six hours. Submarines, therefore, had no difficulty in staying down during daylight hours, but it was essential to have time to re-charge on the surface every night.

One way to detect the enemy when running submerged was the periscope; this could be used in daylight but was of no use on a dark night against unlit targets. There was also a limit to its use in rough weather both because of the height of the waves and the difficulty of keeping the submarine accurately at the right depth. The only other method of detecting the enemy was by asdics. This was normally used passively and was the only way to detect that ships were about when the submarine was running submerged at below periscope depth. Usually in good visibility by day, the periscope would see the enemy first; but in bad visibility, asdics would often give the first warning. On the surface, both by day and night, the only way to detect an enemy, whether a ship or an aircraft, was by lookouts using binoculars. On the surface, asdics was of little use to detect ships.

By far the most effective way to make a torpedo attack was from a submerged position using the periscope, but this could only be done in daylight. The target could then be positively identified, the course and speed plotted, and the torpedoes accurately aimed. However, in calm weather, the torpedo tracks might well be sighted in time for the target to take avoiding action. Manoeuvring to attack also required considerable skill. At night, when nothing could be seen through the periscope, a torpedo attack had to be made on the surface. It was then harder to identify the target, to estimate range, course and speed, and there was always the danger that the submarine would be sighted. However, submarines were faster on the surface than submerged and had a better chance to close distant targets. Attacks could also be made with the submarine dived deeper than periscope depth by using asdics, but this method was the least accurate of all and the chances of success were low.

Passage making in wartime could be made most expeditiously by running on the surface using the diesel engines day and night. A distance of about 300 miles could be made in twenty-four hours. Proceeding on the surface by day was, however, hazardous when attack by aircraft or enemy submarines was likely. Passage-making under these conditions was, therefore, normally made by proceeding submerged by day and only running on the surface at night. This reduced progress to about

130 miles in a twenty-four hour period.

Turning to personnel, of the 49 submarines in commission, five were commanded by Commanders; twenty-nine by Lieutenant Commanders and fifteen by Lieutenants. In short, the Submarine Service overall was a bit long in the tooth. The ratings who formed the submarine crews were, like the officers, almost without exception volunteers. They were long service ratings enlisted for twelve years or to complete time for pension and had to be in the 'very good' category for conduct.

The numbers actually manning the submarines of the Royal Navy totalled some two hundred and seventy officers and two thousand five hundred men; this figure includes spare crews in each flotilla and the number required as a drafting margin, as well as those under training. This accounted for 1.7% of the total strength of the Royal Navy and Royal Marines. The ships' companies of the four depot ships and the shore base at Fort Blockhouse, who were from general service, amounted to another two hundred and fifteen officers and two thousand men. This total of some five thousand needed to man and support the submarine branch was 3.9% of the total strength of the Royal Navy and Royal Marines, which stood at 129,000 in mid-1939.

The training of British submarines for war can only be described as patchy. Training in making submerged torpedo attacks by day was excellent, both by individual officers when qualifying for command and for submarines in commission. Attack teachers' valuable training devices were installed in all depot ships and in the submarine base at Fort Blockhouse. The only defect in 'attack training' was in the spreading of salvoes of torpedoes. Spreading of full salvoes against warships was understood and practised, but the use of reduced salvoes of two, three or four torpedoes had not been studied. This is perhaps understandable as British submarines were not expected to attack merchant ships for which such reduced salvoes were mainly required.

On the other hand, training in night torpedo attacks on the surface was at best poor and at worst non-existent. The reason for this was the fear of a collision leading to the probable loss of a submarine. Practice torpedo attacks by asdics were sometimes undertaken, but were not properly analysed; few Commanding Officers had any confidence in this method. Crash diving from the surface and diving deep from periscope depth to avoid being rammed were exercised *ad nauseam*, but the training of lookouts by day against aircraft or at night against darkened ships was also extremely poor. The use of the gun in a surprise attack from submerged was frequently practised and British submarines were well ahead of other navies with this tactic.

The exercise of submarines in long patrols was just satisfactory during fleet exercises by the three operational flotillas, but the only chance the training submarines had was during the period of an exercise known as the 'Rear Admiral (Submarines)'s War' which took place each summer. A certain amount of practice in evasion of anti-submarine measures was obtained during exercises with asdic fitted ships. The main hope of survival in war, however, was based on optimism and knowledge that hydrophones had proved of little use against German U-boats in the First World War and that there were no indications that asdics had been developed by any of our potential enemies.

To recap, British submarines were designed to: attack enemy warships; act as forward reconnaissance vessels for the Fleet; act as a defensive measure for harbours; and train ASW forces. Their training reflected these roles.

So, what did they actually do and how well did they do it? First of all, consider their area of operations. In essence, operating areas followed the threat and ranged from Norwegian and Russian waters, through the Bay of Biscay, into the Mediterranean, and out to the Far East. The bloodiest battle was fought in the

Mediterranean against the Axis replenishment route to North Africa and, at one stage, losses reached 66% of submarines operating in that Theatre.

Their roles were: anti-surface warfare with torpedo and gun; anti-submarine warfare; clandestine operations with agents; forward surveillance; reconnaissance operations with COPP; minelaying; harbour penetration and shore bombardment; cargo and troop carrying; towing X-craft; carrying human torpedoes; channel marking for invasion forces; ASW training; and air/sea rescue.

By the end of World War Two, British submarines, supported by allies from Holland, Poland, Norway, France, and Greece, had sunk two million tons of enemy shipping and fifty-seven major war vessels. They sank thirty-six enemy submarines, the overwhelming majority by catching their prey on the surface. They also famously achieved the first ever sinking of another submarine when dived when Lt Jimmy Launders in HMS VENTURER sank U-864 off the coast of Norway on 9 February, 1945.

They achieved all this during 2,603 patrols – 1,064 on the Home and Atlantic Station; 1162 in the Mediterranean; and 404 in the Far East. Allied submarines operating under British control conducted 380 of them: 131 by the Royal Netherlands Navy; 117 by the French; 49 by the Poles; 33 by the Greeks; 24 by the Norwegians; 20 by the United States; and six by the Italians after the Armistice. The duration of the patrols ranged from 55 days by HMS TANTALUS (Rufus Mackenzie) which carried him 11,692 miles, to about a week by the 'H' boats. HMS H-28, by the way, was the only British submarine to have conducted patrols in both WW1 and WWII.

As well as many enemy reports of contacts out of range, these patrols elicited 1,732 attacks by torpedo, using an average salvo size of 2.8 weapons, of which 688 were successful in that they achieved one or more hits. This is a 40% success rate. So what of the failures?

- 30% were of indefinite cause - probably an accumulation of the breakdown below.
- 18.6% was through using too small a salvo size (failure to pay attention to lessons learned pre-war).
- Bad conditions (i.e. 'high sea state' = poor depth keeping; 'poor visibility' = snow) accounted for 13.6%.
- 10% was caused by material failure of the torpedoes (although only 2.17% of the weapons fired actually failed) the major cause being gyro failure.
- Weapons running underneath the target – 8.3%; the minimum depth setting of the MkVIII was eight feet.
- COs got their estimations wrong in 7.8% of the cases (usually overestimating target speed).
- In 6.4% of the cases the enemy were alert to the approach of the weapons and evaded.
- The remainder, 4.5%, were due to drill error.

The lack of gyro-angling was a severe limitation on the COs, resulting in many cases of missing the 'DA', which makes the results above all the more impressive. It is also worthy of note that of the 980-odd vessels sunk by Royal Navy submarines in the Mediterranean, 72% of them were in escorted convoy.

There were also 1046 gun actions – usually against caiques, schooners and the like - although 51 of these were against minor war-vessels. Here, the success rate reached 91%. On top of that, there were 65 attacks against airfields, bridges, railway lines, oil tanks and port facilities. Captain Shrimp Simpson of the 'Fighting Tenth' was a great believer in these operations since they tied down large numbers of opposition gunners and technicians for their protection and repair.

British submarines and their allies laid ninety minefields consisting of 3,187 mines. 52, or 1.6%, of the mines laid were successful. There were 49 storing trips to Malta. 'X'-craft were towed on ten occasions and 'Charioteers' were carried on eleven occasions. There were 53 convoy escort patrols in North Russia. Nothing was yielded, although the prime targets for these boats, the German pocket-battleships, did not appear.

What was of the cost of these successes? Of the 206 full-sized boats operated by the Royal Navy during World War Two, 74, or 37%, were lost. The greatest losses were in the Mediterranean and in that theatre, 49% were lost. 37 of those boats were lost to the mine and this statistic is indicative of the amount of time Royal Navy boats spent in shallow water in pursuit of their quarries. The allies under opcon lost a similar percentage: 7 Dutch; 3 French; 3 Greek; 2 Polish; 1 Norwegian and 1 Russian.

The saddest statistic among these sad statistics is that eleven boats under RN Opcon were lost to blue-on-blue or self-afflicted incidents, and there were many other narrow squeaks. Three were lost to aircraft, one to a submarine, two to escorts, and two had collisions with Merchant ships. There were three submarine accidents that might equally have happened in peacetime.

On putting some faces to these impressive, but faceless, statistics, Cdr M.D. Wanklyn stands out as incomparably the leading British submarine 'Ace' of the War. The vast majority of the submarine captains were regular naval officers, but of the officers of the Reserves who obtained command, the names of Lt Cdr A.D. Piper of the RNR and Lt Cdr E.P. Young of the RNVR, might be singled out as outstanding.

Not all enemy ships were sunk by torpedo and the casualties from mines laid from submarines are included in the above totals. The leading minelayer was Lt Cdr L.W. Napier in HMS RORQUAL who laid 800 in sixteen fields. He was followed by Capitaine de Corvette H Rousselot of the French submarine, RUBIS with 525 mines.

The total number of gun actions during the war was 1,046. Gun actions varied greatly; some were dangerous encounters with minor warships or defensively armed merchant ships and others were simply the destruction of an unarmed caique, junk or schooner. Examples of fine gun actions are the destruction of the Japanese Sub-chaser No5 by HMS TRENCHANT (Cdr A.R. Hezlet) and HMS TERRAPIN (Lt R.H.H. Brunner), and the Japanese Special Minelayer No 2 by HMS TALLY HO (Cdre L.W.A. Bennington). Also of note is the destruction of a whole convoy of small ships and its escorts by HMS STATESMAN (Lt R.G.P. Bulkeley) and by HMS STORM (Lt E.P. Young RNVR).

The merit of submarine captains is not measured alone by the damage they do to the enemy although this must be considered paramount. There were seven captains who brought their seriously damaged boats back from patrol in very difficult circumstances. These were Lt J. H. Eaden (HMS SPEARFISH), Lt Cdr JW McCoy (HMS TRIUMPH), Lt Cdr P.S. Francis (HMS PROTEUS), Cdr L.W.A. Bennington (HMS TALLY HO), Lt D. Swanston (HMS SHAKESPEARE), Lt J.A.R. Troup (HMS STRONGBOW) and Lt R.H.H. Brunner (HMS TERRAPIN).

There is another category of submarine captain that is important. This is the indirect leadership of their brother captains by their example and performance on patrol. These men were not necessarily, but often were, the more senior and experienced officers in the flotillas. In the 'Phony War' period and the Norwegian campaign the names of Lt G.D.A. Gregory and Cdr E.O. Bickford and, later, Cdr G.M. Sladen might be cited. In the Mediterranean in the early stages, there were Cdrs Rimington and Dewhurst, and in the Bay of Biscay and later in North Russia, Cdr H.F. Bone. At the height of the Mediterranean campaign, Lt Cdr M.D. Wanklyn and Lt Cdr E.P. Tomkinson set a splendid example; they were followed by Cdrs W.J.W. Woods, J.W. Linton and A.C.C. Miers and, later still, by Lt G.E. Hunt. In the Far East, Cdrs L.W.A. Bennington and A.R. Hezlet set the pace.

Finally, as examples of endurance there were Cdrs W.D.A. King and R.H. Dewhurst who were in command of submarines at the outbreak of war and still there when the war ended. There are many other comparisons that can be made, although they may not be considered very important. For instance, the greatest number of patrols made during the war by a Commanding Officer, which was 37, was made by Lt Cdr A.F. Collett. Cdr Bryant made 27, Lt Cdr Colvin 22, Lt Cdr Crouch, 24, and Luitenant ter zee van Dulm, 19. Lt Cdrs Mars and Maydon made 21, and Capitaine de Corvette Rousselot twenty while Lt Cdr Wanklyn made 25.

These figures do not take account of the length of patrols, which varied from five to six weeks in the Pacific to as little as ten days from Malta. As noted earlier in this account, the longest patrol of the War was by Lt Cdr Mackenzie in HMS TANTALUS, which lasted 55 days. The greatest number of torpedoes fired by a single Commanding Officer totalled one hundred exactly and was by Lt Cdr Wanklyn in HMS UPHOLDER; Cdr Bryant came next with 94. The greatest store carrier was Lt Cdr Napier with seven trips in HMS RORQUAL and the largest number of special operations, which was nine, was performed by Lt Cdr Ainslie jointly with Cdr Cayley, Lt Cdr Collett and Capitaine de Fregate de l'Herminier.

Stories of submarine exploits during the war are legendary. Wanklyn in HMS UPHOLDER, Miers in HMS TORBAY, Linton in HMS TURBULENT were all awarded the VC and personified the skill and courage of all the crews. Special Forces operations figured largely in the tapestry of operations, as did the achievements of the mini-submarines, the 'X'-craft, in crippling the German TIRPITZ (described by Churchill as 'the beast'), and the Japanese TAKAO. British human-torpedomen were extraordinarily brave men, usually destined for a one-way trip.

Let me finish with Honours and Awards. A DSO (Distinguished Service Order) was usually awarded to a CO for sinking a major vessel, a DSC (Distinguished Service Cross) for those of lesser importance. A DSO for a Captain was usually accompanied by two DSCs for other officers, and a handful of DSMs and MiDs for the ship's companies. Nine Victoria Crosses were awarded for exceptional performance, and two George Crosses were awarded for outstanding bravery (HMS UNITY).

78 out of the 303 Commanding Officers who conducted war patrols received the DSO; 25 received bars to the Order and 6, two bars. COs also received 64 DSCs, 14 bars to the DSC, and in one case two bars. Only one officer not in command received the DSO (Distinguished Service Order) and that was Lt Cdr (E) H.A. Kidd, the engineer officer of HMS TORBAY and HMS TANTALUS; and he had already received the DSC and Bar as well as being mentioned in despatches.

227 DSCs, 16 with a bar, and one with two bars were awarded to officers not in command (usually the First Lieutenant and Engineer). 232 were mentioned in despatches. 1,010 Distinguished Service Medals went to ratings (usually the Cox'n and CERA), 64 with a bar, and one with two bars. Another 830 sailors were mentioned in despatches. In 'X'-craft (in addition to their four VCs) seven DSOs and two Conspicuous Gallantry Medals were awarded, plus eleven DSCs (including three bars and one second bar) with four DSMs. Seven MBEs were bestowed on passage crew members, and there were 36 MiDs. Finally, the 'Charioteers' won three DSOs, three CGMs, three DSCs, nine DSMs, and eleven MiDs.

"Of all branches of men in the Forces there is none which shows more devotion and faces grimmer perils than the submarines…Great deeds are done in the Air and on the Land; nevertheless, there is no part to be compared to your exploits."

8

A Flawed Contender: The 'Fighter' Submarine, 1946-1950

Malcolm Llewellyn-Jones

PREFACE

"By 'Fighter' is meant one of our own submarines operating as convoy escort or with a hunting group."[1] "This particular type of submarine operation, the 'Fighter', is not to be confused with the normal anti-submarine role of our submarines on patrol in enemy controlled waters or on passage routes, where they would be unsupported by surface forces. This latter [role] has already been approved as the primary role of the Submarine Branch."[2]

THE REVOLUTION IN ANTI-SUBMARINE WARFARE

The last year of the Second World War saw revolutionary changes in anti-submarine warfare with the German deployment of schnorkel-fitted U-boats able to operate continuously submerged and the development of battery, or hydrogen peroxide, powered U-boats capable of high underwater speed and endurance. These vessels would not only be more difficult to find and attack, but with long-range homing or pattern-running torpedoes, they could hit their targets from outside the existing anti-submarine screens. Alternatively, they would have the speed and endurance to break through a defensive screen to attack and re-attack from under the convoy. Worse still, if these U-boats were to work in packs and in co-operation with aircraft, then the ability of surface and air anti-submarine units to counter them would be greatly diminished.[3]

These new U-boats represented the benchmark of the post-war anti-submarine warfare (ASW) challenge, because it was assumed the Russians would rapidly adopt the technology.[4] This was a novel and complex problem that was to absorb much of the energy of successive Directors of the Admiralty's Torpedo, Anti-Submarine and Mine Warfare Division (DTASW) throughout 1946-48.[5] There was no immediate technical or tactical solution, nor was it always clear what shape the solutions might take. It was in this climate that radical suggestions flourished.

Although the convoy was still seen to be the primary means of protecting shipping, as the Assistant Chief of Naval Staff (ACNS) remarked in 1947, it had "become essential for us to exploit other means of destroying U-boats."[6] These would include attacks at source, that is, the means of production, and the submarines in their bases or training areas. Attacks would also be made on submarines on passage and in their operational areas.[7] One way of intercepting and sinking the U-boat was by using British submarines in an anti-submarine role off enemy bases. Another idea was the inclusion of submarines as part of a convoy's close escort; it was this concept, known as the 'Fighter' submarine, that is explored by this paper.[8]

THE 'FIGHTER' SUBMARINE

In early 1947, Rear-Admiral C. W. Styer USN noted that Flag Officer, Submarines, (FOSM) was focused on "developing the best anti-submarine target to aid in the anti-submarine defense [sic] of the Empire."[9] This was true enough. Throughout the late 1940s FOSM energetically pursued surface and later submerged co-ordinated attack tactics against ships, a version of the wartime German 'Wolf Pack' tactic.[10] This was, perhaps, to atone for the understandable, if somewhat unjustified, criticism of the submarine branch for not having identified the German tactics before the war.[11] Styer also observed that the British had "no plans for design or building anti-submarine submarines."[12] Although they had no specific plans, the topic was included on the agenda for discussion with Styer during his visit to Britain in early 1947. The anti-submarine submarine was raised at a meeting of the Joint Sea/Air Warfare Committee on 27 January 1947, called specifically to acquaint Styer with the British view of ASW problems.[13] It would appear that this meeting also prompted discussion on the use of submarines as part of a convoy escort.[14]

Immediately after the meeting, Rear Admiral R. D. Oliver, Deputy Chief of Naval Staff (DCNS), harking back to First World War experiments, called for a report on the 'The Suitability of the 'R' Class as a Future A/S Submarine'. Captain Lord Ashbourne, DTASW, quickly demolished the idea that the 'R' Class of 1917-18 had any application to the more difficult technical problems of an anti-submarine submarine in 1947. Nevertheless, Ashbourne thought the idea of an ASW submarine was attractive because:

- The fast submarine can outstrip ASW vessels in rough weather, particularly up wind, whereas another ASW submarine could keep up;
- The ASW submarine should be able to operate sonars more efficiently due to…being…more nearly at the same depth as its target;
- The enemy submarine is less likely to know that it is in the presence of [an] ASW submarine than of a surface ASW vessel;
- The ASW submarine might provide an answer to the, at present, unsolved problem of attacking a submarine which shelters under a convoy.[15]

Ashbourne pointed out that, if used as part of a convoy's escort, or a hunting, group, existing submarine types would be unable to keep station submerged until atomic propulsion became available, and they also lacked an ASW torpedo. When referred to FOSM, Vice-Admiral J. M. Mansfield, he emphasised the overriding problems of identification and recognition of submerged submarines when in contact with the enemy, so that ASW forces were able to tell friend from foe.[16]

By the summer of 1947, DTASW had drafted a series of major appreciations of the anti-submarine problem, including a paper on 'The Submarine as an Anti-Submarine Vessel'.[17] Input to these papers by submariners was complicated by the lack of a separate Admiralty staff division charged with submarine matters.[18] Instead, submarine matters were the responsibility of DTASW, whose first two post-war directors were submariners, supported by a submariner desk officer.[19] Fortunately, the relations between the Naval Staff and FOSM appear to have been excellent, fostered by regular Submarine Liaison Meetings between the Naval Staff and FOSM and the regular exchange of staff paperwork.[20] That said, the differences in 'tactical culture' between anti-submarine and submarine practitioners could only have been exacerbated by their physical and organisational separation.

At the Third Submarine Liaison Meeting in November 1947, DTASW's wide-ranging anti-submarine submarine paper was discussed. The paper concluded that submarines could be effective as ASW vessels when employed in enemy controlled waters, where other friendly ASW forces could not operate. During the discussion, there was less enthusiasm for the idea of a 'Fighter' submarine because of the recognition problem remaining unsolved and of the high cost of building, maintenance and training for such vessels, especially at a time when funds were tight.[21] Even so, it was decided that DTASW should produce a more detailed paper on the 'Fighter', which was completed in some haste by the end of the month. The paper explored the value of operating submarines either as convoy escorts or with hunting groups, but concluded that the use of a submarine in the 'Fighter' role still presented a number of insuperable difficulties.[22]

For example, when DTASW considered the 'Fighter' as a replacement for surface escorts, it would have to operate mainly on the surface because submerged speed and endurance of submarines in the near future was inadequate, even when the use of continuous snorting or hydrogen peroxide propulsion were considered. On the surface, the performance of the 'Fighter's' sonar would be no better than a conventional escort, and she would provide little support to the convoy against air attack. Moreover, the surface qualities needed were likely to degrade its submerged performance, so that she would not be able to engage a U-boat on equal terms. When account was taken of the huge production and maintenance costs, compared to surface escorts, the 'Fighter' remained an unattractive choice.

Alternatively, the paper suggested, the 'Fighter' could be used to augment the surface escort. In this case, if she could be towed by an escort or convoy ship, the need for high surface performance and submerged endurance could be sacrificed for high underwater speed and agility. If released at the right moment, she could hunt down U-boats that were shadowing or evading after an attack, or "ferret" out ones that were hiding under the convoy. All this meant that the boat needed superior acoustic equipment to locate the enemy, though only passing reference was made to the requirement for an effective anti-submarine torpedo. Moreover, operating close to surface ASW forces would pose the greatest difficulties if the recognition problem were not solved – and no solution appeared to be in sight.[23]

Because no fast submarines were available, sea trials were impossible.[24] DTASW therefore proposed that simulations be played on the tactical tables to assess the 'Fighter's' practicality. His intention was that the investigations should be set in the period after 1950 when the threat was assumed to consist of the 25-knot intermediate submarine propelled by hydrogen peroxide. The aim was to inform a future staff requirement. Both HMS OSPREY and the Joint A/S School at Londonderry were instructed to include 'Fighter' submarines in their tactical games.[25] However, these establishments were geared towards training for the short-term problem of the 15-knot fast battery drive submarine. OSPREY proposed that investigations should start with the short-term 'Fighter', whose capabilities, in any case, were easier to construct.[26] Londonderry followed suit, though neither establishment attached a high priority to the investigations, and neither reported until the summer of 1948, having been reminded by DTASW in June.[27]

TACTICAL TABLE GAMES WITH 'FIGHTER' SUBMARINES

Londonderry reported first, after fighting two small tactical table battles during which the U-boat was detected by an aircraft sonobuoy barrier and two surface escorts were detached to search the datum using a conventional 'Kappa' or a 'Nomo' search.[28] The 'Fighter' was then slipped from its towing ship to patrol the gap created by the two searching escorts. The hope was "that the enemy, seeing an apparent gap, would make for it and run into the 'Fighter' submarine."[29] By contrast, OSPREY's report, issued a month later, concentrated on the use of the 'Fighter' outside the escort screen.[30]

A new tactical plan was invented called 'Radish'. This assumed that the 'Fighter' was detached from its towing escort ahead of the convoy, and moved out towards a U-boat datum at maximum speed. She would be accompanied by two surface escorts, which, by operating their noise-making torpedo decoys and steering slightly divergent courses, were intended "to lure the U-boat towards the 'Fighter' submarine", in marked contrast to the concept employed at Londonderry. Meanwhile, the convoy would execute an emergency turn to provide fighting room for the 'Fighter' and avoid acoustic interference. As she approached the position where she expected to intercept the U-boat, she would slow to her best listening speed and start to search.[31]

OSPREY concluded that the 'Fighter' could achieve a greater certainty of detecting the enemy, at least when clear of the convoy, because she could operate her sonar at the most advantageous depth and was less affected by rough seas. Although OSPREY's aggressive tactics detected the enemy more often than Londonderry's, in both sets of games the U-boat usually counter-detected the 'Fighter', because she had to use high speed (and was therefore noisy) while closing on the enemy. Consequently, the U-boat either successfully evaded the attack, or the action degenerated into a submarine dogfight. However, the means of hitting the target with the current weapons and their control arrangements was wholly inadequate.[32]

When attacks were made by the 'Fighter', they were based on bearings from her passive sonar. This technique was in its infancy and attacks took time to execute, which was tactically disadvantageous, so close to the convoy.[33] Long periods in the vicinity of the convoy not only increased the danger of being attacked by friendly ASW forces, but the constant distraction and the need to avoid own forces also increased the chance of the enemy escaping.[34] Overall, Londonderry scathingly reported, "feeling of all those participating was one of unreality, and that another surface escort would have been much more useful than the 'Fighter' submarine."[35] Two months passed by before FOSM, Rear Admiral G. Grantham, commented. He agreed with the conclusions of the tactical games, and stressed the need for a solution to the recognition problem. Without a solution, Grantham thought, "very little use can be made of the 'Fighter' submarine."[36]

THE NEED FOR "A MORE REALISTIC BASIS"

Following discussions in early November 1948 at the Ninth Submarine Liaison Meeting, Captain C. E. E. Paterson of DTASW observed that, after a year of investigations, the results had proved to be inconclusive. These were, chiefly, because the capabilities credited to 'Fighter' were unlikely to be achieved; she was inadequately armed and the recognition problem had been assumed as solved. He believed "the time has come to continue the investigation on a more realistic basis" and to assume *no* solution to the recognition problem.

Paterson proposed that two 'Fighter' types should be simulated: one based on the anticipated performance of the 'T' Class conversion, and the other a specialised 'Fighter' design. Both variants would be armed with wire-guided torpedoes capable of homing in three dimensions.[37] After discussion with the Director of Naval Construction in February 1949, FOSM concluded that it was impossible to generate a sensible 'design' of a specialised 'Fighter' submarine before the sea trials with the 'T' Class conversion. He therefore proposed that tactical investigations should be confined to the assumed performance of the 'T' Class conversion, which DTASW approved.[38]

During February and March, the tactical table games at OSPREY were supported by an experienced submarine commanding officer appointed by FOSM and used acoustic data provided by the Captain, HM Underwater Detection Establishment, Portland, and the Director of Naval Operational Research (DNOR).[39] The detailed report covered the use of a 'T' Class conversion against U-boats operating under, or shadowing astern of, a convoy and those detected ahead of the escort screen.[40] FOSM, however, did not comment on these investigations for four months. The tardy response was probably due to the planning and execution of FOSM's Summer War Exercise involving large numbers of ships, aircraft and submarines. Even so, it is possible to detect a less than enthusiastic support for the idea of a 'Fighter' amongst FOSM's staff.[41]

By September 1949, Captain N. A. Copeman, DTASW, circulated the reports from OSPREY and FOSM to the Naval Staff.[42] The tactical games indicated that a 'Fighter' could achieve a high percentage of detections against U-boats, though the realism of these results could only be confirmed in sea trials. It was also noted that the 'Fighter' had considerable difficulty in converting detections into successful attacks because, lacking a high 'silent' speed, it could neither maintain passive sonar contact nor close on its prey without alerting it.[43] Although higher search rates and rapid target fixing were possible with active sonar, its use would betray her presence and was adamantly opposed by FOSM. The games suggested that she had little value against U-boat detected within 3 miles of the convoy and surface, or air, escorts were able to respond more rapidly even against U-boats out to 12 miles. For longer range detections, she had some value, but would have to snort if the contact was beyond 20 miles, which meant a long transit time.[44] In rough weather, the 'Fighter' might be the only vessel capable of offensive action, but her mobility would be impaired if she were unable to snort due to high seas.[45]

The most compelling reason for using the 'Fighter' was because she pitted herself against her adversary in the same environmental conditions.[46] However, if the target could be brought into firing range, she still lacked a weapon capable of homing in three dimensions to achieve a kill. The slow, stealthy methods preferred by submariners were also ill suited to the dynamic engagements around a convoy. Indeed, once deployed, she could not be readily diverted to another target and was, in effect, a 'one shot' weapon of little help in the defence of a convoy faced with an attack by a pack of modern U-boats. But, above all, was the irreconcilable problem of recognition of friend and foe, making it "doubtful whether surface escorts, submarines and aircraft could ever operate together with efficiency and full mutual confidence."[47]

THE 'FIGHTER' IDEA IS AS "DEAD AS DOORNAILS"

By the end of 1949, new sonar sets and weapons due to be fitted to faster escorts were nearing the end of their development. These promised to alleviate the problem of dealing with the new high-speed submarine types, which, it was assumed, the Soviets would be able to produce in the 1950s. There still remained serious concern over the provision of the large number of escorts that would still be needed in any future conflict.[48] As for the prospect of the 'Fighter', FOSM remained sanguine. While he appreciated the "acute shortage of escorts in any future war,…[he] also observed that there will be an even more acute shortage of submarines which will be capable of fulfilling the role of the 'Fighter' submarine. Whilst agreeing that every possible method of defending convoys must be investigated,… nevertheless… the basic objective, which is the destruction of U-boats, is likely to be better achieved by employing the limited number of submarines on ASW patrol rather than in defence of convoys".[49]

DTASW had come to the same conclusion and proposed no further action until 'T' Class conversions were available for sea trials.[50] This policy was approved by the Admiralty Board at the end of 1949. By early 1950, FOSM was engaged on the training of submarines for anti-submarine patrols in enemy controlled waters, which for the previous two years had been his primary wartime task and enthusiasm for the 'Fighter' amongst his staff continued to evaporate.[51] When Captain B. W. Taylor, FOSM's Chief of Staff, drafted a lecture for the Senior Officers' Technical Course in early 1951, he not only observed that his Admiral "does not favour the 'Fighter' submarine," but for the actual lecture, Taylor also struck out the entire page dealing with the 'Fighter', annotating his notes with "Dead as Doornails. Omit"![52]

In 1954, the idea spluttered briefly into life when DTASW again reviewed the 'Fighter' concept. Continuing delays with the 'T' Class conversions meant that the demands for trials with these boats were "growing faster than they can be met". Work on the 'Fighter' concept was very low down the priority list for sea trials and, for realism, would have to involve a convoy. As providing a convoy could only be sponsored by NATO, "the question of security would preclude the possibility of such a trial". FOSM's staff also noted that the improved surface ship sonar and more flexible Limbo ASW mortar and homing torpedoes, as well as helicopter dunking sonar, had all improved the defences available for convoys. Furthermore, advances in low frequency acoustic detection methods for submarines made "it clear that the most economical use of our own submarines is on ASW patrols operating at quiet speeds", that is, well away from friendly ASW forces.[53] More crucially, a solution to the perennial recognition problem was still "not yet in sight".[54]

There still remained the basic difference in submarine and other ASW unit operations. Surface and air ASW is a team sport, while submariners generally prefer solo hunting. The difference permeates their tactical concepts to the extent that there is an entirely different 'tactical culture' that makes direct co-operation between them extremely difficult. This remains true enough even today, although new advances in covert communication make some degree of co-operation at least possible. However, every transmission by a submarine is a calculated risk, and this includes communications. Receiving transmissions often restricts a submarine to shallow depth, which is frequently neither tactically prudent nor advantageous. The *Manual of Submarine Operations*, 1950 summarised the issue succinctly:

> As the operation of a submarine depends entirely on surprise and the operation of anti-submarine forces on fleeting opportunities where immediate action is essential, recognition systems in themselves can never be the full solution for distinguishing between friend and foe. The only true answer is to ensure that our own forces keep clear of submarine patrol areas and that our submarines are kept out of areas in which our anti-submarine forces are operating.[55]

By 1942, operating submarines in the vicinity of anti-submarine forces imposed such severe tactical restrictions on the escort forces that the practice was soon abandoned.[56] It seems odd, therefore, that the concept of the 'Fighter' persisted for so long after the war. Undoubtedly, the uncertainty of how to deal with the fast, high-endurance submarines prompted consideration of radical concepts.[57] For a long time, the technical and tactical assumptions used in these games were allowed to persist without rigorous examination. Such scrutiny was made difficult because there was no comparative data from sea trials. Moreover, trials at sea would have starkly exposed the difficulties of recognition, and the lack of high silent speed and an ASW weapon.

If the Naval Staff had not been going through a major upheaval during the post-war years; if there been better co-ordination between DTASW and FOSM; and if DNOR been more involved, the 'Fighter' concept might have been put to rest earlier to await a submarine with the necessary performance, perhaps driven by hydrogen peroxide or nuclear power.[58] Perhaps, too, the fundamental differences in 'tactical culture' between submarine and anti-submarine operations played its part. Whether these differences will ever be solved is another story.

A FLAWED CONTENDER: THE 'FIGHTER' SUBMARINE, 1946-1950

NOTES

1 Captain N. A. Copeman, DTASW, Naval Staff, "Report of the Investigation into the Possibilities of 'Fighter' Submarines", *TASW* 297/49, 29 October 1949, Public Record Office, Kew, Admiralty Files (ADM) 1/20414.

2 Minute by Captain N. A. Copeman, DTASW, 3 September 1949, ADM 1/20414.

3 "Development of the Submarine," *Annex A to TASW* 021/46, Revised Edition, 4 May 1946, ADM 1/20960, p. 6.

4 The contemporary abbreviation for Anti-submarine was 'A/S', but in this paper the modern term of ASW will be adopted (except in documentary references). The term 'U-boat' was used contemporarily to denote enemy submarines, including post-war Soviet submarines, and this usage will be adopted in this paper. Similarly the current term 'sonar' is used in place of the contemporary 'asdic'. Some quotations have therefore been modified.

5 Their first comprehensive appreciation was: "The Development of A/S Warfare," *TASW*. 021/46, Revised Edition, 4 May 1946, ADM 1/20960.

6 G. N. Oliver "A/S Problems of the Future – Attack at Source and Harbour Defence,", Office of the Chief of Naval Staff, 8 December 1947, ADM 1/21546. A.C.N.S. referred to "Anti-Submarine Problems of the Future" *T.A.S.W.* 4666/47, P. W. Burnett, for DTASW, 16 August 1947, AIR 20/6381.

7 Discussion with Admiral John Adams, 28 May 1998. The ideas were not new. Commander H. J. Fawcett had developed similar ideas in 1944 and had drawn on experience of the First World War. Commander H. J. Fawcett, Naval Staff, Coastal Command "Possibilities of the Coming [April 1945] U-boat Offensive", 1 December 1944, Churchill College Archives Centre, Cambridge, FWCT 2/4/5. Fawcett had been a staff officer in the Admiralty's Anti-U-Boat Division prior to drafting the paper.

8 The concept of using submarines in the ASW, though not the 'Fighter' role was started initiated in early 1946 by [then] Commander Hezlet, the submariner on DTASW's staff. Vice Admiral Sir Arthur Hezlet, KBE, CB, DSO. Telephone interviews, 22 and 23 September 2000.

9 'Report of Co-ordinator of Undersea Warfare and Assistants' Visit to British Naval Activities, Jan. 19 – Feb. 12 1947,' Forrest Sherman, Deputy Chief of Naval Operations (Operations), Op-31B: ch (SC) A16-3 (17) Serial 003P31, 30 April 1947, Records of the Naval Operating Forces: Commander in Chief Atlantic (CinCLant) Secret Administrative Files, 1941-1949, Box 90, RG 313, National Archives and Records Administration (NARA) 2, College Park, Maryland, pp. 2 and 10. Styer, with others of his staff, was on a month-long visit to the UK covering all the establishments concerned with anti-submarine warfare. He had recently been charged with the co-ordination of all anti-submarine developments in the U.S. Navy.

10 See, for example: "Third Submarine Flotilla Monthly General Letter No. 13 – December 1944," Captain (S/M), Third Submarine Flotilla, H.M.S. "Forth", to Admiral (Submarines), 4 January 1945, Royal Naval Submarine Museum (RNSM) A1944/007 and "Third Submarine Flotilla Monthly General Letter – March 1946," Captain W. J. W. Woods, Captain (S/M), Third Submarine Flotilla, H.M.S. FORTH, No. TSF.0817/A/13, 31 March 1946, RNSM A1946/001. The term 'Wolf Pack' was later dropped in favour of 'Co-ordinated' tactics. "Development in Submarine Tactics since the War," Enclosure in Flag Officer, Submarines' letter No. SM.640/1916A dated 7 January 1948, RNSM A1948/008, p. 2.

11 Vice Admiral Sir Arthur Hezlet, KBE, C.B., D.S.O.*, D.S.C., telephone interview 23 September 2000.

12 "Report of Co-ordinator of Undersea Warfare and Assistants' Visit to British Naval Activities, Jan. 19 – Feb. 12 1947," Box 90, RG 313, NARA 2, Maryland, pp. 2 and 10. Styer, with others of his staff, was on a month-long visit to the UK covering all the establishments concerned with anti-submarine warfare. He had recently been charged with the co-ordination of all anti-submarine developments in the U.S. Navy.

13 It has not been possible to locate the minutes of the meeting, though the calling notice is in: Joint Secretaries "Joint Sea/Air Warfare Committee: Tactical and Training and Technical Investigation Sub-Committees," *Sub-S.A.W.C.II/2/47* and *Sub-S.A.W.C.III/2/47*, 13 January 1947, AIR 15/786. Some highlights of the meeting are in: "Report of Joint Secretaries of the Joint Sea/Air Warfare Sub-Committees on Work Undertaken since 22 January 1947," S.A.W.C. 2/47(5), 20 May 1947, AIR 20/6842; and "Report of Co-ordinator of Undersea Warfare and Assistants' Visit to British Naval Activities", Jan. 19 – Feb. 12 1947, RG 313, NARA 2, Maryland, pp. 7-8.

14 The British were aware of U.S. thinking on the anti-submarine submarine (in their terms the SSK), helped, no doubt, by the close working relationship between RN and U.S.N. staffs at this stage, and aided by DTASW's personal ties with the U.S.N. forged during the war. The Americans, however, only seem to have considered the use of ASW submarines with hunting forces from November 1948 onwards. Lord Ashbourne (son of Captain Lord Ashbourne, DTASW) to author, 29 June 2000; Norman Friedman, *U.S. Submarines Since 1945: An Illustrated Design History Annapolis*: U.S. Naval Institute Press, 1994, p. 252, fn. 17.

15 Captain Lord Ashbourne, "The Suitability of the 'R' Class as a Future A/S Submarine," DTASW, T.A.S.W. 4127/47, 24 February 1947, RNSM A1947/001.

16 *Ibid.* Vice Admiral J. M. Mansfield, Flag Officer, Submarines, to Deputy Chief of Naval Staff, No. SM.023/984, 18 March 1947, RNSM A1947/001.

17 "Development of Own Submarines for A/S Purposes," Part 5 of, *Anti-Submarine Problems of the Future*, T.A.S.W. 4666/47, P. W. Burnett, for DTASW, 16 August 1947, AIR 20/6381. This section of this paper was drafted in June 1947. It has not been possible to locate a copy of *The Submarine as an Anti-Submarine Vessel*, T.A.S.W. 4806/47, though discussion and extracts of it are to be found in ADM 1/20414 and ADM 219/327.

18 "Report of Co-ordinator of Undersea Warfare and Assistants' Visit to British Naval Activities", Jan. 19 – Feb. 12 1947, Box 90, RG 313, NARA 2, Maryland, p. 10. By contrast Naval Aviation had two dedicated divisions, and Board representation by the Fifth Sea Lord, who was also Deputy Chief of Naval Staff (Air). "The Admiralty", BR 1806(48), *Naval War Manual*, Tactical and Staff Duties Division, T.S.D. 122/47, 1 June 1948, Admiralty Library, Chapter 6, pp. 24-28.

19 There were also submarine officers appointed to other staff divisions, such as Plans, Operations, and Tactical and Staff Duties. "Lecture to Senior Officers' Technical Course, Tuesday, 6 February 1951," Captain B. W. Taylor, D.S.C., RN, Chief of Staff to Flag Officer, Submarines, RNSM A1997/188.

20 Rear Admiral R. W. Mayo, C.B., CBE, letter to author, n.d., [received 19 September 2000]; Vice Admiral Sir Arthur Hezlet, KBE, C.B., D.S.O.*, D.S.C., telephone interview 23 September 2000. Admiral Mayo was then a Commander on FOSM's staff and Admiral Hezlet was a Commander in DTASW. The Liaison Meetings seem to have been held every two months, though the minutes (apart from short extracts) have not yet been located.

21 See various comment by Staff Divisions in: Reference Sheet, Captain V. D'A. Donaldson to The Captain H.M.S. OSPREY and The Director (RN), Joint A/S School, Londonderry, T.A.S.W. 289/47(2), 24 November 1947, ADM 1/20414, Appendix B; and 'T.A.S.W. 4806/47 – *The Submarine as an A/S Vessel*, [C. R. Jones], D.N.O.R., 8 September 1947, ADM 219/327.

22 *The Submarine as an Anti-Submarine Vessel: Part II – The "Fighter" Submarine*, Torpedo, Anti-Submarine and Mine Warfare Division, T.A.S.W. 289/47(2), 24 November 1947, ADM 1/20414.

23 *Ibid*, pp. 3-5.

24   The only working ex-German Type XXI U-boat had been lent to the French. The fast *Seraph* Class wartime conversions did not have the endurance to take part in tactical trials, and the first Super-*Seraph* conversion, H.M.S. *Scotsman*, was still over a year away.

25   Reference Sheet, Captain V. D'A. Donaldson to The Captain H.M.S. OSPREY and The Director (RN), Joint A/S School, Londonderry, T.A.S.W. 289/47(2), 24 November 1947, ADM 1/20414; *The Development of A/S Warfare*, T.A.S.W. 021/46, Revised Edition, 4 May 1946, ADM 1/20960, p. 4.

26   "The Submarine as an Anti-Submarine Vessel," Captain W. Banks, The Captain H.M.S. OSPREY, No. 652/11, 6 January 1948, RNSM A1947/003, Appendix, p. 1.

27   Reference Sheet, "The "'Fighter'" Submarine," Captain N. A. Copeman, D.S.C., RN, for DTASW, T.A.S.W. 289/47(2), 21 June 1948, ADM 1/20414.

28   For detail of these searches see: 'The A/S Hunt,' in, "Progress in Tactics: 1947 Edition," C.B. 03016/47, Tactical and Staff Duties Division, Admiralty, 17 October 1947, ADM 239/143, p. 20; "Anti-Submarine Warfare," in, *Progress in Tactics, 1949*, C.B. 03016 (49), Chapter 5, T.S.D. 109/49, Tactical and Staff Duties Division, Naval Staff, Admiralty, 29 September 1949, ADM 239/565, pp. 25-27.

29   "The "Fighter" Submarine,"' Captain R. G. Onslow, Director RN, Joint A/S School, Londonderry, No. 79, 13 July 1948, ADM 1/20414.

30   No games were played to explore the sub-convoy battle or against shadowing U-boats. "The Submarine as an A/S Vessel," Captain W. Banks, The Captain H.M.S. OSPREY, No. 652/11, 20 August 1948, RNSM A1947/003.

31   For 'Radish' see: "The Submarine as an A/S Vessel," RNSM A1947/003, Appendix III.

32   Existing torpedoes could only be set to run at 44 feet, though for the games it was assumed that wire-guided weapons were available with depth settings of 0-100 feet. Reference Sheet, Captain N. A. Copeman, DTASW, to The Captain H.M.S. OSPREY and the Director RN, Joint A/S School, Londonderry, T.A.S.W. 289/47, 26 January 1948, RNSM A19947/003. An effective homing weapon was still some 5 years away. See G. J. Kirby, 'A History of the Torpedo,' Part 4, *Journal of the Royal Naval Scientific Service*, Vol. 27, No. 2 (1972), p. 98.

33   A more scientific method was developed in the Third Submarine Flotilla in the early 1950s. Interview with Commander D. Symes, 30 August 2000. Symes was the Flotilla ASW Officer. 'The Submarine as an A/S Vessel,' RNSM A1947/003, p. 2.

34   "The Submarine as an A/S Vessel," RNSM A1947/003, pp. 2-3.

35   "The "Fighter" Submarine," Captain R. G. Onslow, Director RN, Joint A/S School, Londonderry, No. 79, 13 July 1948, ADM 1/20414.

36   "The Submarine as an A/S Vessel," Rear Admiral G. Grantham, Flag Officer, Submarines, No. SM.021/5253, 26 October 1948, RNSM A1947/003.

37   Reference Sheet [The "Fighter' Submarine'], Captain C. E. E. Paterson, Torpedo, Anti-Submarine and Mine Warfare Division, T.A.S.W. 289/47, 9 November 1948, ADM 1/20414.

38   "Possibilities of a 'Fighter' Submarine," Flag Officer, Submarines, SM.021/526, 18 February 1949, RNSM A1947/003; "Functions of Operational Submarines," Captain C. E. E. Paterson, for DTASW, 7 March 1949, ADM 1/20414.

39   Pressure of other work prevented Londonderry providing any useful information "Report of the Investigation into the Possibilities of 'Fighter' Submarines", Captain N. A. Copeman, DTASW, T.A.S.W. 297/49, 29 October 1949, ADM 1/20414. The data used by OSPREY was not complete, and some was based on the results of trials with the high-speed conversion, H.M.S. SCOTSMAN, and contemporary U.S. trials with an ex-German Type XXI U-boat. "Functions of Operational Submarines," Captain A. Wallis, The Captain, H.M.U.D.E., Ref. 11854/422.5/H.A3, 31 December 1948, and "'Fighter' Submarine," W. E. Dawson, A.D.O.R., n.d., ADM 1/20414.

40   "'Fighter' Submarine," Captain H.M.S. OSPREY, Portland, No. 07, 28 March 1949, RNSM A1947/003. The copy of the report in ADM 1/20414 lacks the accompanying diagrams.

41   This was the first exercise in which all the submarines were snort-fitted, though it was heavily focused on "traditional" submarine co-ordinated attacks on surface shipping. None of the boats was a fast type. "Submarines," in, *Progress in Underwater Warfare*, 1949 Edition, C.B. 04050 (49), Chapter II, 17 July 1950, ADM 239/274, p. 41; "'Fighter' Submarine," 1947-1954, RNSM A1947/003, passim.

42   "Report of the Investigation into the Possibilities of 'Fighter' Submarines," Captain N. A. Copeman, DTASW, T.A.S.W. 297/49, [3 September 1949], ADM 1/20414.

43   It was hoped that propeller-silencing devices, such as 'Nightshirt', would allow submarines to travel at higher speeds without producing loud hydrophone effect (H.E.). Unfortunately, the results with this device proved to be "...rather disappointing." 'Lecture to Senior Officers' Technical Course, Tuesday, 6 February 1951,' Captain B. W. Taylor, D.S.C., RN, Chief of Staff to Flag Officer, Submarines, RNSM A1997/188.

44   OSPREY suggested that a snort speed in excess of 10 knots should be investigated, but FOSM. considered this to be impractical, largely because of the high propulsive power needed. "'Fighter' Submarine," Rear Admiral G. Grantham, No. SM.021/2513, 3 August 1949, RNSM A1947/003.

45   Minute by R. W. Mayo, T.A.S., FOSM, RNSM A1947/003.

46   "Fighter Submarine," Captain H.M.S. OSPREY Portland, No. 07, 28 March 1949, ADM 1/20414, p. 7.

47   Minute by Captain N. A. Copeman, DTASW, 3 September 1949, ADM 1/20414. The recognition problem might have been eased given reliable communications between the 'Fighter' and surface or air escorts, but the prospects of this appeared bleak, especially in rough weather. Trials with a floating aerial had been tried but without success. The projected sound telephone equipment was expected to have a fairly short range and, in any case, was no use with aircraft. "'Fighter' Submarine," Rear Admiral G. Grantham, No. SM.021/2513, 3 August 1949, RNSM A1947/003, p. 2.

48   Minute by [Vice Admiral Sir Rhoderick McGrigor, V.C.N.S.], 7 May [1947], ADM 1/20030. For an early assessment of Soviet submarine capability, which brought the 'the cold light of reason to bear on the bogey of the promised enormous Red Navy of the future' see "Russian Naval Tactics," NID/16, 10 October 1946, and Minute by Commander Peter Cazalet for Director of Plans, 10 November 1946, ADM 1/20030.

49   Commander P. R. Pelly, for D.T.S.D., 7 September 1949, ADM 1/20414; "Report of the Investigation into the Possibilities of 'Fighter' Submarines," Captain N. A. Copeman, DTASW, T.A.S.W. 297/49, [3 September 1949], ADM 1/20414, p. 4.

50   Minute by Captain N. A. Copeman, DTASW, 3 September 1949, ADM 1/20414.

51   "The Submarine as an Anti-Submarine Vessel," Flag Officer, Submarines, No. 7/SM.0147.0, 6 January 1950, ADM 1/21803. In January 1948 the Admiralty had announced that 'In war, the primary operational function of our submarines will be the interception and destruction of enemy submarines in enemy controlled waters.' N. Abercrombie to Commanders-in-Chief and Flag Officer (Submarines), etc., M/T.A.S.W. 289/47, 8 January 1948, ADM 1/24407. For details of the progress in submarine versus submarine practices, especially by the Third Submarine Flotilla, during this period see: 'Submarines,' in, C.B. 04050 (49), *Progress in Underwater Warfare*, 1949 Edition, Chapter II, 17 July 1950, ADM 239/274, pp. 41-43.

52   "Lecture to Senior Officers' Technical Course, Tuesday, 6 February 1951," Captain B. W. Taylor, D.S.C., RN, Chief of Staff

to Flag Officer, Submarines, RNSM A1997/188.

53 Minute by T.A.S., "Introduction of a 'Fighter' Submarine," T.A.S.W. 24/54, 11 February 1954, RNSM A1947/003. For very low frequency acoustic work, see: ADM 1/27354.

54 At about this time the U.S.N. was experimenting with SSKs in co-operation with hunting forces, though, as with the British, the recognition problem remained unsolved. Norman Friedman, *U.S. Submarines Since 1945: An Illustrated Design History* (Annapolis: U.S. Naval Institute Press, 1994), p. 84; Captain V. D'A Donaldson, DTASW, 1 February 1954, ADM 1/20414. Communications between submarines and ships were still a problem in 1963, see: "The Communications Problem for the Nuclear Submarine in the Escort Role," W. E. Silver, D.O.R. Note 3/63, March 1963, ADM 219/642.

55 *Manual of Submarine Operations*, C.B. 03179, T.S.D. 141/47, Training and Staff Duties Division, 30 December 1950, ADM 239/232, p. 32.

56 See: Message, Flag Officer (Submarines) to Admiralty, 1457B/9 August, 9 August 1941; Minute D.O.D. (H) and D.O.D. (F), 13 August 1941; 'Instructions Regarding the Conduct of Submarines in Company with Surface Escorts, Coastal Convoys and Ocean Convoys: Part II, Submarines in Company with Ocean Convoys,' Enclosure to Admiral (Submarines) No. 1639/SM.1105 dated 7 September 1941, ADM 199/1217; and 'Conduct of Submarines,' Appendix IX to Rear Admiral (D)'s No. HD.00570 dated 29 September 1942, ADM 199/758.

57 Apart from the 'Fighter' submarine these included projects such as the 'Zannet' manned flying machine, capable of diving before launching a torpedo. See, for example: "Zannet': A Suggested Amphibious Torpedo Carrier to Transport, Aim and Discharge Torpedoes and to carry out A/S Detection and Attack," W. S. Burn, Chief Torpedo Development Engineer, Torpedo Experimental Establishment, Greenock, TDE.122/94, ACSIL/ADM/47/210, May 1947, ADM 213/444.

58 The escort role was emphasised in the staff requirement for the first British nuclear submarine, H.M.S. *Dreadnought*. Trials with her and surface ships were carried out by the Royal Navy from about 1964 onwards. Vice Admiral Sir Lancelot Bell, KBE, e-mail to author, 22 September 2000; Norman Friedman, *U.S. Submarines Since 1945: An Illustrated Design History* Annapolis: U.S. Naval Institute Press, 1994, p. 260, fn. 2.

ACKNOWLEDGEMENTS

My thanks to Lieutenant Commander Douglas McLean, CD, always my sternest critic, as well as Professor Andrew Lambert, and my colleagues Peter Nash, Warwick Brown, George Karger and John Salmon, all of whom read the paper an added to its balance and substance. Remaining errors of judgement or fact remain, of course, wholly mine.

9

Explorer & Excalibur:
The Walter Boat, High Test Peroxide &
British Submarine Policy 1945-1962.
A Study in Technological Failure?

Declan O'Reilly

"The best thing to do with Peroxide is to get it adopted by our enemies."

The catastrophic losses of Black May 1943 convinced Admiral Dönitz that the initiative in the submarine war was inexorably passing to the allies.[1] His subsequent cessation of U-boat operations was intended to be temporary, creating a breathing space to allow new and untried technology to regain the strategic advantage for Germany.[2] Among these new devices were the Schnorkel, the type XXI Electro-boat and the revolutionary Walter HTP engine. Dönitz had long been interested in radical submarine development, and as the new Befhelshaber Untersee-Boots in 1935 he instigated research into the fast submarine. The most promising alternative technology to standard diesel-electric power was Prof. Hellmuth Walter's closed cycle Hydrogen Peroxide, HTP, engine. [3]

Walter's early ideas were similar to the British Ehrren engine with the exhaust gasses of the motor rejuvenated by adding hydrogen peroxide.[4] It was found that this gave off too much heat and this line of investigation was abandoned. A somewhat sensationalist report of this research was published by the *Daily Telegraph* in September 1936, which claimed that all 30 boats of Germany's new submarine fleet were equipped with this new oxygen-hydrogen motor. Ten days later, the Admiralty concluded that the *Telegraph* had misunderstood possible developments in a German version of the Errren engine arguing that "the superior performance claimed for it has not yet been established on theoretical grounds". [5]

Walter then proposed two simpler hot or cold systems that fed HTP directly into the combustion chamber over a catalyst of porous porcelain stones on which were fixed calcium, potassium or sodium permanganate, mixed with diesel oil and the resulting steam, 930°F, being used to drive a conventional turbine. Both the Navy and the Airforce were enthusiastic and from 1935 onwards jointly funded Walter's research. The fruits of the 'hot system' for the Luftwaffe, which used higher density fuel, resulted in the Messerschmitt Me163 rocket plane.[6]

In 1939, Walter was given a contract to build a small experimental submarine of 80 tonnes displacement. The result was the V80 or *Versuchsboote 80* (research boat 80). This was a streamlined vessel employing cold propulsion and it was built under conditions of great secrecy at Kiel. Even at this stage cooperation with the Luftwaffe was close and the steering gears for Walter's first operational fast submarine, the V80, were based on the control surface arrangements of the Junkers Ju 52 transport aircraft.

In 1940, the V80 underwent a series of tests in the river Schlei. At the end of that year she was moved to the Baltic to avoid air attacks on Kiel and more than 100 trial sorties were made: her highest recorded speed was an impressive 28.1 Kts. One obvious drawback in her design was that she left a large wake of oxygen bubbles that could be easily detected. Nevertheless she was sufficiently impressive for Dönitz, now Admiral of Submarines, to continue with development of fast boats. [7]

The U792-U795 series proved the viability of Walter's Designs and he was then commissioned to build a production version designated 'Type XVIIB'; it was these boats that were captured at the end of the war and formed the basis of Allied evaluation programs. The U792 was involved in a collision, which so badly damaged her rudders that she was never repaired. The U793 served as a floating oil tanker until she was scuttled in May 1945. The U794 was destroyed in an underwater shock wave test and the U795 served as a training boat until it too was scuttled. The British raised the scuttled boats but damage was so extensive that they were scrapped.

Walter's type XVIIB boats fared better. 24 boats of this class were ordered in a crash programme and five were built; they received the designations U1405- U1409. These boats were much larger than the U792 series and displaced 800 tons, with a projected range of 270 nautical miles at a speed of 24 kts. Oberingeniur Grumplet scuttled the U1406 and U1407 on the night of 5/6 May 1945; for his pains the British sentenced him to seven years in prison. The U1406 was raised and given to the Americans whilst the U1407 was brought to Britain and recommisioned as HMS METEORITE where she underwent extensive trials before being scrapped in 1950.

American trials of the U1406 were minimal. But the US Navy was already interested in the possibility of nuclear powered vessels and in 1946 one of the first project designs for a nuclear submarine was based on Walter's Atlantic type XXVIW with the substitution of a sodium graphite reactor for the peroxide generator.[8]

Soviet development of Walter technology was also desultory but in 1946, the Antipin Bureau was created to develop designs based on the Walter Engine. Initial projects such as the 615A, 616 and 617 (Whale) utilised the Walter Type XXVI design. A 'Whale' Class submarine was tested but the project was abandoned after a series of near fatal accidents.[9] Like the American experiments with alternative power sources the Soviet Walter designs were superseded by nuclear power. However both the Americans and the Russians enthusiastically undertook aircraft research based on Walter's engine design for the Me163. The fruits of this work can be seen in such diverse programmes as the Mig 1-270 flown in 1947 and the Bell X-15 space plane.[10]

Walter himself was captured in 1945 and the Admiralty had him brought to Vickers at Barrow to continue work on his engines. Dr. Forsythe was in charge of the group but the arrangement proved unsatisfactory and Walter emigrated to the United States in 1950.[11]

The U1407 underwent a complete refit and began trials in 1948. The results were very promising with running speeds of over 15 kts being achieved.[12] A number of things about METEORITE became obvious. As the surface speed of the submarine was increased the second bow wave moved further aft of the boat's spine. This caused an overall reduction in surface speed. However its underwater handling was highly rated. Several other quirks were noted; first it took a considerable amount of time to load fuel, approximately 8-10 hours to ingest 30 tons of HTP. Second, its surface turning was poor; moreover aerial photographs showed that a distinct oxygen bubble track could be seen on the ocean surface when 'warming through' on pure HTP. However the captain reported that "directly fuel is fed into the combustion camber and when combustion is established the wake disappears, even at 40 feet in a calm sea".[13]

In 1945, the Admiralty had enthusiastically ordered a HTP boat for the 1947 construction programme. Moreover the advantages of hydrogen peroxide as a torpedo fuel were enthusiastically embraced and an extensive programme of HTP torpedo design was also instigated which despite serious failures such as the loss of HMS SIDON in 1955 continues today.[14] Inevitably, by the time of the METEORITE trials a more realistic appraisal of the HTP submarine's viability was possible. In December 1946, Captain Logan McKee USN published an article in *Mechanical Engineering* which outlined some of the fruits of American study of the Walter engine. Capt. Mckee argued that the design of the turbine was unnecessarily complicated and was prone to malfunction. He suggested that this caution could be attributed to fear that the Nazis could interpret design errors as criminal negligence. This led to excessive caution on behalf of designers who understandably disliked the thought of spending time in a concentration camp. Moreover McKee identified fuel supply, with costs running at close to 80 times as much per pound as conventional diesel fuel, as a major problem in developing this design.[15]

The following year a secret Admiralty report argued that, despite their supporters' extravagant claims, both the new Walter boat and the type XX1 class were subject to inherent design flaws, particularly in relation to diving depths. The consensus of opinion in the RN was that the deep dive specifications of the new German craft were obtained not through the improvement of hull design but by major reductions in safety margins. In the case of the XX1, the factor of safety was very close to unity. Any attempt at deep diving beyond conventional 100 metres or so would impose unacceptable strains on the boat that could lead to potentially fatal leaks.[16] The major weakness of the Walter boat, aside from the difficulty of operating the engines, was its relatively shallow operational depth of between 25 and 30 metres submerged. This would make it very vulnerable to surface counter-measures. At lower depths, the power ratio of the engine fell and speed was reduced, although the Royal Navy already felt that this problem could be resolved using an indirect rather than direct system where fuel oil is used to generate steam in a closed boiler-turbine-compressor circuit. The combustion gases would then be discharged overboard by their own pressure to dissipate in the surrounding sea.

New hull designs based on wind tunnel experiments from the R101 airship and welded as opposed to riveted steel meant that it was possible to extend diving depths to 200 metres, 30 metres below the current safe diving depths and a full 100 metres off crush depth.[17] There was considerable confidence, based on tests run in new depth testing tanks at Vickers, that crush depths could be extended further to 400 metres.[18]

Despite potential development problems, in addition to the 1947 demand for two experimental boats designated Ex 14 and Ex 15, an order for 12 HTP submarines was placed with completion scheduled for 1955. This requirement broke down into four boats based at Faslane in home waters, four stationed overseas in Malta and four refitting. Admiralty financial projections for 1949-1950 estimated expenditures of £22.5m for the entire programme. This would include more than £1.5 million for the construction of a new plant to manufacture HTP fuel. Preliminary studies suggested that a plant of 10,000 tons capacity could produce HTP for between £70-90,000; depending on catalyst costs this could be reduced to around £61 per ton at 100% HTP, or reducing to £52 per ton at 85% HTP. Such a plant would take at least three years to come into operation, despite access to American experience, particularly ICI's association with Dupont who were studying HTP manufacture for the US Navy. As a stopgap, it was also estimated that a pilot plant of 2,500 tons capacity costing £350,000 could be built in about 12 months.[19]

Financial considerations were now becoming paramount, particularly as Britain's economic position worsened after devaluation in 1949. In that year Research and Development spending on new HSS, High-Speed Submarine technology, including HMS METEORITE's refit and trials, was estimated to be £550,000.[20] In

December of 1950, a cabinet review questioned the value of R&D expenditures of £57 million[21] with a view to reducing costs. The Admiralty wanted a balanced and orderly building programme of all ships, but this was interrupted by the Korean conflict, which quickly absorbed scarce resources. Doubts about the availability of HTP fuel to maintain 12 operational boats led to cancellation of the 1949 programme. Cancellation was confirmed in the wake of the 1952 Committee for Imperial Defence 'Global Strategy Paper', which outlined the need to limit Britain's world wide defence commitment. Another casualty of Korea and budget restrictions was the UK's early nuclear submarine research programme[22], which was not revived until after the Sandy's defence review in 1957.[23]

HMS EXPLORER was laid down in July 1951 and completed in 1956 and her sister ship EXCALIBUR in 1958[24]. They each cost £1,140,000. The design was similar to METEORITE with the HTP bags and the main ballast tanks fitted outside the pressure hull. By comparison with the METEORITE they were larger boats, with streamlined hulls again based on aerodynamic designs for the R101 airship, displacing 980 tons on the surface and 1076 dived. EXPLORER and EXCALIBUR were 225.5 ft in length compared with the METEORITE at only 136.5, and had a beam of 15 ft 9.5 inches and a draught of 17ft 9.5 inches. More than half the pressure hull was devoted to the power plants including two large compartments aft of the control room that housed the turbine and the main HTP combustion chambers. The forward end of the pressure hull, usually given over to torpedoes in ordinary submarines, served for diesel storage. Crew accommodation was very limited, and was positioned between the diesel and control rooms with the steering gear compartment located right aft in the pressure hull. The hull was fully streamlined and submerged resistance was reduced further by an unusually low conning tower. As an experimental submarine EXPLORER carried no armament and had a range of 500 nautical miles at 6kts and 180/75 N.M. at 12/25 kts submerged. Moreover, the introduction of the new high tensile UXE steel allowed a diving depth of over 200 metres, with a crush depth of 300 metres.

EXPLORER was probably the fastest submarine in the world when she was commissioned in 1956. Admiral Bell-Davies, one of her early commanders, explained that his operational brief was very simple; "try to make the bloody thing work without blowing up".[25] Various trials established that the submarines could achieve extraordinary speeds. EXPLORER recorded 26.5 knots in shallow depths. In 1961 other trials confirmed that high speed of 22 knots at deep depths of up to 100 metres was possible. At full speed the two boats had a reputed endurance of nearly three hours during which the engines consumed 100 tons of HTP. By reducing the throughput to the combustion chamber or by using only one of the two turbines endurance could be increased dramatically. A slow speed, 12 knots, on only one turbine gave an endurance of 15 hours. The difficulties of operating HTP meant that this performance was seldom possible. Admiral Bell-Davies was able to run EXPLORER 's engines at over 25 knots for up to one hour while the experimental American submarine USS ALBACORE, also based on the R101 wind tunnel data, could achieve a comparable rate for a very few minutes.[26]

There were a number of other problems. The HTP or peryhdrol was kept in plastic sacks in tanks in the pressure hull and then squeezed into the combustion chamber like a tube of toothpaste. The tanks had also to be kept open to prevent a build-up of gases and the fuel had to be doused with water to prevent spontaneous combustion. The crews were limited to six officers and 35 men and there was no provision for living quarters so a special tender was provided as a mobile HTP depot. Starting the engine was colloquially referred to as 'fizzing'. One observer remarked that "Fizzing in harbour was like a prelude to doomsday".[27] This same officer went on to remark that EXPLORER was not for the fainthearted and that an award of an MBE to its first engineer was in his opinion not over-generous. Commander Christopher Russell commented that if one looked into the unmanned carburettor compartment flames could clearly be seen dancing on top of the machinery. [28] EXPLORER suffered a serious explosion at Cambelton in early 1957[29] but investigation revealed that contamination of the HTP bags rather than any design fault caused the detonation. A further problem was excessive noise; Admiral Bell-Davies remarked "I was stone deaf at above 20 knots[30] , while Cmd. Russell claimed that she could be heard underwater from the deck of a surface ship.[31] As a result the two submarines earned the soubrettes 'Exploder' and 'Excruciator' due to the unstable nature of HTP.

EXPLORER was decommissioned in 1962 and EXCALIBUR a year later. Both boats were sold for scrap and broken up, so ending an extraordinary era in British submarine development. The torch now passed to nuclear power.

EXPLORER can not be classed as an unqualified success, but it can hardly be called a failure either. Given the realities of the immediate post-war situation, High Test Peroxide was a logical response to the problem of War-time German innovations and did offer radically new prospects not just in propulsion but in overall submarine design and performance. Soviet interest in HTP was clear but they found it too difficult to develop. Relative American indifference was a result of the US Navy's willingness to proceed on a broad front of technological development which eventually produced nuclear engines. However, in 1945, nuclear power in submarines was uncertain, since it was believed that such a power-plant would have to be very large. It was not until the USS NAUTILUS was launched in 1955 that nuclear power became a reality. Even then it was more than three years before the US Navy opted to abandon diesel- electric designs altogether and concentrate on a totally nuclear force.

This option was never available to the Royal Navy simply on grounds of cost. However the RN was able to adopt foreign technology with some ease, as both the 'Ex' Class and the 'Porpoise' Class designs of the 1950s proved. Both were directly inspired by German developments. The 'Porpoise' and 'Oberon' Class diesel electric boats were among the finest conventional designs of their day. Later British designers would prove their considerable capability with the project to marry a British hull and a US reactor for the Royal Navy's first nuclear powered submarine HMS DREADNOUGHT. The building of the 'Ex' Class as well as more conventional diesel electric submarines and finally the 'Swiftsure' Class nuclear boats indicates flexibility rather then stagnation in Britain's industrial base of this period.

A STUDY IN TECHNOLOGICAL FAILURE?

NOTES

1. Fregattenkapitän Günther Hesssler explained that the losses in the spring 43 battle had convinced the 'High Command' that the Kriegsmarine was nearly defeated and that the striking power of the U-boat arm was in imminent danger of collapse. PRO ADM/234/67 German Naval Historical Monograph series *The U-boat War in the Atlantic* Vol. II, pp111-112.
2. V. E. Tarrent, *The Last Year of the Kriegsmarine*, London 1994.
3. Air independent propulsion has been the holy grail of submarine design since 1900. As far back as 1911, the German Navy was experimenting with closed cycle engines and in 1942, the Esso Company had undertaken research into alternative forms of submarine propulsion based on feeding diesel and oxygen as secondary fuel directly into the engine. (Submarine Museum Gosport A1389, p4) AIP still fascinates as an alternative to nuclear power and for a view on recent research see *Maritime Defence* December 1995, p242.
4. Material on the Ehrren Engine can be found in PRO ADM 116/6325.
5. Submarine Museum Gosport, A1963/23, *Report on Oxy-hydrogen Submarine Propulsion*.
6. See Mano Zeigler, *Rocket Fighter, The Story of The Me163*, Arms & Armour Press, 1976.
7. Eberhard Rössler, *The U-Boat: The Evolution and Technical History of German Submarines*, Arms & Armour Press 1981, pp166-188; p266-272.
8. P. R Stokes *Hydrogen Peroxide for Power and Propulsion*, Lecture to Science Museum London, 14/1/1998. *Net pub; www.ee.surrey.ac.uk/SSC/H202CONF/Pstokes.htm.*
9. See Spassky and Semyonov, *Project 617 The Soviet Whale Naval History*, Nov/Dec 1994, pp40-43.
10. See, A. Belyakov & J. Marmain, *MiG, 50 Years of Secret Aircraft Design*, Airlife Publishing, 1994; Milton O Thompson, *At The Edge Of Space, The X 15 Flight Program*, NY 1992.
11. Tom Bower *The Paperclip Conspiracy*, London,1987.
12. PRO ADM 213/1060 Meteorite Trials: Entry 6th April 1949, "Turbine ran for 28.5 minutes without problem at speeds of 13.5-15.2 knots".
13. *Ibid*.
14. Sidon sank with all hands when an HTP torpedo malfunctioned. ADM 1/25919: Loss of HMS Sidon 1955. The Russian Submarine Kursk may well have been lost because of an explosion in her Hydrogen peroxide/kerosene fuelled torpedoes, Washington Post: 19/10/2000, pA22.
15. Submarine Museum Gosport A1980/03/002 Capt. Logan McKee, "Hydrogen Peroxide for Propulsive Power", *Mechanical Engineering*, 1946, pp1045-1048.
16. Submarine Museum Gosport A1990/183 *Submarine Development*, p4.
17. *Ibid*, p9.
18. *Ibid*, p10.
19. PRO ADM 265/52 HTP Costs.
20. PRO PREM8/1162 Defence Production Committee: Annex One, 15/12/1948.
21. PRO PREM8/1162 Defence Production Committee: 31/12/1950
22. For a brief indication of the RN's view see PRO PREM8/1244.
23. PREM 11/2635: Development of N.Sub Anglo US Co-operation 1957-1959.
24. Submarine Gosport A1997/119, "Launch of H. M Submarine EXCALIBUR", *Vickers News*, April 1955.
25. Letter from Adm. Bell Davies, 12/03/1999.
26. Telephone Interview with Adm. Bell-Davies, March 1999.
27. John Winton, "The Worst Hangover", *Naval Review*, Jan 1970, pp31-35.
28. Submarine Museum Gosport, A1994/52 "What They Were Like: EXPLORER & EXCALIBUR"
29. PRO ADM 2451/114 Believed that some seawater had caused corrosion, which became isolated and this led to spontaneous combustion when HTP bags were empty.
30. Letter Adm. Bell-Davies, 12/09/1999.
31. Submarine Museum Gosport A1994/52.

10

The Influence of the Cold War on Submarine Design

Antony Preston

We all know when the Cold War ended. Some might even have thought that the collapse of the Soviet Union spelled the end of their naval careers. I am one of those who suspect that the *first* shot of the Cold War was fired in the Spanish Civil War, but I admit that is a minority view. However, it is not right to assume that it started as the Second World War ended.

In fact, far from being a plot cooked up by that legendary 'military-industrial complex' to keep the US defence industry in full production, the Cold War caught the US military in a weakened state after the cuts made by the Truman administration's well-meaning efforts to balance the books. The US Navy had done very little beyond experimenting with new concepts and faced the risk of block obsolescence. The bloated wartime fleet could never be maintained or modernised, *en masse*, and one-for-one replacement was a fantasy. What was to be done with them all? The Axis navies were gone and, even if the Soviet Union became hostile, its surface fleet was made up almost entirely of obsolescent designs and had only a small 'blue water' mercantile marine.

THE TYPE XXI SUBMARINE - A GIFT FROM GERMANY

The German Type XXI fast diesel-electric boat and the Walther air-independent designs offered a lifeline. Funds could be obtained to unlock the secrets of German submarine design and existing submarines could be matched against each other to test new concepts. Today, the acronym 'SSK' for hunter-killer' submarines is loosely used to cover all diesel-electric boats, when in fact the term did not come into use until the US Navy built a small number of dedicated small, anti-submarine submarines. The wide range of 'GUPPY' (or Greater Underwater Propulsive Power) refit had its echoes in the Royal Navy's 'T' class conversions.

Although submariners on both sides of the Atlantic had taken the lead to avoid cutbacks in funding, political support became much easier after intelligence assessments of the Soviets' strength in diesel-electric boats leaked out. These early assessments did not get the roles and missions of the various types of Soviet submarines wrong; but they grossly over-estimated the Soviet Union's industrial capabilities. Only in recent years has the policy of submarine mass-production become clear; it appears that many of the alleged 'fully operational' Project 613 'Whiskeys' were delivered without engines, sensors or weapons. The Soviets intended the surplus numbers to form a 'materiel reserve' from which damaged boats and, even, exports could be drawn. I do not see a conspiracy in all this overestimation, but it is an example of how intelligence assessments can become wish-fulfilment and how correlation from a narrow database can give a misleading picture.

THE WALTER BOAT AND THE SEARCH FOR SPEED

As soon as submarines started to hunt submarines, it became clear that a speed advantage was essential for the hunter and that streamlining and greater battery power could only go so far. The speed of the handful of Walter Type XVIIBs tested by the Americans and British was impressive, nonetheless. The British built version of a Walter boat, the 'Explorer' Class, was rated at a maximum speed of 27 knots, and the Soviet Project 617 'Whale' (adapted from the Walter Type XI) was designed for 20 knots. The Royal Navy boats were known as the 'Exploder' Class and the solitary 'Whale', S.99, tried to start her Walter turbine 80 metres below the surface and blew an 80mm hole in the pressure hull. Wisely, the US Navy decided to follow another route.

ENTER THE USS NAUTILUS

I am not going to repeat the story of the conception, design and implementation of the USS NAUTILUS; it is already well known. Her importance, however, cannot be over-stated. Here, at last, was a submarine capable of high speed over great distance. Life in the surface warfare community would never be the same again. Although the industrial might of the United States allowed its Navy the luxury of building several prototypes for evaluation against each other, it seemed highly likely that the Soviet Navy could achieve similar results by diverting resources on a massive scale. We now know from all those obliging retired Soviet designers and engineers that, at the time, the Soviet Union could have been slightly ahead of the Americans.

Fortunately, the malevolent personality of Lavrenti Beria made him jealous of any developments he did not understand; if our Russian friends are right, he stopped developments at a critical point in the programme. Subsequently, after Beria had met his violent, but well-deserved, end, the stupidity of his interference was recognised, and the Project 627 'November' nuclear attack submarine (SSN) programme was given top priority. Perhaps we in the West should enlarge our pantheon of heroes who came to the rescue of our navies to put a bust of Beria alongside those of such luminaries as Kim il Sung, Saddam Hussein and General Galtieri.

Speaking of 'also-rans', the British efforts to get into the SSN business are rarely described accurately. As early as 1943, the Admiralty noted that a team should look into ways of harnessing nuclear power for submarine propulsion. No less an authority than the former Director-General Ships, Admiral Sir Ted Horlick, is on record, saying that the permission granted to the Royal Navy by Admiral Rickover to purchase the S5W 'Skipjack-type' reactor plant would have been of much less value had the Douneray reactor not been running in parallel. Cross-fertilisation speeded up the Royal Navy's ability to absorb the new technology.

Be that as it may, the US Navy became the technology leader in nuclear submarine design and, at the same time, imposed rigorous safety standards on its operators. Its example was followed by the only other Western operator of nuclear submarines, the French Navy. It cannot be a coincidence that in 45 years only two US Navy SSNs have been lost, and no British or French, whereas the former Soviet Navy had a frightening series of accidents (for example, the Project 658, K.19, was nicknamed 'Hiroshima' by her crew). Leaving aside environmental concerns, the good safety record of Western SSNs and SSBNs has a military value, even if hard to quantify; confidence in the safety of the platform is an excellent foundation for the development of tactical skills.

With safety raised to a credible level, it was possible for the US Navy to react rapidly to Soviet developments. The delivery of the first 'November' Class submarine in 1959 was followed by the Project 658 'Hotel' Class, a strategic submarine armed with SS-N-4 ballistic missiles from 1959 onwards. The Soviets had pioneered the launch of ballistic missiles from converted SSKs, but in such a cumbersome form that the boats stood a fair chance of being intercepted by conventional anti-submarine forces while surfaced. The US Navy's response was somewhat slower, but infinitely superior; five 'Skipjack' hulls were given a 40-metre section abaft the sail containing 16 launch-tubes for A-1 Polaris missiles, launched underwater. Here was a secure sea-based deterrent, and the five 'George Washington' Class were followed by 36 improved 'Ethan Allen' and 'Lafayette' Class SSBNs, all delivered between 1961 and 1966.

The Soviet Project 659, the 'Echo' Class SSBNs, followed very close on the heels of the 'Hotel' Class, but priorities were changing. The Soviet government had become aware of the threat to Russian land targets posed by carrier-borne aircraft, and the Project 675 'Echo II' was armed with long-range anti-ship missiles (introducing the SSGN category). The second-generation of SSBNs, the Project 667 'Yankee' Class submarine, was clearly influenced by the US Navy SSBNs and had a similar configuration of launch-tubes. The hull-design, however, followed previous Soviet practice. There is no truth in the story that 'Yankee' was built to stolen US plans.

The Soviet Navy produced designs prolifically. It is not my intention here to catalogue them. Rather, Soviet SSBN design settled down to parallel US Navy improvements in missile range and destructiveness (apart from the unique 'Typhoon'). In attack submarines, however, a most interesting divergence emerged. The Soviets were happy to develop individual designs optimised for specific missions, whereas the West stuck to a broad policy of all-purpose designs capable of undertaking a variety of missions. Hence, the extraordinary variety of Soviet designs and the size of some of them, such as the Project 949 'Oscar' Class of SSGNs, of which the ill-fated KURSK was one.

Not until the Cold War was over did the Russian Navy appear to accept that the West had a point and that mission attack submarines have come back on the agenda. The Soviet philosophy was only affordable in a command economy and even that could not sustain the rising costs of the submarine fleet.

MANOEUVRABILITY TO MATCH SPEED

We must retrace our steps to the early 1950s when the US Navy ordered its first submarine intended exclusively for underwater operations. This was the experimental USS ALBACORE (AGSS-569). Although only a technology-demonstrator, she was highly influential, and the term 'Albacore hull' is still used. The idea of a whale - shaped hull had been introduced by the Royal Navy in its 'R' Class submarines in 1917-18, but the ALBACORE matched manoeuvrability, high speed with control systems. Her huge silver-zinc battery is reputed to have used silver supplied by the US Treasury, but only on condition that it was recovered and returned. Speeds as high as 33 knots have been reported, but the trials results are still classified.

The submarines incorporating the new hull-shape and control systems were all distinguished by their high manoeuvrability. The US Navy's 'Barbel' SSK design

7   The 'G' Class Submarine, HMS G-9 (1916)

courtesy BAe Systems

8   The 'K' Class Fleet suppport Submarine, HMS K-3 (1916)

courtesy BAe Systems

9   The 'R' Class Submarine, HMS R-7 (1918)

courtesy BAe Systems

10   The Monitor, 'M' Class Submarine, HMS M-1 with 12" gun (1918)

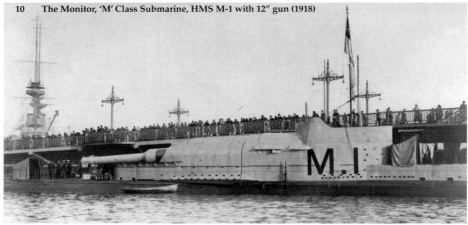

courtesy BAe Systems

11   HMS L-12, HMS H-28, and HMS R-7 Wartime Submarines (1919)

courtesy BAe Systems

12   The 'K' Class Experimental Submarine, K-26 (1923)

courtesy BAe Systems

was made available to NATO and other allies, and 'Albacore' features were incorporated in all future Western SSNs, starting with the 'Skipjack' Class.

DIMUS - A NEW LEVEL OF DETECTION

Many attempts were made to improve Western sonars by adapting German technology, but the first big step forward was the digital multi-beam sonar (DIMUS), that used beam-forming techniques. It was regarded as so important in countering Soviet submarines that it was made part of the technology-transfer package that included the S5W reactor plant for the Royal Navy's first SSN, HMS DREADNOUGHT.

It was that same DIMUS technology that lay at the heart of the Portland Spy Trial of the early 1960s. It is amusing, if slightly embarrassing, to read contemporary press coverage, which claimed that the Soviets had targeted the Admiralty Underwater Weapons Establishment (AUWE) at Portland because of its world-beating expertise in sonar design. In fact, the embarrassment stemmed from the appalling prospect of breaking the news to the US Navy that Britain had given the secrets of DIMUS to the Soviets before the Royal Navy had even got it into its new SSN! Fortunately, Ethel Gee could only remove one drawing at a time by stuffing it down her knickers, and her boyfriend Houghton then developed the film in the washbasin of the bathroom. Reliable intelligence sources have stated that the Soviets were welcome to try and build a working sonar from the resulting prints!

TOWED ARRAYS

The passive towed sonar array was an outcome of the Sound Underwater Surveillance System (SOSUS) seabed passive tracking system. Clearly, SOSUS was limited to use in a barrier defensive system, and if it could be made mobile it would be more flexible at the cost of some degradation of performance because the array would be shorter. Development work was shared between the US Navy and the Royal Navy in the 1970s, and surface ship arrays were soon followed by the first non-reliable arrays for submarines.

By a totally unforeseen turn of events, the first operational use of a submarine towed array was not against the Soviet Navy, or even against a submarine. It was used by the SSN HMS CONQUERER to maintain surveillance on the Argentine cruiser GENERAL BELGRANO in 1982. The connection with the Cold War is that the KGB and GRU would have paid a lot of money to get their hands on the CONQUERER's navigation log with its details of speed and depth of water while streaming the array. It also explains why that navigation log had to be shredded.

'ALFA' AND 'PAPA'

The Soviet Navy produced two outstanding design concepts that had a profound effect on Western submarine design. These were the Project 705 'Alfa' SSN and the Project 661 'Papa', also intended as an attack boat, but using cruise missiles. 'Alfa' became very well known when selective details were leaked to the Western media, whereas 'Papa's' remarkable characteristics were, for some reason, downplayed, possibly because they were not understood.

Some of the 'Alfas' had titanium hulls and all had an unmanned reactor plant, resulting in a relatively small, very high-speed boat. Their role, not understood properly for many years, was to act as 'interceptors', racing out to attack hostile submarines already located by other means. They relied heavily on shore support, but Soviet automation technology was simply not mature enough to provide reliability. Titanium has great benefits, and the Soviet engineers, who mastered the art of working this somewhat intractable metal, deserve great credit. But it is the most expensive way to build a submarine. The 'Alfas' were known to their crews as the 'Golden Fish'. The concept was not repeated and they had short service-lives.

'Papa' also had a titanium hull, but her designed speed of 38 knots was handsomely exceeded, and her maximum speed of 44.5 knots remains a world record (until 'Seawolf' figures are released by the US Navy). Fortunately for the West, the power plant proved very unreliable, and the cost was so exorbitant that only one prototype was commissioned.

NEW WEAPONS FOR NEW THREATS

Weapons are easier to adapt than submarine designs when new threats appear. Reports of the 'Alfa' led to pressure for a new generation of high-speed heavyweight torpedoes, and for good measure exaggerated estimates of the 'Alfa's' diving depth added a requirement for full speed down to 1000 metres, a daunting task for the engineers. Out of this scare came the US Navy's Mk 48 ADCAP and the British 'Spearfish', and their performance became a benchmark for foreign competitors.

The Soviet penchant for tactical missiles eventually led the US Navy to arm its submarines with, first, the Sub-Harpoon missile and, then, with the Tomahawk cruise missile in a nuclear anti-ship version and a conventional alternative, and the better-known land-attack version, the Tomahawk Land Attack Missile (TLAM). With TLAM and its successors, the submarine had for the first time a major ability to influence military operations on land, a dream of submariners for 90 years.

These advanced torpedoes and missiles bring with them an added need for greater volume. The age-old cry of "keep it small" misses the point. Modern weapon systems demand adequate command and control (C2), and that means capacious control rooms, cooling for computer cabinets and so on. The integrated Type 2054 sonar suite in the Royal Navy's 'Vanguard' Class SSBNs needed 17 cabinets in its original form, and a strategic system such as the D-5 Trident II requires its own separate fire control system. These requirements are not compatible with small submarines, which is why the more potent SSKs are so large.

CONCLUDING THOUGHTS

The wheel of fate spins, and it may be that we are back in the position that submariners found themselves in by 1946. With the end of the Cold War, what are all those SSKs that have been acquired around the world for? As 'mobile minefields', they have a limited role in coastal defence; but there can be no assumption of a uniform level of efficiency. Submarines require highly trained operators and small forces of small SSKs may not be able to afford that luxury.

In the right hands, a powerful SSK and an SSN are potent weapons; but such professional excellence is expensive. As the Iraqis and the Argentines have learned the hard way, owning expensive technology does not guarantee victory. And as the once mighty Soviet Navy shows, efficiency can vanish through neglect and under-funding. No navy can be complacent about the lessons of the Cold War, particularly not the 'winners'.

PART III

RN SUBMARINES & SUBMARINERS INTO THE 21ST CENTURY

11

The Submarine Contribution to Joint Operations: The Role of the SSN in Modern UK Defence Policy

Commander Nick Harrap

In this chapter, I intend to try to put the role of the SSN into the context of modern defence doctrine and to outline the significant and continuing contribution the flotilla can make to joint operations and thus wider defence policy. I rather hope that the force of the argument will stand alone without embellishment!

Let me first begin with a quote from current British Maritime Doctrine. It reads as follows:

> The fundamentals of British maritime doctrine, now encapsulated within BR 1806, are the overarching concepts from which future operational and tactical doctrine should flow. The redirected focus of core naval operations towards power projection in the littoral has highlighted the importance of the maritime enabling role at the operational level. We can only play our part if we understand operational art as practised by our sister services and our allies, and they understand how to integrate and employ maritime power to best advantage.

During recent years, the focus of maritime attention has shifted from countering the Cold War threat in the North Atlantic, towards littoral operations, power projection from the sea and the ability to influence the land battle ashore. This has been a significant change in thinking which has resulted from the changed political face - and priorities - of western nations. British maritime doctrine is quite clear that there is now an opportunity to take full advantage of the potential of maritime power and deploy it in direct support of UK interests wherever in the world they might be engaged.

Since these changes were brought about, the Royal Navy has introduced a wide range of initiatives and studies to embrace the concept of, and justification for, the move towards this revised doctrine. The results are enshrined within the philosophy of the maritime contribution to joint operations (MCJO) and, in particular, within the detail of the associated sub concept papers produced under the guidance and direction of the Assistant Chief of Naval Staff (ACNS).

The stated purpose of these sub concept papers is to define and develop MCJO in the context of joint force expeditionary operations in order to provide a framework for realisation of the concept.

They deal with the operational capabilities required to shape and dominate the different dimensions of the modern battlespace. The submarine's ability to contribute in these newly defined arenas is not always well understood and sometimes subject to 'legacy thinking'. The modern SSN has much to offer the joint force commander both now and for the foreseeable future.

What I want to do now is to articulate and illustrate the wide utility of the United Kingdom submarine flotilla within the MCJO framework in support of national and multi-national objectives, and at all military levels of warfare. I also aim further to show that the SSN is intrinsic to British maritime doctrine and, by extension, to United Kingdom defence doctrine.

I look, particularly, to address the roles and employment of the SSN force undertaking joint operations. I do not intend to cover the politico-strategic considerations in the use of either the national deterrent or sub-strategic Trident. These stand-alone and although they are, perhaps, the ultimate extension of maritime contribution to joint operations, they are not considered within the concepts of manoeuvre or expeditionary warfare.

Nor do I intend to address capabilities that might be provided, other than those already scheduled to enter service through endorsed equipment programmes. It would be unhelpful for me to try to advertise capabilities that cannot be delivered.

Additionally, I have to make some assumptions. Firstly, I assume that post-Strategic Defence Review (SDR) force levels will be maintained throughout the time-frame covered by the current strategic plan; secondly that the Tomahawk Land Attack Missile (TLAM) capability will be extended to all SSNs in the flotilla; and, lastly, that a covert means of delivering and extracting special forces will be brought into service with the advent of the Alamanda and, later, the Chalfont projects.

To examine the use of the SSN as a political and military tool, firstly at the strategic and operational levels of warfare, it is of note that the submarine flotilla has long extolled what have become known as the 'Seven deadly virtues', all of which are key aspects of performance, or features inherent in the platform. Current doctrine states that: maritime forces must be capable of influencing events and actions above, on and below the surface of the sea. The oceans provide a three dimensional space in which maritime forces can manoeuvre.

All of these virtues are thus still relevant today - perhaps more so than ever before.

Flexibility. The capability to change role almost instantaneously, without equipment reconfiguration and without changes in, or redeployment of, personnel. No arrangements have to be made for host nation support. The submarine is constrained only by broadcast limitations - or communications windows when undertaking task group support operations - in that the transmission and receipt of an instruction takes a finite length of time. It is, however, true that some roles are mutually exclusive. Prime examples are provision of indications and warnings and TLAM strike - the one inherently covert, the other necessarily overt in its execution.

Mobility. The SSN is capable of high speeds, for sustained periods, independent of the surface and with no requirement for an accompanying logistic train. This allows for a Speed of Advance (SOA) potentially in excess of 500nm per day for as long as is required. It further allows efficient and effective employment in support of task group operations, bringing real meaning to the term 'fleet submarine'. This inherent agility allows close range force protection or sanitisation operations ahead of the task group. It almost certainly means that the SSN can be in the vanguard of follow-on forces to shape the battle-space at the direction of the joint force commander.

Stealth. The SSN represents the only true ability to operate independent of the surface, up threat, regardless of who exercises sea control or air superiority. In this manner, it may be possible to conduct operations either alone or in conjunction with Special Forces that are exactly in keeping with the precepts of manoeuvre warfare. The impending advent of the dry deck hangar and the ability to deploy the Swimmer Delivery Vehicle (SDV) covertly represent a significant capability enhancement and force multiplier. The contribution to, and the effect on, the campaign estimates might be critical. Added to this is the psychological dimension. The mere threat of submarine presence has a coercive effect of its own and should not be underestimated.

Endurance. There is no requirement for dependence on outside authorities either for support, or for withdrawal, from an area if the situation changes. All life support services can be provided onboard on a continuous basis. In combination with mobility and stealth, this capacity serves to give the widest range of military and political choice in campaign planning and execution. The only limitations are expenditure of food and weapons.

Reach. Of itself, seapower provides ready and unique access to huge areas. The SSN is capable of taking this concept further, exploiting the environment to the full, including areas not accessible to other forces such as the marginal ice zone and under the ice canopy. This facilitates a variety of operational employments at the time and place of choice. It can range from mere physical presence to the delivery of selectively targeted ordnance, 'behind enemy lines' and regardless of who dominates the battle-space.

Autonomy. This virtue embraces the ability to operate alone and without support at the direction of whoever exercises overall command, as a self-contained unit of force - with broad utility - rather than part of a force package, if that is what is required. The SSN is capable of self-protection and offensive action without assistance from other units.

Punch. The punch ranges from the determination of the enemy's centre of gravity through intelligence gathering and the provision of indications and warnings, through force protection, to precision strikes against land targets at a range of 1,000nm and to an accuracy of 25 feet.

Maritime doctrine, in addressing the nature of maritime power, rightly states that joint integration is crucial. The right tool is required in the right place at the right time. Commanders of joint forces have to be able to recognise the distinctive attributes of each of the components, in order to play each to its strengths. It goes on to list the distinctive operational attributes of maritime forces: access, mobility, versatility, flexibility in response, adaptability in roles, joint and multi-national attributes, sustained reach, resilience, lift capacity, poise and leverage.

This view is further echoed in joint doctrine. With the clear exception of lift capacity, the SSN is able to display all of these attributes, often in large measure; in fact, although the terminology is different, they reflect the seven deadly virtues to a considerable degree. The application of maritime power, through the SSN, allows potential employment across the full range of crisis and political activity and confers the ability to give an almost infinite range of signals. The SSN allows the sensitive application of force or influence - and intervention at the time and place of political choice - to enable the exploitation of joint assets.

Let us look now a little further down the spectrum - at the use of the SSN as a force *enabler* - the operational and tactical levels of warfare.

Sea control is defined as the condition in which one has freedom of action to use the sea for one's own purposes in specified areas and for specified periods of time and, where necessary, to deny or limit its use to the enemy. Sea denial is defined as the condition where one party denies another the ability to control a maritime area without either wishing or being able to control it himself. They are neither mutually exclusive nor the same; either may be considered as a precursor to, or implicit in, force projection. The former ensures freedom of action above, on, and below the surface of the sea. The protection of maritime forces as an operational function is concerned with preserving the combat power of the force. Maritime power projection exploits sea control to achieve access to the coast and to deliver power ashore. Inherent in this, be it in a 'blue water' open ocean setting or a 'brown water' littoral context, is the principle of force protection.

The same virtues outlined earlier are as important and as exploitable at these levels of warfare, effectively the operational and tactical levels, as they are across the strategic and operational levels. The full warfare spectrum is encompassed. Many roles can be conducted simultaneously while the SSN remains alert for others. Concurrent operation across all levels of warfare is both possible and achievable.

All of these inherent strengths contribute to the ability of the SSN to assist in shaping the battle-space for follow-on forces - but although they are strengths and demonstration of ability, what capability do they enable and what benefits do they bring to the joint force commander? I shall touch on three distinct areas in which the contribution of the modern UK SSN is unique.

First, the task we have always described as 'indicators and warnings'. This term is widely used, often glibly and, when put on the spot, many do not really understand what it means. It is not just a question of sitting off a hostile coast counting ships coming in and out of harbour or aircraft taking off and landing. There is a great deal more to it than that. There are those who would argue that this is a submarine card that is often overplayed and that there are other assets far better able to obtain the kind of intelligence inherent in this task than the SSN. For a lot of the information, this is probably true but there is much that the SSN can obtain that is not available to other sources - or is simply shut down if there is any danger of a known satellite being able to exploit the situation.

We have seen submarines obtain electronic intelligence (ELINT) information from systems that were not operated when collection satellites were overhead. We have intercepted communications made during similar periods. We have been able to exploit microwave links and platform-to-platform communications - and we have been able to do all of this in near real time. In addition, we have been able to conduct environmental assessments, close range photography, obtain acoustic intelligence, and pass tracking information in similar time-scales. With the impending advent of closer links with Special Forces and the advent of new technology, we will be able to do more.

The second distinct area is that of offensive ASW. The days of trying to incorporate a submarine into the close range ASW screen are gone. This concept inhibits the strengths of the SSn and danger of blue on blue is too great. Over recent years, the idea of operating submarines in a different manner but still in support of the task group has been tried with varying success. Today, the advent of high integrity, near real time transfer of information, expanded bandwidth and high data rate transmission make this a much more attractive and realistic concept. More and more frequently, requests are coming in for SSNs to operate in direct support of, or integrated with, the battle group with a wide ranging remit and often at considerable range from the group itself.

Offensive ASW is an integral part of battle-space dominance and this is defined as exerting control over the environments of the entire battle-space; the surface, subsurface, air, land and information environments, and the electromagnetic spectrum. As the technological revolution continues, it is these last two that represent the biggest challenges and opportunities for the SSN flotilla - and I shall return to these very shortly. Before I do, I want to touch briefly on the third distinct area to which I alluded a moment ago - land attack from the sea.

The use of Tomahawk allows the SSN to achieve the application of force or influence at a time and place of political choice at minimum political risk and with a low probability of unwanted damage. This makes it, for the moment at least, 'the precision weapon of choice'. This excellent and yet flexible capability is coming into service throughout the flotilla as the boats go through major upkeep. Not all will carry Tomahawk all the time, of course, and some doubt still remains over the eventual total buy, but this is a fearsome weapon.

The advent of the Tomahawk missile system into the SSN inventory has given the UK the ability to reach out from the sea over a longer distance than was ever possible before and to assist in shaping the battlefield to achieve its objectives. Approximately 70% of the world's population, and therefore by definition the majority of the largest urban areas, are within 100 miles of the coast. Just about everyone lives within 1,000 miles of the coast. This means that the UK, via the RN's TLAM system, has the capability to attack not only the maritime defences of a country, but also its high value assets and political centres far removed from the traditional front line

Throughout the history of the Submarine Service, there have been numerous occasions when a submarine has attacked land targets but, until now, these attacks have been confined to coastal facilities. The use of the submarine to land Special Forces behind the enemy front line to attack targets inland is, of course, also a well-proven method, and continues to be an option even today.

But let me draw briefly on the experiences of HMS SPLENDID during the Kosovo campaign. This TLAM equipped SSN delivered to Permanent Joint Headquarters (PJHQ) a stealthy, autonomous land attack platform, requiring host nation support only to re-arm, from day one of the conflict all the way through to the conclusion of the FOSM air strikes. HMS SPLENDID was on station, with only a very few days out of theatre, for re-supply and minor maintenance. She was a sustainable asset that could, and indeed did, keep up the pressure on the Milosevic regime by launching TLAM strikes by night and during weather that prevented tactical aircraft from pressing home their attacks.

Admittedly, in the Adriatic, there was little ASW threat; nevertheless, it is obvious that the TLAM equipped SSN could operate in a hostile ASW environment and still deliver a significant weight of weapons on to high value targets. This is an extremely effective force multiplier for the chief of joint operations to have at his disposal, and as more UK SSNs are fitted with the TLAM system, FOSM will be able to provide a continual SSN based land attack capability throughout an extended crisis. This is especially important as the RN and the other UK forces move inexorably towards the 'littoral warfare' concept and away from the ASW orientated arena of the cold war, as I described above.

Tomahawk has proven ability to operate in all weathers, with remarkable accuracy and at a precise time, and it has shown a demonstrable ability to get through to the target. This gives the UK a very valuable weapon with which it can affect the whole course of a conflict with, potentially, a single shot. In addition, imaginative and meticulous mission planning can minimise the risk of any collateral damage. Significantly, there is no risk to our own people. What a weapon for the politicians to have in their armoury!

This all sounds very rosy - but where are the problem areas? Where are the capability shortfalls that limit the ability of the SSN to contribute to what is known as 'battle-space dominance'?

This concept is defined as embracing control over the environments of the entire battle-space: the surface; subsurface; air; land and information environments, and the electromagnetic spectrum. As the technological revolution continues, it is these last two that represent the biggest challenge to the SSN flotilla. The MCJO concept has clear implications for the priorities of the [future] equipment programme [and it] must influence the design of new equipment. The single most important issue is that of connectivity.

Joint battle-space digitisation describes the communications and information technology architecture of the future battlefield. To play a major role within the joint force demands access to high bandwidth satellite links, connection to a tactical wide area network and the full use of Internet protocols. Current submarine connectivity is lagging the advances being readily made in other capability areas, let alone the commercial world. Exploitation of these advances is crucial to the contribution of the SSN. The lead-time for new and visionary equipment is long. If full use is to be made of the submarine in the modern warfare arena, every technological avenue - military or commercial - must be explored in order to increase the ability to integrate these versatile and potent units into the joint effort. The cost benefits of so doing are self-evident and fully in accordance with endorsed doctrine.

I end with a few thoughts. The SSN is not a legacy of the Cold War. Its attributes and abilities reflect exactly modern maritime doctrine. The SSN has broad utility and offers a wide range of options to politicians and campaign planners, at low risk. It can deploy early and quickly, exercise full freedom of the sea, changing role and area of operation at will. This posture can be maintained almost indefinitely. It can be an instrument of diplomacy, coercion, or war fighting employed directly or obliquely. The multi-faceted capabilities of the SSN, in contributing to the overall effort in both political and military 'battle-spaces', are dependent on remaining abreast of current technological advances. Failure to invest in the future has the potential to sideline a capability that offers the widest ranges of strategic, operational and tactical choice.

12

Submarine Capability – 'Astute' Class and Beyond: Introduction and Capability Management

Steve Ramm

INTRODUCTION AND CAPABILITY MANAGEMENT

In this chapter, I intend to look forward beyond 'Astute' and therefore I shall principally be looking at the UK Underwater Equipment & R&D programme and what changes we have introduced to deliver the product that we require.

I am responsible for Equipment Capability from the Underwater Battlespace – part of the MOD's Central Customer Organisation. In order to set the scene, as it has direct bearing on the future of submarines, I shall briefly describe what 'Capability Management' is and how it is affecting the way that we do business.

The seeds of capability management came from the Strategic Defence Review of 1998. This re-emphasised the change in defence posture that had progressively occurred throughout the preceding decade and placed the focus for future operations firmly on expeditionary warfare and, for maritime forces, on the littoral world-wide. But it went further than operations and sought to reorganise fundamentally the whole of the acquisition process throughout the UK defence supply chain. There were four principal drivers for change that pervade the whole of the equipment life-cycle and, to many, these have now become very familiar:

- The first is that the UK armed forces were, and still are, facing less predictable threats and being asked to conduct a wider range of tasks including constabulary or peace keeping operations. Many of these threats are asymmetric and operations are being conducted under increasingly restrained rules of engagement.
- As a result, defence equipment is becoming increasingly complex and diverse, but military flexibility demands shorter acquisition cycles.
- UK defence procurement has continued to show time and cost over-runs that significantly exceed the performance targets agreed by the Ministry of Defence with our Treasury Department.
- The defence industry is restructuring, with companies merging or allying both within the UK and across Europe, requiring a new MOD relationship with industry.

These changes pose significant challenges to the Equipment Acquisition area and, by extension, to the R&D that supports much of the Equipment Procurement Programme. But we must not forget the end users' needs – the delivery of equipment capability is one of the five contributing pillars of overall operational effectiveness. Whilst the Military Commander delivers this by maintaining flexible, well-equipped units with trained, multi-skilled crews, it is the job of the Equipment Capability

Customer to get capable equipment to the front line as early as possible. All of this must be affordable and there are other higher priority claims on the public purse.

From the acquisition perspective, 'capability management' is fundamentally about equipment provision and the Balance of Investment decisions required when providing that equipment. In short, 'capability management' is about selecting the best way of generating a capability by delivering both the performance demanded by military commanders and minimising the development time and costs to put that equipment into service.

Thus, the aim of a 'Capability Manager' in our submarine environment is to provide an integrated and holistic approach to the whole problem of Underwater Warfare and where we can contribute to other areas. The Underwater Battlespace Department has direct responsibility for more than submarines and more than ASW. It directly sponsors the delivery and sustainment of equipment capability from ASW to mine warfare to Maritime Survey and has inputs in addressing capabilities in other areas such as Strike, ASuW and Special Forces. The investment in these areas has to be balanced to provide the most capability for the least cost.

'Capability Management' is a new concept and, as for any period of change, we expect it to take from between three to five years before all the changes have been fully incorporated and ingrained into our organisational culture. Even so, we are already beginning to see some of the benefits in terms of the capability trade-offs that can be performed – and the future promises a great deal more.

CURRENT UK UNDERWATER RESEARCH REQUIREMENT

Turning to the future programme, research is the key to our future capability as an integral and essential part of the acquisition process; it provides options for development that are practical, achievable and cost-effective. Research must act as a catalyst to further the Smart Procurement aims of being 'better, faster, cheaper'.

FASTER ACQUISITION

The 'faster' category relies on improving the acquisition process itself and this in turn depends almost solely on speeding the procurement selection and approvals processes, rather than specific research. Nevertheless, researchers must appreciate that the aim is to transfer technology from the laboratory to an equipment programme; without the associated exploitation route, the research customer may as well spend his resources elsewhere.

The UK's submarine platform's characteristics have been determined until after 2017, when the Future Attack Submarine (FASM) comes into service. Therefore there are severe constraints on our ability to introduce new or enhanced capability into submarine platforms. Incremental acquisition is the key as it offers a means not only to get technology into service quickly but also to upgrade it affordably through its service life. Researchers, however, must be able to convince industry that a technology is sufficiently 'de-risked' so that it can be offered back to the MOD. There are two strands to achieving this:

- The first is to design equipment that can be continuously upgraded through its service life – this almost certainly means the use of Commercial off-the-Shelf (COTS) technologies
- The second is the greater use of technology demonstration programmes and the engendering of a build-test-build philosophy into UK research and development. An example of this is the demonstration of sonar adaptive processing that should provide significant sensor improvements in the noisy littoral environment – part of the 'Acoustic Quick Wins' initiative started last

autumn. It is already at sea today. Another illustration is multi-statics with the submarine platforms exploiting the surface ship, Maritime Patrol Aircraft (MPA) or remote sensor active acoustics. And again, there are long range acoustic communications to reduce Water Space Management (WSM) issues. In the weapons area, we are currently looking at early pull through of mature technology during Technology Insertion periods, rather than waiting for major weapon upgrades.

It is in the 'cheaper' and 'better' categories that research can really excel. To translate our aims into capability terms, we are looking at how we provide more capability for less cost or, at worse, the same capability for less cost. Technology is seen as a cornerstone to achieving these aims and we are seeking either cost reduction, capability improvements or, ideally, a combination of the two.

CHEAPER ACQUISITION

The 'cheaper' category is undoubtedly the driver in current defence spending. If we can reduce cost in one area, then those savings can be re-invested elsewhere to the benefit of defence as a whole. The UK is aiming to manage Whole Life Costs that are a combination of Unit Production Cost and Through-Life Operating Costs. The unit production cost, being the cost of the platform or weapon system, is relatively easy to measure; but for through-life costs, measurement methods are still maturing. Nevertheless, there is strong evidence to suggest that there is significant scope for reducing these costs. Conducting research into cost reduction is not being prescribed; instead, we are asking for exploitation of new technologies that could lead to substantial reductions in the costs for both new and in-service equipment.

I already have a substantial part of the research programme looking at these types of technologies.

Firstly, towed arrays; we are initially looking to remove as much of the electronics from the array as possible and, in the mid-term, looking to fibre optic technologies to substantially reduce total costs whilst potentially improving performance. For submarine towed arrays, we also have work in place to improve 'reliability', thereby making savings from the sizeable support costs of 'clip-on' systems whilst removing some operational deployment and tactical exploitation limitations at the same time.

For hull mounted arrays, we are investigating whether large thin conformal hull arrays could out-perform towed arrays, especially in the shallow and deep-water littoral. The use of large hull arrays with vertical adaptive beam forming will reduce ambient noise and enable improved passive sonar capability. This would lead to considerable cost savings and enhance tactical manoeuvrability by replacing the need for towed arrays, in some environments, altogether. Even so, towed arrays will probably continue for the blue water operations. The first large hull array is being fitted to one of our submarines now as part of the sonar-type 2076 incremental acquisition programme.

Reducing manpower costs is seen as a significant objective and, for this, improved information management and human factor techniques, largely produced commercially, are seen as offering savings. However, some risk remains in applying these principles to the demanding environment of underwater warfare.

In platform terms, we can also reduce costs of externally mounted systems especially on both surface ships and submarines. Although more expensive to purchase, composite materials will help to limit corrosion damage thereby saving support funding downstream. The emphasis here is on improving manufacturing and integration techniques and also proving that these complex substances can withstand the maritime environment, particularly under shock conditions.

Finally, on cost issues, the UK is looking at simulation techniques to reduce the costs of lengthy equipment testing and acceptance. With a limited number of platforms, we can no longer afford to spend weeks conducting first of class acceptance on increasingly complex systems, especially sonar. We are developing a Synthetic Acoustic Environment that can simulate a sonar system from the noise input through the hydrophone to the display. This should eventually enable us to test the system in all modes and all environments.

BETTER ACQUISITION

In the 'better' category, we need to return to the Strategic Defence Review and the concept of operations being fundamentally expeditionary and joint. This had a significant impact on the Underwater Battle-space. It was essential that all underwater assets, especially submarines, should begin to demonstrate more generic capabilities and wider utility in support of the land battle rather than the single overriding capability of deep water ASW operations, their major role during the Cold War. In terms of capability shortfalls, we are essentially looking at the following three new areas.

The first is how to integrate underwater assets with wider maritime, air and land forces. In the short term, this will enhance submarine utility and in the longer term, it will permit integration of static sensors and Unmanned Underwater Vehicles (UUVs). Wider integration clearly means better communications and connectivity. The acquisition process, rather than R&D, is leading the way here and is benefiting from advances in the civil sector. Connectivity and continued interoperability with our own and allied forces is the key to the submarine's utility and the biggest challenge for the future.

The US has set the standard and we are grateful for their continued assistance in this area. For the near term, UK research has been concentrating on the most difficult problem of improving communications in both capacity and redundancy. Here, we are nearing the end of our work on the Recoverable Towed Optic Fibre (RTOF) buoy but have also made significant progress over the past year in acoustic communications. While ranges are still comparatively short, we now have methods to pass video pictures acoustically with almost no errors, a substantial achievement given the vagaries of underwater sound propagation.

We need to reduce the effort required to achieve sea denial and, preferably, sea control. This commits a significant number of our assets to performing force protection duties rather than being used for power projection in support of the land battle. We therefore need to use sensors and weapons as force multipliers by divorcing them from the mobile platform. The submarine's unique attributes for sustained covert operations is well known and it is these attributes that we need to build on, particularly in the littoral environment, in preparation of the battlespace.

In this area we see Remotely Deployed Sensor Systems as having the most potential. UK work, now at a technical demonstration phase, has been concentrating on providing a system at an affordable price for which COTS technology may well prove to be the answer. We now believe that a 50km 10-node system can be provided for a unit price about the same as that of a top-of-the-range Mercedes saloon. The concept is for the launch platform, or a UUV, or a comms uplink buoy to satisfy the monitoring requirements. We also see the UUV as an enhancement in this category. While the UK's submarine-specific work continues to review launch and recovery options, we have significant work in other areas, especially mine warfare, with which to provide the sensors payload for these vehicles.

The final area is to improve the self-protection of underwater units. Submarines and surface vessels are capable, but also major, assets. If they are to be totally versatile, they must be able to be put in harm's way and therefore demand appropriate levels of self-protection.

In the littoral, the mine threat is of particular concern. Here we require some innovative research to enable the tempo of force projection to be maintained without the need for laborious and time-consuming mine clearance operations. There are many strands to this research including radiated noise signature, electro-magnetic signature, mine avoidance sonar, mine hunting, and one shot UUVs.

The torpedo threat remains a problem and we have work in hand on torpedo detection, classification and localisation as well as softkill countermeasures.

CONCLUSIONS

Today's numerically smaller UK submarine service faces a broader tasking than ever before. This will demand significant capability enhancements that will only be possible through:

- Capability Management enabling the military commander to be provided with the right kit at the right time; the best capability within the performance, time and cost limitations imposed.
- A platform is not a capability; it is what we put in our submarines. It is the connectivity, sensors, weapons and trained people that give it the capability.
- Affordability is paramount.
- Timely upgrades through the use of COTS. Build-test-build programmes will help provide capability earlier.
- This demands far greater co-operation between MOD and industry, research establishments, academia and allies.

13

Operating SSKs in Shallow Waters

Bo Rask

The opportunity to present this paper, is a personal privilege for me, and it is an honour to have been invited to the RN Submarine Centennial Conference. I served 1983 in HMS OTUS (Lt Cdr Sandy Powell), so I have strong personal memories from serving in RN Submarines. To do so as a member of a junior submarine service to the Royal Navy's is both thrilling and demanding. It is also a strong recognition of the Swedish way of operating submarines.

Sweden has operated submarines since 1904, so we are now in the middle of the process of preparing a programme for the Swedish Submarine Service's centennial celebration in 2004.

This paper, however, is concerned with the way in which the Swedish Navy operates its submarines and why it has come to that solution. This will be done by giving a brief outline of our submarine history and the improvements in our submarines battle potential over the last thirty years; providing an overview of our hydrographic and operational conditions and the implications it has on submarine warfare; and by discussing some tactical and operational demands in the littorals.

SWEDISH SUBMARINE HISTORY - IMPROVEMENTS IN BATTLE POTENTIAL

Although Sweden has not been involved in a war since 1814, she has maintained a relatively large and well-equipped Defence Force; this has mainly been due to the fact that Swedish policy has been to stay outside treaty organisations.

The Swedish strategic defence concept has always placed great importance on her Navy. Furthermore, the importance of submarines in the armed forces as an essential component of a balanced fleet has never been disputed, although the number of boats has been reduced over the last few years, due to overall reductions in the annual defence budget.

The first Swedish submarines were, in fact, built about 1880 as export products. The submarine program in the Swedish Navy, however, started in 1904 with the delivery of RSwN HAJEN ('The Shark'). The submarine was designed by the Navy and was constructed by the naval shipyard in Stockholm. Since then the Swedish Navy has operated about 80 submarines and with, two exceptions, they have all been built in Sweden.

Since 1945, six submarine classes have been designed and a total of 27 submarines have been built. These submarine classes have all been continuously evolved from one generation to the next each to meet the RSwN's specific requirements. These include the requirement that the submarines should be well capable for submarine warfare in the littorals. The Swedish Navy's main operational area is in the Baltic, the Bay of Botnia and in Kattegatt and Skagerack.

The basic technical concept for today's boats – the 'Västergötland' (A17) and 'Gotland' (A 19) Classes - is around thirty years old. The main advantage of this is that the concept is well proven and that in turn means they are safe, both in design and cost. The cost of development, therefore, can easily be predicted.

However, the development of the technical concept has seen a dramatic increase in our submarines battle potential and endurance over the same period. The battle potential consists of several different parameters, and has evolved as follows:

- Detection ranges with passive sonars against cavitating targets have increased by a factor of more than ten;
- Target handling capacity has increased more than fifty times;
- The ability to identify targets with passive sonar due to DEMON and LOFAR techniques have increased considerably;
- The ability to fire and simultaneously steer both heavy and lightweight torpedoes against different targets has increased more than four times;
- The torpedo firing range against cavitating ships has increased at least by a factor of three;
- The hitting probability within the individual torpedo has increased significantly, mainly due to passive homing and wire guidance;
- Today, it is routine to attack purely on passive information;
- Indiscretion rates have improved significantly due to better batteries and more effective generators and most of all due to the use of air independent propulsion, (AIP);
- Resilient mounting of noisy machinery and use of static converters instead of rotating and other improvements have reduced the revealing range considerably;
- The ability to act in a multi-target environment and acoustically jammed environment has increased considerably. Today it is better the more frigates and other active systems transmit; target acquisition is therefore easier.

The endurance - both operational and tactical - of the boats has increased by a factor of two over the last thirty years. Over the past twenty years or so, these technological developments have benefited submarines, but in the long run it will always be the commanding officers' knowledge of the hydrographic and hydroacoustic conditions - the acoustical environment – that really counts.

The Baltic Sea is sometimes called the 'submariners' paradise' and the 'submarine-chasers' hell'. The reason for this is the very special hydroacoustic and navigation conditions that prevail in the area and the excellent conditions for seeking targets provided by the channelling effect of geographical constraints.

The basic criteria for a submarine are that it should be able to act covertly, to conduct surprise attacks, and to have great firepower and endurance. It is a matter of course that submarines should be able to operate in the entire volume of water. The submarine that can make the best use of the hydrographic and hydroacoustic conditions will be the submarine that is most efficient in conducting and executing its tasks whilst, at the same time, the risk of being detected and attacked by the enemy is minimised.

This was just as important to Lt Cdr Max Horton in the submarine HMS E-9 (Flag Officer Submarines and Commander SW Approaches during WWII) and for Lt Cdr Francis Cromie in the HMS E-19 during WWI. Together, with their gallant crews, they fought for their country and for Russia in the Baltic Sea from 1914 to

1918. They waged a successful submarine war against German and neutral Swedish shipping in the Baltic Sea after an almost miraculous passage through the Flint canal in the Sound whilst under the guns of the German destroyers.

The sea environment around Sweden was also exploited by the few brave Finnish submariners during WWII who fought against the Soviet Navy with daring mine-laying missions and torpedo attacks in the narrow Gulf of Finland, the Northern Baltic Sea and the waters around Åland. They were so successful that in the Paris Peace Treaty in 1947, Finland was not permitted to have submarines!

Soviet submariners also waged a successful campaign against German and neutral Swedish shipping. During discussions about naval warfare in the Baltic Sea during WWII, one often hears how the Germans, by deft mining and air operations, managed to blockade the Soviet Baltic Fleet at Kronstadt and, thereby, prevented the Soviet Navy from all further activities until the last months of the war. Regarding the Soviet submarine fleet, however, this is incorrect. Instead, the daring and ruthless Soviet submariners managed to make successful and skilful passages through German submarine nets and minefields in the mouth of the Gulf of Finland, in 1942 and 1943. Those feats demonstrated a spirit and bravery that is perhaps unique in the history of submarine warfare. Robust and functioning equipment even then made this offensive activity possible.

To utilise the entire water volume is just as important today. Foreign submarines have systematically violated Swedish territorial waters many times, especially during the eighties and nineties. They cleverly made use of the hydrographic and hydroacoustic conditions to carry out their tasks, well aware of the problems this created for the submarine-chasers

It was during this period that the Swedish Submarine Service was put into action as attack submarines (SSKs). The operational missions therefore shifted from SS to SSK. The Swedish Submarine Service was given clear orders to sink enemy submarines with lightweight torpedoes in what subsequently proved to be quite a thrilling time!

HYDROGRAPHIC AND OPERATIONAL CONDITIONS - IMPLICATIONS FOR SUBMARINE WARFARE

When considering the coast and surrounding waters of Sweden it is important to recognise that Sweden has, since 1945, been the focal point between two strong opposing military alliances: NATO and the Warsaw Pact. In fact, the whole of Sweden was located to the East of the borderline (the Iron Curtain) in Central Europe. The world during the Cold War was, in many respects, on the brink of a Third World War. That was as imminent in the Baltic as it was anywhere along the Central Front in Europe.

The Soviet Union was, at that time, identified as the principal threat to Sweden. The enormous Soviet military potential gave the Swedish military planners a severe headache. The strong Soviet Baltic fleet and its Air Force had both the range and precision in their weapons to threaten the Swedish naval forces simultaneously on both the Swedish and the Soviet sides of the Baltic. The Swedish military calculated that the Soviets most likely had radar contact with all ships and aircraft over the whole Baltic region. It also estimated that all Swedish submarine bases in the Baltic were vulnerable to enemy air attacks.

Submarines that could take the war to the enemy and that could operate hidden from the air threat were, therefore, of key importance to the Navy, and to the defence of Sweden, a neutral country. The major difference between Lt Cdr Cromie's submarine engagements in 1915 and the activity of Swedish submarines today is that the periscope is no longer the primary sensor for surveillance. The periscope demanded a tactic that required the submarine to work close to the surface. The horizon can be seen with the periscope a distance, maybe, of 10 to 15 kilometres depending on target height, and the periscope's height and visibility. In contrast, modern sonar can detect cavitating ships at distances five or ten times greater – up to 75 kilometres. To improve the possibilities for a submarine to reach its attack position with periscope surveillance it was generally necessary to have target information from the submarine command. These instructions were transmitted on radio using a low frequency that required the boats to stay rather shallow, due to the poor penetration of radio waves through the water.

Every submarine captain wants to receive radio traffic, and specifically that directed to his own submarine. The result was that Swedish submarines were more often close to the surface rather than remaining at greater, and therefore less vulnerable, depths. Tactically this was wrong and potentially dangerous. Naturally, this situation did not lead to a better understanding of hydrography and hydroacoustics.

The need for periscope and command assistance decreased when sonar systems were modernised. When this happened, activities near the surface decreased and Swedish submariners could start to explore the secrets of the depths. The results, and the benefits, came quickly. Once accessible, the hydroacoustic conditions are just some of the operational aspects that makes the Baltic Sea so different.

Other important factors are the short transit distances to the operation areas. Swedish submarines can therefore operate in their assigned areas for considerably longer periods than in other Seas. As a consequence, the demand for high transit speeds to reach the assigned area is also reduced.

At the same time, however, the risks increase. In the Baltic, it is difficult to find safe snorkelling areas that are free from shipping, enemy patrol areas (search areas) and airborne ASW. The short distances and the limited geographic area mean that large areas of the Baltic Sea can be permanently under surveillance by ship and airborne radar. The risk of detection is therefore considerable. The air threat has continued over the years and has served to drive further technical developments. Today's AIP system is the result of this endeavour to get away from the dangers close to the surface.

Another important factor for submarine warfare in the Baltic Sea is the greater safety of the submarine whilst at sea than when in its base area. This fact has generated the need for a strong and flexible logistic support organisation. The submarine's home base could therefore be anywhere around the coast that could provide support for the submarine operating in the open sea, thereby giving the Navy options to choose from among any number of 'bases'.

The Swedish SSK submarine is also capable of using the seabed while conducting repairs or recharging the main batteries between missions. The submarine's own generators are capable of charging the main batteries to full capacity and it can be fully replenished, including weapons, within one night, just by using small tenders.

The Baltic Sea is not deep. The average depth is some 67 metres. In some areas, however, the depth can reach 100, 200 and, in places, depths in excess of 400 metres. The seabed topography can significantly vary from very rugged profiles in some parts to quite flat in others. This has a significant effect on passive and active sonar ranges and can reduce the effectiveness of homing anti-submarine torpedoes at lower depths, near the seabed. But the shallowness of the Baltic Sea also increases the threat from mines. During WWII, most of the Baltic Sea was declared dangerous to mines. In sensitive areas, for example outside bases, harbours and some choke points, where the shipping is channelled, the mine threat can be considerable. The mine threat demands a thorough knowledge of the large differences in the earth's magnetic field and effectiveness of three-dimensional degaussing systems.

Add to these considerations the varying salinity in the Baltic from almost fresh water in the far North to 34 promillie on the West Coast and in density from 1 up to 1.027. This makes it important to have a weight-compensating tank big enough to handle the submarine and a full weapons load in all areas.

The water surface temperature varies during the yearly seasons from minus two degrees on the West Coast in the winter to around 20 degrees Celsius in the summer. The summers have caused some problems over the years and have required the Navy to develop cooling systems effective enough for its submarines to operate in the warm water close to the surface. Today there is a Swedish submarine *en route* for the Mediterranean to conduct exercises and to verify whether or not the latest changes in the submarine's cooling system are good enough to engage in operations in that theatre.

This temperature change causes very large seasonal and geographical variations in sound velocities. In the summer, sound propagation in the channel appears between two points with the same, or almost the same, speed of sound. The channel width determines the range: a wide channel – longer wavelengths – 'fit' into the channel and longer ranges are obtained. In the winter, very long ranges are obtained, but it also considerably more difficult to hide from ASW forces.

If the sound channel is used in a correct way, good conditions for surveillance, localisation and classification of cavitating targets are obtained in the low frequency range at distances exceeding half of the width of the Baltic Sea. The summer water also provides excellent protection for a submarine when it is close to the surface. Tactical use of the sound channel gives a submarine early warning of the threat (so it can be avoided) and good information about target positions.

The sea bottom material itself also varies significantly within the Baltic region from hard crystalline bedrock and morainic deposits to deep, gaseous mud. One of the main reasons for this is, of course, that the area frequently has been de-glaciated. This combination of changing seabed topography and hydrographic conditions causes particular problems for surface ship hull-mounted active sonars. Transmitted energy deflects sharply to the bottom (particularly during the summer period from May to October) thereby reducing active sonar ranges to less than 2,000 metres, even when using variable depth sonars. Rocky bottom conditions will also generate numerous false contacts. The limited depth causes reverberation between the bottom topography and the surface. Normal spherical spreading is non-existent; instead, a channel effect is the norm. That means that the energy is absorbed in the seabed, and that Lofar systems do not give the same passive ranges as in the open deep ocean. In another example, the optimal frequency used for active sonars is much higher than it would otherwise be used in the oceans.

As noted above, cavitating targets can be detected at distances exceeding half the width of the Baltic Sea; this was also an important operational lesson learned. The true Baltic Sea consists of two deep water areas and one shallower one along the Gotland axis from North of the island of Kopparstenarna via Gotska Sandön and Fårö, and South of Gotland, from the Hoburg Bank via the Midsea Banks and the Slupska Bank.

Despite scanning in the low frequency range, it turned out that a submarine located West of the Banks could not detect targets East of the Banks. Around the Banks the depth is just some ten metres. There simply is not room for the long waves at these depths. This effectively reduces the range of East-West detection ranges.

The conclusion is obvious. When using submarines for surveillance, where long ranges are important or desired they have to be directed to areas on the 'correct' side of the banks; otherwise, they will not be put to optimal use.

Another important discovery during the systematic intrusions in Swedish territorial waters was the importance of great water depths in order to obtain the longest ranges. As in the sound channel, there is not sufficient room for long waves when the water is shallow. The result is shorter ranges. Swedish submarines are now equipped with advanced surveillance sonars in the low-frequency range that can best support their tasks in deep water.

Sweden's submarine crews have learned the importance of knowing hydrography and hydroacoustics. Used correctly, they offer opportunities for early target detection whilst giving protection to the hunted submarine. At greater depths, there is often a saltier layer that forms a true hydroacoustic lid. Under the lid the submarine is at a depth that provides further protection.

Visual distance under water is quite low in the Baltic, up to between 10 and 12 metres. On some days of the year, however, algblooming occurs all over the Baltic resulting in vision being reduced further to less than one metre. This increases the difficulties in intelligence gathering.

Off the archipelago coast of Sweden, there are many islands. For example, the archipelago around Stockholm has about ten thousand islands, both large and small; between them there is an inshore depth of up to around 120 metres. Outside the archipelago, the bottom topography is almost the same as the islands, except at a greater depth. This causes 'shadow zones' behind the mountains on the seabed where a submarine can hide.

The large differences in the earth's magnetic field also has significant importance to submarine warfare. All submarines today are protected by a degaussing system taking care of the three dimensional magnetic field. The degaussing system is controlled through a sensor (probe) and a computer. The probe measures the magnetic field of the earth and the interaction from the submarine; then, automatically by computer, it adjusts the current in the three-dimensional degaussing system.

In the Baltic Sea there is no tide. The currents are weak and are only affected by the air pressure variations. Truly rough seas are rare. There are several geographical constraints – choke points – where shipping is concentrated.

With good passive sensors and long-range homing torpedoes, it is often possible to hover, to sit at the bottom, or to move very slowly and still achieve a good attacking position. This saves energy and limits the time needed to recharge batteries. It also enhances sonar performances and reduces the risk of detection. If detected, Swedish submarines are designed to resist the shock from a standard mine (or depth charge) explosion at distances quite close to the submarine. This is achieved by rubber mounted floating platforms.

In view of the threats to the country, the conclusion is that a submarine, when used in a correct tactical manner, has a better chance of a successful outcome than for those engaged in ASW. To summarise, the hydrographic and hydroacoustic conditions in the Baltic Sea provides submarines with:

- very long passive ranges – and normally short active ranges;
- easy avoidance of enemy surveillance by hiding on or near the bottom or in a warmer layer or in under a saltier layer;
- simple navigation;
- easily maintained depth;
- base areas in the archipelago that allow great flexibility for deployment and maintenance;
- good attack positions due to the fact that enemy shipping is naturally channelled to specific places (choke points).

Due to these factors, the Swedish Navy knows that a submarine in the littorals should be able to utilise the whole water volume and operate in water depths that vary from just 15 metres down to 300-400 metres and also from, or near to, the bottom to the surface. A submarine will use the background topography to its own advantage by operating as close as possible to the vertical or horizontal bottom, or try to be in a position on the bottom, yet still be able to use its sensors and weapons.

All Swedish submarines currently in service have extremely good manoeuvrability both in the vertical and horizontal planes. For example, it is not a problem to go backwards with the submarine submerged. Due to the shape of the submarine's hull and its rudder configuration, a turning radius of less than the boat's own length is possible even at low speeds. The control system makes it very easy for the only helmsman to control the submarine both in depth and heading at the same time, regardless of the speed.

The submarines are designed and built to be able to safely hit the seabed at low speeds without sustaining any substantial damage. Of course, when approaching the bottom this is done as quietly as possible. The rudder configuration makes it possible to sit on the seabed with very little risk of damaging the rudders and propeller. The sonar arrays (even the FAS) will continue to function even if the submarine is sitting on the bottom.

It is also possible for the submarine to launch both heavyweight torpedoes (torpedo 2000), and lightweight torpedoes whilst resting on the seabed.

SOME TACTICAL AND OPERATIONAL DEMANDS IN THE LITTORALS

It has been mentioned above that a submarine is safer at sea than in the base area. This supports an increase of operation times and minimises the time spent in base areas. But it demands large stores of fuel, carbon dioxide absorbent, oxygen, supplies, and/or auxiliary engines alongside the usual diesel electric propulsion. The primary disadvantage of the conventional diesel electric submarine is the need to come to periscope depth to recharge the main batteries. This is a major tactical drawback. Furthermore, the continuous advances in the development of airborne radar and infrared sensor capability have increased the threat against a snorting submarine.

In order to reduce the time required to snort and, thereby, improve the indiscretion ratio, the RSwN has sought to identify an AIP technology best suited to its needs. In 1988, an AIP prototype system was installed in a 'Näcken' Class submarine for sea trials. Subsequent tests, trials, and refinements to the design resulted in the decision to install Stirling engine plants, in addition to the normal diesel engines, in all three of the new 'Gotland' Class submarines, and recently in two, and hopefully soon in all four, 'Västergötland' Class submarines.

By using AIP, the submarine commander can select his operational profile. When the threat against the submarine is acute, the battery is used. For lesser threats, the AIP is used; and with even lesser threats, the regular diesels are used while snorkelling. Today's AIP system supplies sufficient energy to keep the battery loaded ('floating the load') and still run the submarine at normal submarine speeds. This means that for 80 – 90 % of the time the submarine in the patrol area can be covered when operating on AIP. For greater speeds the battery is used.

The Stirling system is inherently silent due to the fact that the combustion takes place in a continuous and controlled manner. The low noise is further reduced by double-elastic mounting arrangements; airborne noise is reduced by an acoustic hood. In addition, the exhaust gas is let out into the sea in a controlled way through a unique arrangement that leaves, in practice, no trace of bubbles or heat. An AIP capability improves the submarine's indiscretion ratio significantly. With Stirling engines on board, underwater tactical endurance can be increased from a few days to several weeks.

Operations in the littorals also demand that the passive sensors give a high bearing resolution in a multi-target environment (high background noise). They should cover a large part of the frequency band to make it possible to avoid interference from strong active transmitters. Wide frequency coverage is also important for good recordings when collecting acoustic intelligence.

Other demands are the usual ones, when constructing and building submarines: low target strength; low noise level; and an efficient degaussing system. The need to sit on the bottom now and then is an important staff requirement.

The weapon development follows the construction of a modern submarine closely. The Swedish Navy believes in a combination of heavy and lightweight torpedoes and ground attack missiles. The commander has to have optimum flexibility when facing a multi-target situation. It also strongly believes that such ground missiles can be installed in its submarine weapons inventories.

A better way operating with and exchanging information with the surface commander in the area is also equally important. That means satellite communications. Swedish submarines have been reluctant to communicate like this before, but now it is paramount to develop the capability to do that. Even so, let it never be forgotten that it is always the submarine commander who decides when to put up the communication mast!

Sweden has confidence in the strength of its submarine force today. The Submarine Service is on the right track to meet its current and future tasks and knows where to go. This was not the case a couple of years ago. It has evolved the tasks for its submarines over the last years from the traditional missions in defending Sweden from invasion. These missions were mainly attack missions with torpedoes, mine-laying missions and reconnaissance missions, to missions were the conventional submarine is effective. The new role is to further enhance special operations and different sorts of intelligence gathering, roles that really need a quiet submarine with long endurance on station.

The current deployment of Swedish submarines in the Mediterranean is therefore an important step: out of the 'submariners' paradise' and onwards to meet new and different challenges.

14

The Submariner: Who or What is he?

Jeff Tall

When the submarine was introduced into the order of battle in 1901, the first challenge of Captain Reginald Bacon, the first Inspecting Captain of Submarines, and apparently the only man in uniform with any enthusiasm for the craft, was to man it. But from where was he going to find what he wanted amongst the men in a navy that, in his own words,

> *"….had spent the whole of their lives in masted ships. Gunnery had increased but little since the time of Trafalgar. Muzzle loading was still universal. Fifteen hundred to two thousand yards was looked on as a probable battle range. Ramming was still a battle tactic, and explosive charges at the end of the lower boom were fitted to damage any ship that missed ramming, or tried old-time boarding tactics. Steam propulsion was looked on as a convenience rather than a dominant factor which involved new tactics".*

But find them he did. Sailors no doubt were attracted by the additional two and sixpence a day, but what about the officers? Perhaps they had all done naughty things to their Commander-in-Chief's daughter, and so their careers were going nowhere; or were they genuinely inspired by the potential of the new craft? Looking at the list of men who did sign up early – Horton, Nasmith, Laurence, Little and many, many more – the latter is surely true.

Conditions of service were bad enough at the start, but as the country went to war what could possibly induce a young man to join a life redolent of sardines in a can and with a high chance of ending up just as dead?

Rudyard Kipling attempted to define the submariner in 1916 when he sought to find the origin of the sobriquet that had become attached to the service, still only in its fifteenth year of existence.

> *"No one knows how the title 'The Trade' came to be applied to the Submarine Service. Some say the cruisers invented it because they pretend that submarine officers look like unwashed chauffeurs, others think it sprang forth by itself, which it means that it was coined by the lower deck, where they always have a proper name for things. Whatever the truth, the submarine service is now 'the trade'; and if you ask them why, they will answer 'what else can you call it? The Trade's 'the Trade' of course!"*

A very similar sentiment was expressed by another observer many years later. Following his analysis of the circumstance of every British submarine loss, Evans concluded that "the small dank and foul smelling interior (*of a submarine*) crammed with noisy and temperamental machinery, was no place for the faint-hearted; it took first class men to withstand the unsavoury conditions and to perform skilled work with efficiency and with at least a modicum of cheerfulness." So, from the very beginning submariners had to be submarine 'types'.

In short, there was a submarine 'type' who wanted to belong to a 'trade', but this is still far too nebulous to lead to an understanding of why men sought to sign up. Perhaps a ready source of recruitment, consistent with the prevailing view that submariners were 'pirates', would have been the goals, as suggested by Lieutenant Commander Williams-Freeman of HMS H-9 in 1915 when he wrote, "I cannot conceive why they hang a man, when the foulest crime to be seen would be punished two-fold if they gave him life, and put him in submarines!"

But was it really necessary to empty the country's jails to man the submarine branch?

Telegraphist William Halter of HMS D-4 recounts his experience in 1914,

> "It was an exclusive service because nobody but a submarine rating was allowed in a submarine. We got more pay and a very stiff medical examination. Your character had to be perfect to get in and we were regarded as something a bit special. We went to HMS DOLPHIN for training, messed in the hulk and slept in the Fort (Blockhouse). Discipline was quite comfortable and after instruction you could lie in the sun on the ramparts; a very different Navy altogether. When we got in the boats we were so near the officers... every one was close to each other. No red tape, no falling in and out."

A better clue is provided by Captain WR Fell, a veteran of the Great War submarine operations and mentor of 'Charioteers' (human torpedomen) and 'X' craft (miniature submarines) during the Second World War, when he stated

> "To serve in submarines is to become a member of the strongest, most loyal union of men that exists. During the First War and the twenty-one years of peace that followed, the Submarine Branch was an integral part of the Royal Navy, subject to its discipline and obeying its laws. But it was still a 'private navy', inordinately proud of its tradition, jealous of its privileges, and, if slightly inclined to be piratical, the most enthusiastic, loyal and happy branch of the Service".

Fell goes on. "Scores of people ask, Why did men join submarines and how could they stick in them?" There are many answers to that question. For adventure and fun at the outset; then because of the intense interest, and because of the variety of tasks that must be at one's fingertips. The submariner must be a navigator, an electrician, a torpedoman, a gunnery type, and even a bit of a plumber. He must know men and get on with them; he must use initiative and tact and learn to enjoy hard living. He must accept responsibility when young, and not misuse it. There is every reason why he should join and delight in joining submarines, but the greatest joy of all is the companionship, unity and feeling that he is one of a team.

Certainly, the experience of Lieutenant Leslie Ashmore bears out Fell's words concerning adventure. He relates " I had ambitions to get into some branch of the Service that would give more scope to a junior officer. Watchkeeping and coaling were eating into my soul". He found himself visiting the ship-building firm of Vickers Ltd in Barrow, Britain's principal builders of submarines and

> "The sight of so many of these sleek little craft in various stages of construction seemed to suggest a solution to my yearnings. It was therefore not entirely by chance that I struck an acquaintance ashore with two officers, considerably

my seniors, whom I knew from their conversation were submariners standing by HMS E8 which was nearing completion. The attraction of their mysterious trade for me must have been very obvious and I was soon being questioned by the senior of the two, Lieutenant Commander Halahan, captain designate of E8, as to what I was doing and whether I would like to transfer to submarines.

Evidently Halahan thought me likely material for, next time he visited the Admiralty, he pulled various strings with the result that I received orders to join the Submarine Depot ship HMS BONAVENTURE at Newcastle. In those days, entry into the submarine service was as simple as that. There were no organised training classes and the young enthusiast learnt the rudiments of his trade by going to sea as a 'makee-learn' in an active service boat."

Although training became more formal as time progressed, nevertheless learning on one's feet continued as a basic principle. The 1940 experience of Lieutenant Phil Durham, though not typical, nevertheless underlines the principle. As a midshipman Durham had seen active service in a battleship, an anti-submarine trawler (of which he was second-in-command), a 'County' Class cruiser, a destroyer and a battle cruiser, and had earned a Mention in Dispatches. And yet, his goal remained service in submarines. While awaiting training class, he filled his time by joining the training submarine HMS L-26, and spending a fortnight of "daily seagoing, diving, gunnery and torpedo practice" after which he "had made drawings of air and electrical systems and was able to trim and handle L-26 dived". His enthusiasm made sense of the "bewildering mass of pipes, gauges, dials, levers, switches, hand wheels, air bottles, electrical control boxes for rudder, fore and after planes and centrally, the aluminium ladder leading to the conning tower and the outside world."

Like Ashmore his talent too was spotted by a senior officer, in this case the revered Commander Jackie Slaughter, who sent him off to join the recently captured German U-570 (which was re-commissioned as HMS GRAPH) with a warning to the Commanding Officer of Durham's lack of experience, but suggesting that since he had no knowledge of a how a modem British submarine was handled, he had "nothing to unlearn in finding out how a 'U-boat' worked."

It was not until the trainee submariner got to sea that the real test of character began. Ashmore described conditions in the 'C' Class in 1915 as,

"primitive in the extreme. There was one bunk for the Captain, but all the others had to sleep on the deck, there being no room to sling hammocks. When diving, the atmosphere quickly became foul, fumes from the petrol engine adding their quota to the normally fetid air.... Sanitary arrangements consisted simply of a bucket passed up through the conning tower on surfacing. The periscope was raised and lowered by hand winch. By the time we had been dived for some fifteen or sixteen hours it was as much as one could do to operate it."

He also declared that "during these early patrols I got to know the characters and temperaments of my fellow officers and of the ship's company in a way and a speed only possible in the cramped space, enforced intimacy, and shared responsibility of a submarine."

THE SAILOR'S LIFE

Dwelling further on the conditions that Ashmore alluded to during WWI, not much had changed in WWII. Add to the smells the daily grind of watchkeeping and the hardships involved in conducting even the simplest functions, one must wonder if the enthusiasm of Ashmore and Durham (and thousands like them) was not totally misplaced. A letter home from Signalman Gus Britton of HMS UPROAR in 1944 summed up the sailor's life and routine.

> *"We have lockers about the size of coffins... and a small table in the fore-ends. Hanging from the ceiling there are about fifteen hammocks, so if you want to move around you have to do so in a crouched position... Potatoes and cabbages are piled in one corner and, as it is as damp as Eastney beach, after six days there is the horrible smell of rotting vegetables and refuse is only ditched at night; and on top of that there is the smell of unwashed bodies. At the moment we are doing about eighteen hours dived every day so you can guess that it is pretty thick at night. Before I go any further, don't' think that I am complaining because I really love submarines and this sort of life, and I wouldn't swap it for anything.*
>
> *What a blessed relief when, at night, comes the order 'diving stations' and about ten minutes later 'blow one and six'. The boat shudders as the air goes into the ballast tanks and then up she goes! I am at the bottom of the ladder and then the captain opens the hatch and up rushes all the foul air just like a fog, and if I did not hang on I would go up with it as well. Beautiful, marvellous air. We are provided with top-notch waterproof gear but the water always seems to find a weak spot to trickle into. Up on the swaying bridge, with a pair of binoculars which you try to keep dry to have a look around between deluges of water, soaked and frozen you say to yourself 'why the **** did I join?' Then when you are relieved, you clamber down the ladder, discard all the wet gear and go into the fore-ends, have a cup of cocoa, turn in and, as you fall asleep, you think 'well it's not such a bad life after all.' "*

GUS

Gus Britton MBE must be one of the greatest ever sailor submariners. There is no greater accolade than the fact that his obituary appeared in both *The Times* and *The Telegraph*.

Waiting For The Gunlayer

I could see Monte Carlo
If it was not so dark and rough
And pouring with rain
I could be in my hammock
In the stinking fore ends
But the gunlayer's late again.

I thought we'd roll over
When we surfaced last night
Staggering beam on to the sea
With the diesels pounding
And the mistral blowing
Gosport's where I'd rather be.

The new Sub-Lieutenant's eager for war
An eager know-nothing twit
But when the hunting begins
And we are the fox
His ardour will cool a bit.

The crew of that U-boat
We missed yesterday
Are ashore, dancing, drinking and fighting
While I'm out here
Peering into the night
And my lice biting, biting, biting.

Dawn's coming up
And it's 'clear the bridge'
Ready to take to the deep
But when the klaxon blares
And the boat plunges down
The gunlayer will still be a sleep.

RELATIONSHIPS

Relationships determined the quality of life onboard, and that would have started with the Captain. However, he had a couple of people above him that would set his tone. At the top was Flag Officer Submarines, and the first rung of the Command Ladder down was The Captain (S/M). There were many great Squadron Commanders, but perhaps the most famous was Captain Shrimp Simpson of the Fighting Tenth. Here is what he had to say about Max Horton.

"From this time (1941) until the end of the war I served either directly under Sir Max Horton or in direct correspondence with him on personnel and material needs. He was the most important man I have ever got to know well. He was a 'lone wolf' and the reason for our friendship was in part due to my never serving on his staff; I could not have stuck the pace.

His father was an Englishman and a stockbroker, his mother a Jewess from a well-known banking family. Thick set with a big head and mobile expression dominated by ever-alert eyes, his whole being expressed obvious physical and mental power far above the normal. People either cared deeply for Sir Max or hated him. He was, I noticed, so strongly influenced by first impressions that he seldom, if ever, changed his opinion of a man's character and ability, and this was occasionally unfair. During the war the vast majority of his subordinates formed a deep affection for him though many feared his ruthlessness. He worked quickly and decentralised fully.

So far as war events permitted he played golf every day from 2 pm to 5 pm, and to compensate for this worked after dinner until about midnight. He was a good golfer playing off a nine handicap, which more correctly should have been a four, his ability being in his concentration and determination to win which made his short game very accurate. This daily exercise refreshed and invigorated him marvellously.

His favourite quotation was from Proverbs, Chapter 29, verse 18. 'Where there is no vision, the people perish'; but I also remember his "What were the first things I did on hearing that war was declared? Why, to buy a gross of golf balls and a gross of whisky, of course". His views on promotion were equally strong, "You are wasting your energy putting X at the top of your promotion list, Simpson. I will support you in any award for gallantry you may make, but a man who consistently shields his subordinates and takes the blame for their errors is unfit for higher command".

The next rung is the view of the Captain S/M by his COs.

If Simpson was proud of his men, they regarded him with something akin to reverence. His concern for his COs and crews was obvious to all, yet he "never shrank from fair and firm administration of justice", in the words of Anthony Daniell. "He was imbued with a generous humanity and humour that was readily sensed by everyone with whom he came into contact. That was the main ingredient that made him an apparently effortless leader of men". "Shrimp made the flotilla", Ben Bryant writes, adding that he had "tremendous stamina". He needed it; he was practically "watch on, stop on" twenty-four hours a day, seven days a week. Nearly every signal you got on patrol from (S)10 was fairly certain to have been drafted by Shrimp, personally.

He loved his sailors: If a rating was found in the gutter of the base, sleeping off the previous night's drowning of sorrows, Shrimp would say, "Get that body out of sight". He understood. He knew his men. They loved and respected him. The general view of him can be summed up thus: With these terrible decisions on one pair of shoulders he should have been twice as tall and twice as broad. How could one man take all that he did and survive for so long?

The next is the view of the CO by his officers, but first give thought to the CO. A distinguished Admiral at the end of WWI made the following comments about the inherent qualities that were required:

> "In surface vessels there are several factors which may bring success - in spite of the commanding officer. A ship may be a good shooting ship; an excellent chief of staff, mistakes on the part of the enemy, assistance from other vessels are some of these factors. In submarines none of these counts. One man only, the commanding officer, can see, and he only with one eye. No one can help him. Germany had some four hundred submarine captains during the war, but over sixty per cent of the damage they did was accomplished by but twenty-two of these four hundred officers. The inference is obvious. The one and great difficulty in submarine warfare is to find a sufficiency of officers such as I have portrayed, officers who will rise superior to the incidental intricacies of these complicated vessels, who will make their opportunities and then take advantage of them when found under conditions of hardship and acute discomfort.
>
> Fortunately, not every nation can produce such men; and if they cannot we can safely let them have as many and as large submarines as they like."

One such man, amongst many, was Ben Bryant. This is what Edward Young had to say about him.

> "Ben Bryant was one of those men who are big enough to give you confidence in yourself by assuming you can do your job without appearing to check up on you. He believed in taking the game of war seriously; nevertheless it somehow always seemed a game. He strove continuously to make himself and his men as efficient as possible, and was out to hit the enemy with all he knew, but he did so with such an air of gay bravado that half the time you had an odd feeling that you were playing at pirates. With his erect height, his sea-dog beard and arrogant eye, he was the typical submarine captain of the public imagination. He had a fine command of the English language, which he used to good effect in recounting yarns in the wardroom, inventing ballads, or expressing his opinion of some ineptitude on the part of one of his officers or men. He had the rare gift of being able to switch, without loss of dignity, from commanding officer to entertaining messmate".

There you have it in a nutshell.

But what was Ben's view of his men? He spoke of his Engineers with great affection.

"The Engineer Officer, apart from his direct responsibilities in the engine room, was the technical adviser, mentor and guide to all. At this time he was a warrant officer and nearly all of them had tremendous experience, having worked their way up.

It was very difficult, though not impossible in those days for these warrant officers to get promoted much farther. Thus they remained in similar appointments for many years. They were great characters and of great ability. To them the submarine service, mechanically, and the junior executive officers in advice, owed a great deal."

And despite the fact that he called his Autobiography, *One Man Band*, this was his view of his ship's company:

"No man (other than a submarine captain) relies more completely upon each and every member of his crew. A good submarine crew is far more than a team; they are as near as possible during attack, a single composite body using the CO as their eye and their director."

Alistair Mars, on taking over his first active submarine command, HMS UNBROKEN, cleared the lower deck and delivered the following message to his ships company:

"I shall be an exacting captain. I know what I want down to the smallest detail and I'm going to get it. You can promise your wives and families that you will return to Britain the crew of a successful submarine."

This was no small promise at a time when half our submarines entering the Mediterranean were being sunk. He continued,

"I have, however, another important duty - to destroy the enemy wherever he may be found. And we shan't shirk the job of finding him. Therefore we have two jobs - to be successful and to survive. To achieve these I need every ounce of loyalty and strength you can give. Remember that I am the sole arbiter of what is good for you, and my orders are to be obeyed implicitly. You may expect work, work, and more work. If any of you joined submarines to get away from discipline you are in for shocks. You will learn more discipline with me than you dreamed of - the proper sort of discipline, self-discipline.

I don't give a damn what you do ashore, so long as you are ready for your duties at the appointed time. This doesn't mean you can run foul of the shore authorities, and when you do, don't forget that I shall have to punish your misbehaviour. Your officers are young, but they have the weight of my experience and training behind them. Obey them without question, for even a bad order well executed leads to a better result than a good order ruined by indecision. A bad order can be countermanded, a slackly obeyed order leads to confusion. In a submarine confusion means disaster.

One final thing. What was good enough in other submarines will not be good enough here. Nothing is 'good enough' for me. I'm going to have the best, and only the best - and you're going to give it to me."

That may seem a pretty hard message to deliver, but in war there was none other if a boat was to be successful and survive. Max Horton delivered a clear message on loss of concentration:

"It is essential to keep the standard high - nothing can be neglected - it is not a kindness to overlook slackness or mistakes. It is really great cruelty to do so - cruelty to wives and relatives of the man you let off and his shipmates and to yourself. There is no margin for mistakes in submarines; you are either alive or dead"'

There is a memorandum called "Famous Last Words" written whilst on patrol by Lieutenant Commander Cayley of HMS PARTHIAN after something had really upset him. It is entitled, *"All right, mate, I've got the weight"*

" 1   *On a recent occasion of going up to the bridge, I was closely followed by a relief lookout. After a few seconds I heard him make the above remark, or words to that effect, to his predecessor, who immediately went below.*
  2   *The night in question was dark. It took me five minutes to see efficiently. My eyesight has recently been tested and pronounced good.*
  3   *It would appear therefore that, while the lookout in question was getting accustomed to the darkness, the ship had a blindspot and was open to surprise.*

ADVICE TO LOOKOUTS

  Do not arrive on the bridge and think to yourself: "It's a black night, so I don't suppose that I'll see much anyway." The night is NEVER really black (fog excepted), except when the following conditions occur together:

- *There is no moon (not even behind the clouds)*
- *The sky is overcast*
- *It is raining or snowing. Therefore, do not say to your relief: 'ALL RIGHT, MATE, I'VE GOT THE WEIGHT' until you are quite satisfied that you can see the horizon clearly, and that you could pick out objects between yourself and the horizon."*

Signed: RD Cayley Lieutenant Commander in Command. All Lookouts Initial.

Other lessons were passed in actions as well as words. In his book *Crash Dive*, Telegraphist George Dickison tells the story of how one day in HMS SAFARI he was cuffed round the head by Ben Bryant for polishing the ring of the magnetic compass. It was obvious that lessons had to be pushed hard and early.

As well as training and so on, to avoid being sunk, submariners were terribly superstitious. Gus Britton for example, a huge man and a naval champion swimmer, always carried with him a really manky and moth-eared teddy bear that is proudly on display in the RN Submarine Museum. Ben Bryant tells another amusing story,

"There was an amusing sequel to our misfortunes. The regulations still prescribed compulsory church on Sundays. Apart from the regulations, I believed that men, living as submariners on patrol lived, wanted something more than material comfort. I held a little service each Sunday, although it was unpopular with some as it interfered with precious sleep. On the previous Sunday the Coxswain reported hands mustered for church, but the prayer book could not be found. Our solitary prayer book was an Admiralty issue and I had a shrewd idea why it had been lost. I was tired so I let it go and cancelled church.

The following Sunday the Coxswain, without instructions, reported hands mustered for church. I pointed out that there was no prayer book, but he said it had been found; and there it was, somewhat the worse for a sojourn in the bilges. We had missed church, we had had a shockingly bad week, and it was obviously bad joss. Never again would the little Sunday service be missed in either HMS SEALION or HMS SAFARI. One could not afford to take chances with joss".

But what went on if joss failed and a submarine came under attack? How can any of us here understand what it is like to be attacked and depth-charged, with the precursor of an attack being the transmissions of an enemy asdic, firmly in contact. To Edward Young those pings were as though someone were tapping on the hull. I thought of Blind Pew's stick in *Treasure Island*. For Ben Bryant,

"The swish, swish of the propellers of the hunter passing overhead, the waiting for the explosion of the charges as they sank slowly down. Had they been dropped at the right moment? Were they set to the right depth? The knowledge that there is no escape; that you must just wait for it. Then the shattering roar, the lights going out, the controls going slack as the power is cut, and the paint raining down. Then silence and the faint sounds of running water where a gland has started to trickle. It seems magnified one hundredfold - a serious leak is what you dread. For a few there is something to do, to make good the damage, provide alternative methods of control; others just have to wait for the next attack. For the CO being under attack was an absorbing business, you had far too much to think about to have time to be frightened. I always imagined it was very much worse for the crew, though most of them were kept pretty busy in controlling the boat as you twisted and turned, speeding up and slowing down. However they never seemed to mind though critical interest was taken in the performance of the chaps up top - all of whom judging by the remarks, had not only been born out of wedlock, but, blessed with amazing stamina, were credited with an almost continuous indulgence in the sexual act."

But what were attitudes generally to escape?

"Actually the active submariner was not particularly interested in these efforts. Like all who live dangerously, the 'it couldn't happen to me' philosophy was all pervading. The thing was to guard against mistakes, back your own judgment, and not worry about things over which you had no control. Anyhow the best bet for your own survival was to see that your boat survived."

Escape training was taught to new inductees, but not always with the desired result. Captain RO Shelford was Staff Officer Personnel during the war and he had more to say on the subject of both escape and the losses that the Submarine Service was suffering.

"Later in the war when we were forced to conscript men into submarines, the effect of this introduction began to have very serious repercussions.

New entries came into DOLPHIN, and were given a first aid lecture and an escape course before going up to Blyth. I always thought this was a curious introduction for young volunteers who were not sure what they had let themselves in for. First they were given a lecture by an enthusiastic young doctor on fractures, arterial bleeding, and epileptic fits; then they were hustled up to the escape tank, filled with theories about how submarines get sunk, and were then firmly submerged beneath fifteen feet of water. It would not have been surprising if, by the time they left for Blyth, many of them must have felt that they had joined a suicide service.

When you take a man and divest him of his clothing, and rig him in an ill-fitting pair of slips and a breathing apparatus, and stand him on the edge of a deep tank full of water, you strip him not only physically but mentally as well. If that man is not an enthusiastic volunteer, and, so far as he knows, has been enlisted in a service which to him appears to be hazardous in the extreme, his last shreds of confidence are liable to break down at that moment. I had so many distressing scenes with men who, already covered in war medals, begging me to help them get back into destroyers, trawlers or motor torpedo boats - anything, in fact, rather than submarines - that I eventually approached the captain of the base on the subject. He promised to take the matter up with Admiral (Submarines), and from then on there was an improvement in the amount of publicity given to our submarines and their activities. We emphasised that escape training was only precautionary, and after that hundreds of them went happily on their way when they realised that the sinking of the submarines they were about to join was by no means inevitable."

So where do these stories lead? The experiences and the characters described above could be taken from any era of the Royal Navy Submarine Service's history, but can we have the same confidence in our ships companies of today. In the 1970s, a wartime veteran remarked,

> "Since I had joined the Branch (Captain J.S. Stevens, Captain (S) 1st Submarine Squadron), Submarines had developed from the tail end of the 'handraulic' era of the 'H'- and 'L'-boats and their predecessors, via Patrol Submarines of increasing sophistication culminating in the 'Oberons', moving on to the first Nuclear Fleet Submarines coming in to service. The techniques by which a submarine sank or damaged her prey had changed from depending largely on the skill of her Captain manoeuvring by eye and aiming his torpedoes visually, to complex electronics and computer type processes."

The foundation of the rather unique kind of relaxed, yet firm, discipline in Submarines in earlier times had been the sharing of discomfort and danger by all ratings with their officers with whom they lived in very close proximity. The size, crew numbers and modern comforts in the nuclear underwater vessels of up to 8,000 tons, combined with a higher standard of education and requirements for a larger number of technical skills, demand a different form of leadership, but there is no doubt at all that this is forthcoming.

With the years of building and trials behind her, HMS VALIANT is today a fully operational ship of the Royal Navy, ready to take her place, with other units of the Fleet both in war, should it occur, or in pursuing the peacetime roles of the Navy. Although based in Scotland with the Third Submarine Squadron the long endurance and sustained speed, which are the chief attributes of her nuclear power, will enable HMS VALIANT to operate throughout the world without recourse to foreign bases or external support.

The significance of the fifth HMS VALIANT does not, however, lie solely in the contribution she will make to the might of the Navy's submarine force, important though it is. She does too, represent a major engineering triumph for this country. The successful installation and operation of the first British Nuclear Marine Propulsion Plant in an operational submarine is no mean achievement: and one of which the BAE SYSTEMS building yard at Barrow-in-Furness, together with its many sub-contractors, may justly feel proud.

But although there is much to be marvelled at in terms of technical advance, it remains a fact that the equipment and machinery will only be as good as the men who operate, maintain and repair it. It is true that the Ships' Company are today better paid, better fed and better accommodated than other generations of submariners could have believed possible. However, it is also true that in order to get the maximum out of this complex ship, the crew must work as hard as ever in the past, they must spend longer at sea than ever before, and the degree of professional skill expected of them is of a very high order.

The message about comradeship and teamwork was echoed at the end of WWII by Rear Admiral Sir George Creasy, who followed Max Horton as FOSM, although not a submariner, obviously understood his men well;

> *"Two points stand out, I think. The constant struggle of the Submariner with the element on and in which he works - the sea; and the grand companionship engendered between officer and officer, officer and man, and man and man by service in submarines."*

> *In the Book of Common Prayer will be found a section entitled 'Forms of Prayer to be used at sea'. The first prayer sets out in words of wonderful simplicity and magnificent prose the Naval man's petition to God for His help and protection in the performance of his duty, and in that prayer the sailor asks to be preserved 'from the dangers of the sea and the violence of the enemy'. Note the order. The 'dangers of the sea' we have always with us, in war and in peace, and the Submariner has them in full measure, living as he does so close to the sea when he is on the surface and so much in the midst of the sea when he dives.*

> *Comradeship: Submarine operations demand a most exacting standard of teamwork. Every man in the boat has his individual job and on the correct and efficient performance of that job the efficiency of the boat will depend and the safety of all may depend. Living in inevitable intimacy and dependent each on the other, the Submariner acquires a deep-rooted confidence and trust in his shipmates. Truly they are, in the Shakespeare phrase that Nelson used, 'a band of brothers'.*

> *To those splendid men and to their more fortunate comrades who survived, the Allied cause in general and the Royal Navy in particular owes a deep debt of gratitude. They enhanced the traditions they inherited from the Submariners of 1914-18, and they have passed on to their successors, the present and future Officers and Men of our submarines, a standard of fighting efficiency and brave endurance of which every British man and woman can justifiably be proud."*

So perhaps there is, after all, an explanation of 'The Trade'; but let a United States Air Force Officer have the last word on the subject. Colonel Bradley Gaylord was onboard HMS SERAPH for 'Operation Kingpin' in 1942 (the pick-up of General Giraud from Vichy France) when he noted in his diary

> *"How could you have claustrophobia among these smiling boys whose easy informality was so apparently a thin cover for the rigid discipline on which every man knows his life depends upon the other fellow. It is so completely infectious. You suddenly realise that here is one of the essential points about war: there is no substitute for good company. The boys in the Submarine Service convey a spirit which quickly explains why they would sooner be in submarines than anywhere else".*

15

'Perisher': The Making of a Submarine Commander

Martin MacPherson

"What makes a Submarine Commanding Officer?" The answer is self-evident - it is 'Leadership'. However, my problem is, of course, that since numerous distinguished commentators, historians and analysts have found it impossible to define the qualities required of a successful leader, I am unlikely to produce any earth shattering revelations about this Holy Grail. All of us would probably agree that we can, "recognise a leader when we see one".

There is some truth in this maxim, but it does assume that the individual is in a situation that allows him to display his leadership talents. The problem facing the Commander, or Head, of a Submarine Service is that he needs a method of identifying the officers with command potential early and a system that nurtures this potential until it is sufficiently mature to be trained in the arcane tactical skills required of a CO. You might argue that history shows that we are pretty good at this. By any standards, Horton and Nasmith; Wanklyn, Linton and Miers (to name but a few) were outstanding submarine Commanding Officers; but we shall never know if there were even better potential COs who, through no fault of their own, failed to attract the selector's eye. In short, I submit that the selection process is every bit as important as the training.

What, then, should the talent spotter be looking for? What are the special qualities that distinguish the outstanding CO from the ordinary? And what training does he require to develop his latent ability? I shall attempt to answer these questions by delving into the historical archives and drawing a few conclusions, before looking at the evolution of the 'Perisher' and assessing whether it has delivered.

Command of a submarine in war must be one of the greatest responsibilities it is possible to have placed upon one. To discharge that responsibility successfully at the age of 23, as John Roxburgh did in the Mediterranean in 1942, is almost unimaginable today. Ben Bryant, that distinguished Captain of the submarines HMS SEALION and SAFARI, expressed some interesting views about the subject of age. He wrote:

> I was just 28 when I was given my first command, which is young for peace time. During the war we had operational COs of 22, but I think, on an average, probably the best years of a submarine CO's life are 25 to 30 - old enough to have experience, self confidence and judgment; young enough not to think too much. At 35, most men are getting too old and over cautious. In fact, I commanded a boat in war till well into my 38th year, but I had been at it non-stop. I know that I was potentially a much better CO, despite the later accumulation of wisdom and experience, at 28 than at 37.

Clearly, the perceived wisdom at the end of the war was that you should be ashore by your mid thirties. This of course raises an interesting debate about today's selection process, which produces nuclear submarine COs in their mid-to-late thirties and officers of well over forty at sea in command are by no means unusual.

Captain Fell was a 'Teacher' on two occasions between the wars. He believed that a submarine CO should be something of a dictator; but he also emphasised the importance of accepting responsibility:

> The submariner must be a navigator, an electrician, a torpedoman, a gunnery type, and even a bit of a plumber. He must know men and get on with them; he must use initiative and tact and learn to enjoy hard living. He must accept responsibility young and not misuse it. There is every reason why he should join and delight in joining submarines, but the greatest joy of all is the companionship, unity and feeling that he is one of a team which only he as CO can let down. The supreme moment, the moment of truth, for the CO is in his attack: then, his judgment and actions alone can bring success, failure or death. He has no one to hold his hand, to advise or correct a fatal move. His eye alone can see, and his instinct sense the correct and only tactic to pursue; on him rests all responsibility. When he feels the faith of his ship's company behind him, knows that they trust him and will carry out or even anticipate his slightest command, then indeed he is a proud man.

Ben Bryant also neatly encapsulated the difference between submarine command and that of any other ship:

> One's first command is always a milestone. One's entire submarine career 'till then has been watching and learning; now is the chance to really put one's own ideas into effect. It is easy to think how much better one would do oneself and criticise others, but it is a very sobering feeling when it is all yours. I have had a number of much bigger commands since my submarining days, with hundreds of men for each man I had in my submarine, but I know no other job that is so completely yours and yours alone.

Under these circumstances, it is self evident that a CO needs to be eager to accept responsibility. It is worth remembering that, during the Second World War in the Mediterranean theatre, the Commanding Officer knew with absolute certainty that to conduct an attack against a screened target would inevitably result in a prolonged and heavy counter-attack and yet there are virtually no examples of COs passing up an opportunity. The moral and physical courage displayed by almost all Commanding Officers in such circumstances, when the odds were often heavily stacked against them, is inspiring. Ben Bryant's description of being depth-charged vividly illustrates the sort of responsibility placed on a CO.

> The swish, swish of the propellers of the hunter passing overhead, the waiting for the explosion of the charges as they sank slowly down. Had they been dropped at the right moment? Were they set to the right depth? The knowledge that there is no escape; that you must just wait for it. Then the shattering roar, the lights going out, the controls going slack as the power is cut, and the paint raining down. The silence and the faint sounds of running water where a gland has started to trickle. It seems magnified a hundredfold – a serious leak is what you dread.

To be totally responsible for extricating your submarine and your crew under such circumstances must be the ultimate test of responsibility. His description goes on to say:

> For the CO, being under attack was an absorbing business, you had far too much to think about to have time to be frightened. I always imagined that it was very much worse for the crew. However, they never seemed to mind, though critical interest was taken in the performance of the chaps up top – all of whom judging by the remarks, had not only been born out of wedlock, but blessed with amazing stamina, (and) were credited with almost continuous indulgence in the sexual act.

This short passage provides evidence of three further qualities necessary for success, namely: *courage* (both moral and physical); *care and consideration* for one's ship's company; and a *sense of humour*.

Another example of the sort of moral courage required, or at least downright honesty, is provided by the Teacher in the late seventies who told an Australian student on completion of the 'Perisher' that:

> The only reason I'm passing you is so that I can come to Sydney later to defend you at your court martial.

At least he knew were he stood and did not leave the course with any misconceptions about his ability.

Honesty is also evident in the Teacher who wrote about a contemporary of mine: "I would go to war with this officer but not to a diplomatic reception." He was dead right, although the Naval Secretary subsequently disregarded the report and sent him off to be a Defence Attaché, with predictable results.

I have stressed the virtues of *honesty* because I believe that the ability to be honest with oneself is an absolute necessity. No two Commanding Officers have the same mix of skills, and the ability to analysis one's own strengths and weaknesses and adopt courses of action that maximise the former and minimise the latter is crucial. A plan that will succeed admirably for one CO may end in disaster for another, simply because he has been dealt an equally good but different hand in the lottery of life.

Stamina is undoubtedly a fundamental requirement of any CO. It was arguably more important in the past when the CO was, by necessity, something of a 'one-man-band'; but it is nevertheless important in the nuclear submarine as well. Whilst the Executive Officer is also command qualified, he is, by definition, unlikely to have acquired much command experience. Shrimp Simpson, the outstandingly successful CO of the Tenth Flotilla in Malta in 1941/42 was clearly in awe of the physical stamina displayed by one of his COs. He wrote in his autobiography that:

> Teddy Woodward found that it suited him best to play the game of war in reverse. The pace he set himself during rest periods in Malta would have put most men in hospital. He would arrive at Lazaretto from the rigours of leave in Malta's 'watering holes', which seemed never closed to Woodward, looking pale and in need of complete rest. Sailing on patrol was an escape from the dangers and then he set out bravely to meet the dangers and demands of yet another holiday.

I am not sure that this recipe for success would meet with universal approval today, but it clearly worked then. *Delegation* is an art that requires practice; it involves trust and confidence in one's subordinates and it is therefore necessary to train them to accept the extra responsibility you intend to place upon them. Clearly, Woodward had established an excellent understanding with his First Lieutenant in this respect. Another example of successful delegation from the Second World War is provided by John Roxborough when he wrote in the foreword to Shrimp Simpson's autobiography:

> *Few officers (and Shrimp was only a Commander at the time) can have been given such an unfettered directive to operate an important command as he was in January 1941 by Admiral Cunningham from his headquarters in Alexandria; "If you don't get results and don't dispose your forces to suit me, I will soon let you know. Until then, you have a free hand to act as you think best to achieve your objective." The results Shrimp achieved with his submarines from Malta undoubtedly prove what a sound leader he was.*

In the same book, Shrimp Simpson painted pen-pictures of five of his more successful Commanding Officers, which neatly summarise the qualities required:

- Woodward – a young officer of exceptional physical stamina. He had a good eye for the periscope attack – his theory and mathematical ability put him in the top flight.
- Tomkinson – He had great qualities of concentration, a strong will and tenacity. His ability, presence and intelligence made him a born leader. He had a gay personality with a gentle manner.
- Wraith – was a very modest man with a great sense of humour who in action was entirely self confident.
- Cayley – was light hearted and almost flippant but behind his cheerful appearance was a shrewd, tough and brave man who volunteered for special duties and undertook them with a sound balance of caution and determination.
- Wanklyn – was a precise person with a good brain – a quick calculating brain. He was self confident and modest.

Far be it for me to attempt to draw conclusions about these men, but the lessons of history do suggest that our successful Commanding Officers shared a number of common qualities. These are just as much to do with character and personality, traits that they were born with, as they are to do with professional skills. All accepted responsibility eagerly and were self-confident; they were strong willed, tenacious and determined; they were brave; and they possessed great physical and mental stamina. They all cared passionately for their ships' companies, had a strong sense of humour and many were surprisingly modest. Their professional experience and training had developed quick calculating brains, the ability to delegate, presence, and 'a good periscope eye'.

So much for the qualities that the selection boards should be looking for. What about the training? The tried and tested vehicle used by the Royal Navy is, of course, the Commanding Officers Qualifying course, to give it, its formal title. The requirement for formal training in the art of submarine command was first recognised in the First World War and the first 'Periscope Course', as it was then known, was conducted in 1917. There were three students on the inaugural course. In the intervening 83 years, only just over a thousand officers have been welcomed 'to the most exclusive club in the world' and, of these, 79 have lost their lives in command.

I mentioned earlier that one of the skills potential Commanding Officers acquired through training was a 'periscope eye' and for the first 50 years until the mid sixties, this was exactly what the 'Perisher' was all about. But what is, 'periscope eye'? Many distinguished submarine officers have attempted to define 'it', but about the only consensus achieved is that if you have not got 'it', you will never make a CO. This does not help much, but in an attempt to get to the bottom of this conundrum it is necessary to recognise that until the early 1930s a submarine had very few instruments to assist in the torpedo attack. What aids they did have, were rudimentary and, as a result, a submarine attack was essentially a matter of judgment by the CO. He alone could see what was going on and, further, his vision was limited to one sector at a time, rather like looking round with a telescope; he had to be able to piece the picture together in his head as he swept round the horizon. A student in the late twenties wrote:

> *'Perisher' was a particularly happy experience, almost devoid of book-work and was a concentrated effort to develop in the students a sense of location and a clear mental picture of one's own position relative to a target, throughout the time when the submarine is being manoeuvred blind, since the periscope can usually only be used for less than five per cent of an attack. This sense of relative position in the Captain's mind's eye is what the success and the safety of the submarine chiefly depend upon. It should be quickly developed in the simple case of a merchant ship steering a straight course at slow speed, first sighted many miles distant, but the sense must be developed so that the Captain will act both correctly and immediately when confronted with, for example, an aircraft carrier escorted by eight destroyers zigzagging at twenty-five knots in a visibility of only two miles. The flair for holding a correct mental picture comes easily to a few, but most are capable of becoming safe rather than brilliant submarine captains; the one essential is constant and frequent practice.*

Another CO of this vintage wrote that:

> *A good eye, self confidence and an ability for mental arithmetic were sufficient to gain proficiency. In attack there is no time to explain or take advice and the CO's decision must be instant. And yet there is a long delay before that decision takes effect. Five seconds late in putting the wheel over now and five minutes later you will find yourself that five seconds too late to get your sights on.*

In short, before the advent of the analogue computer to calculate the Deflection Angle or Aim-Off for your straight running torpedo, 'periscope eye' was the one and only essential prerequisite; 'Perisher' developed it and subsequent practice honed it.

The advent of the 'Is-Was' and, subsequently, the 'Fruit Machine' as standard torpedo attacking instruments made little difference to this basic credo. You could not be a Submarine CO if you lacked 'periscope eye'. The debate was lively, but Teacher was writing in 1938 that:

> *I found that there were two distinct classes of submarine CO. One class was only successful when the COs made full use of the available instruments or had a highly trained crew to feed them information, but if, in the last moments of the attack, the enemy zigzagged or a destroyer on the screen distracted their attention, then they missed. The other class attacked almost entirely by eye. Their percentage of hits was far higher than that of the class who relied on instruments. My own natural instinct was to attack by eye, but I knew the day of instruments was coming and trained myself to use the few we had, to help me.*

117

Submariners tend to be conservative creatures, but by 1942 things were beginning to change. It is interesting to note Shrimp Simpson's remarks about one our most successful wartime COs, Teddy Woodward, who subsequently built the 'new' DOLPHIN Attack Teacher in 1943 and was regarded as the most effective Teacher of all.

> *He had a particularly good eye for periscope attack while, at the same time, his theory and mathematical ability put him in the top flight of those who relied chiefly on instruments, [when time allowed such lethargic assessment].*

Simpson's premise here is, of course, that the ability to attack successfully using instruments is all well and good; but the ability to react instinctively and not get 'lost in the box' remained the paramount consideration.

By the middle of the war, potential Commanding Officers were being trained in the new DOLPHIN attack teacher. One of their number described its workings:

> *The student entered an underground full scale working model of a submarine's control room, and when he looked through the periscope he gazed at a complete surround of canvas realistically painted to represent sky, horizon and sea. From one section, moving on a clockwork trolley, came his target doing any speed and zigzag, either alone or escorted, which the instructor may have set on the clock. Refinements to make the instruments more realistic were steadily added. On a bad day you might have a run of unsuccessful attacks; and your gloom would increase when you remembered that these model attacks were carried out in perfect visibility, with no rainstorms to blot out your target, no breaking waves to obscure your view, and none of the navigational anxieties you were liable to have when operating in shallow water. If you made a mess of it in ideal conditions, when there was no question of anyone's life being at stake and you could consider the problem academically, what disasters might you not be responsible for when you were trying to do the same thing in earnest?*

At this stage, the course had lasted six weeks and, having spent two weeks in the Attack Teacher, the course then went to sea for a further four weeks in the Clyde before qualification and subsequent appointment in command. Edward Young's description of his 'Perisher' sea time in 1943 is identical to the routine we were still using forty years later when I was Teacher. There are good reasons for this. Submarine development was slow in the post war years. When I joined submarines twenty years after the end of the war, we were still using fairly primitive derivatives of the Second World War Fruit Machine, the same straight running torpedo and the same manual plots. Nothing much had changed and 'periscope eye' was still the fundamental qualification.

I say nothing had changed, but in reality it had. The primary role of the submarine had changed. It was now declared to be Anti-Submarine as opposed to Anti-Surface and one would think that this would have introduced significant changes to the way we conducted the training of the CO. In reality this is a false premise; policy can be changed at the stroke of a pen, but designing, procuring, and fitting the equipment to deliver the new capability can take anything up to twenty years. A look at the significant changes required to achieve this new capability is illuminating.

The advent of the Royal Navy SSN in 1965 brought with it speed, mobility, endurance and an element of stealth, but HMS DREADNOUGHT could by no means be considered an ASW platform. ASW torpedoes were in their infancy, the sonars were experimental, and the torpedo fire control equipment came out of the ark. Furthermore, she had no automated Action Information System (AIO) and she made a noise like an express train.

The advent of the 'Polaris' SSBN in 1968 was an outstanding achievement but, given the massive investment in equipment 'through life', it is worth remembering that on commissioning the best passive long range sonar available was the 186 – a set that had had its genesis in the early fifties and provided little confidence in our ability to detect the enemy on a good day with the wind behind.

The first automated AIO system of any consequence did not go to sea until 1973 in HMS SWIFTSURE and the first combined AIO and Fire Control system finally saw the light of day in HMS SCEPTRE in 1978. During the seventies, huge strides had been made in the field of sonar and the advent of the towed array at the end of the decade probably signaled the end of the interregnum. However, it was not until the arrival of the 'Trafalgar' Class in numbers in the mid-eighties that the Royal Navy could truly say that the shift to a primary role of ASW had been achieved.

During the twenty years between 1965 and 1985, Command Training had to evolve but the catch-phrase was 'Evolution not Revolution'. Change to the 'Perisher' had to cater for a range of appointing options for the newly qualified Commanding Officer and provide him with a multitude of new skills that had never been required before.

This theme of constant change was occasioned by a number of factors, which included:

- The reduction in the number of Diesel Submarine Commands available for successful 'Perisher' candidates;
- The requirement for all Executive Officers in nuclear submarines to be 'Perisher' qualified;
- The demise of the Second World War straight running Torpedo – the Mark 8 (but not before it had accounted for the BELGRANO in 1982);
- The steady shift towards greater concentration on Cold War Operational roles;
- The greater emphasis on ASW;
- The introduction of Over the Horizon ASUW weapons (Sub Harpoon);
- The shift to an all nuclear submarine Flotilla.

The inevitable result was that the syllabus has got larger and larger and the course got longer and longer. At the same time, more and more practical training has had to be conducted in shore trainers, which, these days, are a far cry from the 'new DOLPHIN Attack Teacher' of 1943. The other significant change is that officers now require greater doctrinal and tactical knowledge than in yesteryear and certainly require a greater depth of technical knowledge in the weapons and propulsion disciplines.

Nothing in this world ever stands still; no sooner had the Royal Navy acquired a true submarine ASW capability that was second to none, than the game changed. The Cold War ended and now ten years on we are in the middle of another fundamental revolution in submarine warfare. Operations in the Littoral and Projecting Power from the Sea have introduced the requirement for a whole new fist of skills for the future Commanding Officer to learn. These skills include: Land Attack; Integration with the Battle Group or Task Force; Special Operations; Intelligence Gathering; Support of Surface Forces; etc. etc.

In short, the 'Perisher' will have to go on delivering; evolution, not revolution, will continue to be the secret. Our future submarine Commanding Officers will need all the natural attributes, skills, strength of purpose and character that were so evident in their forbears. The requirement to make instant instinctive decisions, not get 'lost in the box' and retain the relative picture will remain the *sine qua non* for future generations of Submarine COs. I look forward to discussing the relevance of 'periscope eye' at the centenary celebration of the 'Perisher' in 2017. Now, that should be a party!

16

Where Do We Go From Here?

*Norman Friedman**

A century after practical submarines entered British (and, for that matter, US) service, their presence in our fleets is well established. However, in the aftermath of the end of the Cold War, there is inevitably a nagging sense that these expensive, magnificent ships, so vital in the struggle against the Soviets, may be less relevant now. After all, they were seen mainly as anti-submarine platforms, yet our likely adversaries have nothing like the Soviets' underwater fleets, and the Russian submarine force is noticeably dwindling. Even the role of the undersea deterrent, so important in keeping the Cold War cold, may seem less vital right now. What is the future of our submarines in a post Cold War world of great uncertainty and enormous local instability, but probably not - for now - of great power threats?

In what follows, I shall use numerous US examples. I can only hope that this is fair to the Royal Navy; of all the navies of the world, the US Navy is surely closest to the Royal Navy in its thinking and in the sorts of strategy that it espouses. I recognise, of course, that US and British governments have different priorities and operate under different conditions.[1]

This question can be approached in several complementary ways. One seeks to imagine future scenarios and requirements. A second is historical; a third is technological.

Any discussion of future requirements must begin with national strategy. As far as I can tell, neither the United States nor the United Kingdom has ever officially articulated a meaningful national strategy; but many scholars have discerned strategic continuities. For both countries, the great virtue of sea power is that it keeps problems at arm's length. It allows a government to intervene as it wishes without making an excessive commitment. To some extent one can imagine a sea power or maritime strategy in which the emphasis is on small but highly mobile forces, which can be inserted as desired, as an alternative to a garrison strategy in which forces are deployed in a variety of overseas bases, for the use of which special agreements are required. To the extent that maritime forces are forward-deployed so that they are within range of potential problems, they represent a mixture of the two strategies. It seems fair to say that since the end of the Cold War Britain has shifted from a garrison strategy (involving large forces fixed on the Continent) to something more like the maritime one. To what extent governments either appreciate or exploit sea power in this way is of course very variable, but the potential determines the nature of their sea power. Intervention may be a show of potential action (for deterrence or coercion) or it may entail actual combat, perhaps mounted from the sea. Information gathering is often a prerequisite.

From the strategic point of view, naval forces offer a combination of mobility and persistence, the latter achieved without the consent of local governments (naval forces can also easily withdraw without consent). In a post Cold War context, one great value of persistence is that the forces should not feel any urgent need to act, hence need not escalate a delicate semi-crisis situation. That cannot be said of aircraft (which have greater mobility but virtually no persistence over the target). Ground forces require local agreements for their existence, and merely inserting them raises the level of a crisis. Withdrawing them is often an admission of defeat which can exacerbate a crisis. Conversely, in order to avoid the loss of face consequent upon withdrawal, governments may well feel impelled to throw in larger forces, which in turn raise the effect of further withdrawal, etc.

These considerations help decide what submarines can do for the governments who buy them, and what their most important characteristics are likely to be.

Crystal balls tend to be cloudy, and the Cold War is not so far behind us that the shape of its aftermath is clear. It does seem obvious that the threats our governments perceive tend to be localised rather than, as in the Cold War, global. For a submarine, then, there is a distinct difference between the transit and the operational environments, to an extent unknown during the Cold War. There are also inevitably sanctuaries - probably very large ones - in which rules of engagement will preclude attacking enemy ships or submarines. With the end of the Cold War, the fixed sensor systems, such as SOSUS, which tracked most submarines in the North Atlantic and North Pacific are also being retired. That, too, changes the submarines' operating environment. The fixed systems are gone because they do not cover likely operating areas. To some extent specialised surveillance ships, such as the US TAGOS, may make up for the absence of fixed systems in forward areas. However, it seems fair to suggest that whatever benefits the US and British submarine forces gained from fixed systems will not be available in future conflicts.[2]

Threats also tend to be far from home. For Americans that was always true, but for the United Kingdom there was an enormous difference between the possibility of, say, the Soviets overrunning Europe and reaching the Channel, and the possibility of a new and disastrous war in, say, the Gulf. In the first case, the nearby threat is mortal, and it is logical to support local defences. In the case of submarines, local defence stretched north into and beyond the Greenland-Iceland-UK Gap. In the wake of the retreat from the commitment 'East of Suez' it was logical, for example, to buy the 'Upholder' Class diesel-electric submarines specifically to monitor the Gap, and to imagine basing them in Scotland for their entire twenty-year lives. Clearly the pre-Cold War Royal Navy thought on a global scale (and, indeed, for years concentrated on the needs of a Far Eastern war), but before World War II it enjoyed a worldwide network of bases. No operating area was more than a few thousand miles from a base. Long transits without replenishment were not a serious issue; ships did not need very long endurance. These considerations applied to submarines as much as to surface ships.

For submarines, high-speed transit equates to nuclear power; there is no real alternative. It is certainly possible to run diesel submarines over vast areas, but not at such high transit speeds. Moreover, their crews are likely to be in considerably worse condition at the end of such runs. It is also possible to use flo-flo merchant ships to carry submarines to a distant operating area. That, too, is not entirely satisfactory. I will, therefore, assume that for the Royal Navy, as for the US Navy, the requirement for operational flexibility and for long reach equates to the decision to concentrate solely on nuclear submarines. I would note that in the aftermath of the Cold War the French seem to have reached a similar decision. Russian thinking is not so clear, because it is so tied up with issues of export sales (apparently necessarily of diesel submarines) and with the problems of infrastructure formerly spread over the whole Soviet Union, and now perhaps inaccessible to the Russians themselves. The Russians have said officially that they prefer a mix of nuclear and

13   The "Monitor", 'M' Class Submarine M-2 with Seaplane (1927)

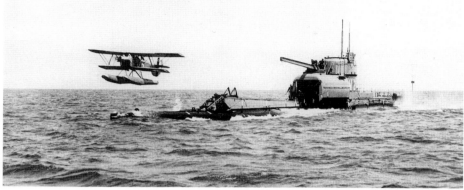

courtesy BAe Systems

14   HMS L-55 Undergoing reconstruction by Soviet workers in Kronstadt (1928)

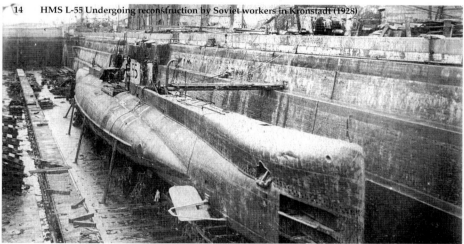

courtesy Camilla Kuznetsov-Aug'yarov family

15   The 'O' Class Submarine, HMS OSIRIS (1928)

courtesy BAe Systems

16   The refurbished L-55 paraded under Soviet colours on the Neva River (1930)

courtesy Igor Kozyr

17   The 'River' Class Submarine, HMS SEVERN (1934)

courtesy BAe Systems

18   The 'Porpoise' Class Submarine, HMS NARWHAL (1935)

courtesy BAe Systems

19   The 'U' Class Submarine, HMS UNITY (1938)

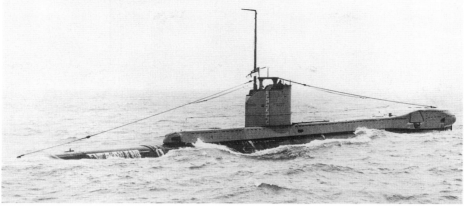

courtesy BAe Systems

20   Mine -loading on HMS PORPOISE (1943)

courtesy RNSubMus

21   The 'S' Class Submarine HMS SERAPH (Formerly P69, then P219) (1943)

courtesy BAe Systems

22   The 'V' Class Submarine HMS VENTURER (1943)

courtesy BAe Systems

23   The 'Fruit Machine' torpedo course calculator (circa 1944)

courtesy RNSubMus

24   The 'X' Craft (1944)

courtesy BAe Systems

non-nuclear submarines, but it is not clear how seriously that is taken; it may, for example, be seen as an inevitable high-low mix for affordability.[3]

Now it is entirely irresponsible to imagine a few fixed scenarios for the next ten, let alone twenty, years. The rule seems to be that crises arise suddenly (or at least unexpectedly, for decision-makers), and that they are far from home. They seem, moreover, to be randomly located. Quickly getting forces to crisis areas becomes a major concern. Moreover, crises are more ambiguous than in the past. Governments may well find it difficult to decide when, or whether, to intervene. They want to be able to intervene, or to withdraw without excessive loss of prestige. The value of choice is difficult to quantify, but it is enormous. Similarly, forces should be capable of remaining in place while a crisis escalates or evaporates, preferably without any resort to local agreement (coercion is difficult if a local government can choose not to allow forces to remain in place).

To complicate matters further, it is by no means clear just what sort of crises will be worth our governments' attention. It seems dubious that any rule can be made to fit all the cases of both intervention and avoidance of post-Cold War crises. For example, very few areas of the world can be characterised as so vital that they are worthy of major military sacrifice (because of its oil, the Gulf may be the key exception). It can be argued that Kosovo was vital because it had the potential to boil over into a general South European war, but intervention there was usually justified on humanitarian grounds. The news media have pointed out that Western forces had not intervened in some other extremely nasty local or internal wars. One crisis in which the United States intervened, Somalia, was substantially less bloody than many others in the same continent, Africa, and the United States lacked any long-term ties to Somalia.

The conclusion one would draw is that it is impossible to know in advance which crises will and will not draw intervention. Forces have to be extremely mobile, and extremely flexible.

Another point well worth making is that great power competition, on a scale something like the Cold War, can come back. Submarines last about thirty years, and a great deal can change in such a period. Moreover, with the end of the Cold War, the rate of change in international relations seems to have accelerated considerably, back to something like its rate in, say, the inter-war or pre-1914 periods. To get some idea of just how long thirty years is, remember that thirty years separated the end of World War I from a point well into the Cold War. During that period Japan went from being a close British ally to being the main threat to the British Empire and then to being a crushed ex-enemy seemingly with little future. That we have just emerged from a period of great stability is suggested by the similarity between the world situation of 1948 and that of 1978, thirty years later, so different from the comparison between 1918 and 1948. It follows that major capital investments, such as submarines, ought to be flexible enough to operate in the contexts both of localised conflict (as we are experiencing it in the aftermath of the Cold War) and great-power conflict, either as hot or as cold war.

Problems are likely to be global, not least because we depend on global sources for our resources. Yet we are unlikely to be able to depend on any sort of global base structure. That is particularly the case for local crises, in which the local powers may be unable or unwilling to accept our presence. The situation in the Gulf since 1991 is a case in point. Even if we have access to local bases, we lack the sheer number of separate battle groups or naval formations necessary to maintain forward forces in many places at once. Inevitably, we will usually find ourselves redeploying forces at high speed from one place to another.

All of this means that submarines are most likely to find themselves operating in littoral areas, perhaps often on the Continental Shelf (say, at depths of 600 ft or less). Most of the world's population lives near the coastline, and most crises happen there. Alternatively, one might say that seaborne access is so important that in a crisis near a coast, which Western governments would willingly tackle, they would probably be forced to avoid were it well inland. Put differently, distance from the coast is necessarily a factor in whether to intervene. The deeper the crisis, the more the intervener must rely on ground forces, which can be trapped if local powers decide not to allow them out.

Continental shelf operations in turn mean crowded waters and, probably, complex bottom topography. Diesel - but not nuclear - submarines can hide by sitting on the bottom, and they can be found only by using active sonar (which may give away the hunter). Heavy local shipping provides dense noise which can hide the hunting submarine but which will also hide her quarry.

Then, there is the history. Go back to the last great break in world affairs, the end of World War II. There was a widespread feeling that not only submarines, but perhaps navies themselves, were obsolete. On the one hand, it seemed that with the advent of nuclear weapons, the sort of relatively slow-motion war in which sea power was vital was finished. Surely the future belonged to heavy bombers and ultimately to missiles. On the other, even if it were accepted that nuclear weapons would not entirely usurp other military roles, the likely enemy, the Soviet Union, was a land power. The sort of interdiction so successfully executed by American and British submarines during World War II would hardly touch the Soviets. At least in the US Navy, submarines survived in the first post-war years because, without them, the anti-submarine force would have been unable to understand the threat it faced. There was also no doubt that the Soviets had, and would continue to develop, a large submarine force capable of threatening the vital sea communications of the West.

There were, it seems, two distinct reactions to the radical change in affairs among the submariners. Some maintained that in fact the Soviets were vulnerable to submarine attack, that they had vital coastal shipping the destruction of which might be quite disastrous to them. At least in the United States, the conclusion was that the Submarine Service that had been so effective against Japan would be equally effective against the Soviets. The other point of view was that the submarine's role against the Soviets would necessarily be different, but that it would exploit the same fundamental virtue - stealth – that had made submarines effective against Japan. It turned out that the new primary submarine missions were, in effect, extensions of missions which had been secondary during World War II: intelligence-gathering, countering enemy submarines, and bombardment (which ultimately became the strategic deterrent). It took about a decade for the wartime submarine forces to transform themselves into the Cold War ones we know so well. Some of the new roles were in place, at least tentatively, within the first five years; another, the deterrent mission, took more than a decade to reach a mature form.

On this basis, that the minor roles of the past may become the principal roles of the next era, we might emphasise the direct support of surface groups. There was considerable interest in direct support during the Cold War; at one time nuclear submarines were envisaged by the Royal Navy as independently-powered variable depth sonars.[4] The great problem was poor communication, which also meant non-existent Identification Friend or Foe (IFF). Yet it seemed that only a nuclear submarine could reliably detect other nuclear submarines, and the American 'Los Angeles' Class was initially justified by the direct support role. The consensus seems to have been that direct support was both ineffective and dangerous, and that it was better to place submarines in an indirect, or associated support, role. Now communication may be far better, and a submarine launching Tomahawk cruise missiles in support of air strikes can be quite valuable. Given localised rather than global conflict, we cannot use past ASW techniques, such as the GIUK barriers. Instead, submarines must be dealt with at source. Alternatively, we may think in terms of "preparing" an area by blocking or trailing potentially hostile submarines. This is not too far from evolved direct support.

The other Cold War role that unmistakably points to the future is reconnaissance. During the Cold War, it was often, though hardly always, concerned with ASW.[5] To the extent that future operations will be in littoral areas, covert reconnaissance of some sort will be essential, and at least the US Navy is already fitting its submarines to probe potential mine fields using unmanned vehicles. It is also the case that, although a submarine may be unable to detect very many signals which, say, a satellite or airplane or UAV will miss, it is also the case that these more overt platforms may be defeated when an enemy turns off emitters. The submarine, being stealthy, may pick up many more signals that an enemy may wish to conceal. Because she may be able to support Special Forces, a submarine may be able to support operations to tap into key land lines. As radio intercept successes are more widely publicised, such a capability may become more and more important, as governments reduce their reliance on radios and cellular telephones.

Recent experiments, in which submarines controlled unmanned aerial vehicles (UAVs) and received their data, suggest another form of reconnaissance.

One other historical point should be made here. Because they are stealthy, submarines generally are not credited with a useful presence role. After all, presence requires that someone be seen, and that may be an unacceptable risk. However, there were some interesting Cold War exceptions. During the Vietnam War, the US Navy stationed an attack submarine off Hanoi-Haiphong, which it was not permitted to blockade. The commander of this submarine periodically ran underwater alongside Warsaw Pact merchant ships, suddenly raising his sail out of the water. Their captains were suitably impressed, and apparently the North Vietnamese decided that the United States had ten or twelve attack submarines just outside the harbor, waiting to close it down.

The tactic worked because the North Vietnamese lacked any credible ASW capability, and in this case invisibility in effect multiplied the single submarine. That the United States did not exploit the resultant fear does not affect the point, that a judiciously handled submarine can exert very impressive presence. The technological implication is that the submarine needs excellent situational awarness, particularly in shallow water, where it may find itself in the midst of considerable coastal traffic.

Any reader of the naval reference books will probably realise just how little ASW capability Third World navies seem to have. Certainly, their submarines threaten Western warships operating in their waters; but it is not at all clear that they have the training or the capacity to threaten Western submarines.

The wartime presence effect of submarines is better known. The Argentine fleet remained in port after HMS CONQUEROR sank the cruiser BELGRANO. To the extent that Argentine carrier-borne aircraft would have been a real threat to the Sea Harriers over Falklands Sound, that degree of presence must have been quite important. However, in most cases governments will badly want to avoid actual combat, so the US case from Vietnam seems more relevant than the British one from the Falklands.

Then there is technology. Submarines offer some very important advantages, albeit at a cost. The most familiar advantage is stealth: a submarine can operate freely in areas nominally under someone else's control. So far as I can tell, the submarine's advantage is actually increasing, since most navies underinvest grossly in any sort of wide-area ASW. That may change, but for the present most countries in the world probably cannot detect submarines at any great distance, even if the submarines run at very high speeds. There seems to be nothing in the Third World, for example, equivalent to SOSUS or even to its rather weak Soviet equivalent.

Because the submarine relies on stealth for self-protection, she is a solitary actor. Usually that is taken to mean that she is ill equipped for close support of surface forces, a point to which I will return. However, it also means that a submarine can be sent, alone, on a mission that might otherwise require a mutually supporting group of surface ships. That ability to operate alone may become more and more important in a world of multiple, widely separated crises.

Another important technological point is that, at least in the open ocean, a nuclear submarine is capable of very sustained high-speed transits. Usually this capability is discounted on the ground that high speed carries with it high radiated noise; surely that is incompatible with stealth. However, for the next decades, it seems likely that we will be concerned mainly with localised crises. Those with whom we will be concerned are unlikely to be able to detect anything, however loud it may be, more than a few tens or hundreds of miles from their coasts. So high transit speed may be quite valuable as a means of responding to critical situations. Moreover, because of its stealth, a submarine can respond without automatically affecting a delicate situation.

One might cite the Falklands as a case in point. In 1977, it seemed that a crisis was imminent, and Royal Navy nuclear submarines were sent to the South Atlantic, to be ready to act in the event the situation worsened. Because they were invisible to the Argentines, they did not affect the delicate diplomacy which defused the crisis. Five years later, the Royal Navy quietly sent attack submarines back. This time, the crisis exploded. The submarines were in place to deal with the cruiser BELGRANO. Note that the dispatch and return of the submarines entailed no public fuss, whereas the dispatch of the surface task group was inevitably a very public event. The task force could not have been dispatched prior to the opening of hostilities.

Both in 1977 and in 1982, the submarines functioned in their traditional anti-ship role. In 1982 they were also used as pickets, to detect Argentine sorties as they left the mainland. However, in neither case could attack submarines directly affect the Argentines on the mainland. During the Cold War, there was some interest in tactical nuclear weapons which a submarine could launch at land targets. For example, the US 'Subroc' anti-submarine rocket could be used against a shore target. Tomahawk of course offered strategic or semi-strategic capability. Since the Cold War, both the US and Royal Navies have used submarine-launched 'Tomahawks' to attack land targets. The US Navy found it interesting that a submarine could transit alone, and thus could fire 'Tomahawks' without any requirement that a substantial number of ships operate. That was quite aside from the stealth with which the missile could be deployed.

On the other hand, an attack submarine has limited volume, and she carries only a few weapons. The US Navy stretched its submarines by adding vertical launch tubes external to the hull, but clearly that solution was disliked: it limited the flexibility of the submarine's armament. Since nuclear weapons are probably unusable in the near term, the question must be whether the small number on board a submarine suffice for anything more than a demonstration attack. One possibility is that the weapons are most useful as 'enablers', e.g. to destroy enemy air defences so that carrier-based bombers can operate more freely. In that case small numbers exert very useful leverage. Another possibility is that exotic warheads make the missiles more effective. In recent years the use of graphite fibres, which are used to short out power stations, has received much publicity in connection with attacks both on Iraq and on Serbia. Probably no other legitimate warhead offers a missile the size of 'Tomahawk' any sort of area capacity.

Yet another point worth making is that in many cases the true target of attack (or threat) is not really an area target at all: it is the enemy government, which may mean nothing more than the Presidential palace or bunker. In that case, the combination of precise navigation and a deep-penetration warhead may offer enormous coercive power, particularly if they come from a platform, a submarine, against which the local government is entirely powerless.

It would seem, however, that any technology which greatly increases a submarine's weapon stowage will be well worthwhile. Modern nuclear submarines are vastly larger than their diesel predecessors, but they seem not to show a proportionate increase in the number of weapons. That is partly because so much of the bow is necessarily taken up by large sonar arrays. It is possible that, as in early sketches of the USS SEAWOLF, the use of conformal arrays may free up bow volume. In the US case, the conformal array could not be used because there was insufficient computing power; but that limit surely will soon be breached.

Speed and stealth already exist, although there may be changes in propulsion technique. As in the surface ship world, there is current interest in electric propulsion. It offers inherent quieting, hence simpler construction (no rafting, at least for main reduction gears). On the other hand, it does not offer the sort of simplification and economy claimed for surface ships. It is difficult to envisage distributing smaller nuclear power plants throughout a submarine, as one can imagine distributing gas turbine generators through the hull of a surface ship. It is, however, possible to imagine displacing hydraulic systems and using electronics to achieve control. It is also possible that eliminating hydraulic piping would make a submarine inherently quieter. The key is probably a large-capacity superconducting motor, which seems to be a practicable proposition. At a much further remove might be a reactor capable of generating electricity directly, without producing steam. If indeed such a reactor is feasible, then again it would greatly simplify the layout of the submarine, and the elimination of the steam plant would indeed make the submarine quieter. Yet it is not at all clear that such a reactor is feasible, or that the considerable cash outlay for its development will be forthcoming; there is probably no urgent civilian application.

An all-electric submarine might use some form of propulsion other than a propeller or pump-jet, such as the long-heralded flexible skin (as in some fish), if that is indeed worth while. There seems to be no current reason to imagine that it would be, but the point is that electric power need not be fed into a motor turning a shaft. In theory, the flexible skin would provide both propulsion and steering.

Another possible change in propulsion would be the introduction of the long-heralded polymer ejection technique, which would drastically reduce the submarine's frictional resistance for a brief period, and thus would offer the submarine high yet quiet burst speed. This was probably more important during the Cold War, when Western nuclear submarines faced fast Soviet nuclear submarines. In a post Cold War world it might be attractive for torpedo evasion.

Over the last few years the super-cavitating 'Shkval' rocket torpedo has gained considerable publicity. In effect, a torpedo is a small submarine; whatever performance it can achieve, surely can be achieved by a larger craft with a suitable power source. On this basis, a magazine recently suggested that future submarines might rival 'Shkval's' 200 knots, or might even be able to transit at supersonic speeds which, under water, would mean more than 3,000 knots. Right now this is the purest fantasy. If, however, we begin to see transit speed as a matter of strategic value, then we might become interested in really high speeds, to be used only in the open ocean, far from detectors. At present the choice is always between really fast transit, which means an airplane, and the ability to loiter near the area of interest, which means a surface ship or a submarine. The strategic ambiguities of the present (and probably of the near future) favour the ability to loiter, because the last thing that is wanted is immediate attack on the area of interest. Imagine, then, an airplane capable of fast transit *and* long term loiter, with substantial weapons and sensor capacities - the atomic airplane, perhaps, of the 1950s.

Perhaps it is worth pointing out that none of this favours a revival of non-nuclear submarines. For non-nuclear submarines, the current favourite propulsion technology is an air-independent adjunct system (AIP) which allows the submarine to loiter for up to two weeks without snorkelling, i.e., without making very much noise. That is certainly useful if the submarine has to operate in an area of very heavy ASW surveillance. It seems unlikely that any such system will be effective for a navy requiring long transits, and there must even be questions as to whether the added complication of an air-independent system is worth the operating and maintenance costs, not to mention any additional shock vulnerability.

For the longer term, it is possible that a submarine could be powered by a fuel cell, without any diesel engine. Such a submarine could run entirely submerged for a significant length of time. If she could replenish her oxidiser from the atmosphere, she might rival a nuclear submarine in transit speed (breaking periodically to snorkel oxygen). Even so, chemical means of storing energy are nothing like as compact as nuclear. Comparing the fuel cell to a nuclear submarine, one would balance off energy storage against the weight of the engine and its auxiliaries. The smaller the submarine, the smaller the contribution of the fuel to overall propulsion weight, so that it might be possible to build a very compact fuel-cell submarine; but anything large would have to be nuclear. If this equation is correct, it would mirror the torpedo situation: for high performance, batteries can power lightweight torpedoes, but it takes internal combustion (i.e., more dense energy storage) to power a heavyweight at high speed.

WHAT IS LIKELY TO BE COMING?

Perhaps the most striking developmental technology is the combination of unmanned underwater vehicles (UUVs) with a new kind of acoustic communications. Current UUVs are long-endurance torpedo-like devices capable of independent operation over several days. The US version is intended to explore potential minefields, dumping its data to the waiting submarine on its return. Assuming this sort of UUV is effective, it exploits the submarine's inherent stealth to probe a likely objective area entirely covertly, even perhaps to monitor the act of mine-laying. Given the serious problems of mine countermeasures, the ideal surely is to evade minefields altogether, and it is best not to give away the fact that this or that area is of particular interest.

For about the past three years, experiments in underwater communication have proceeded to the point where a link can now transmit clear pictures over a range of ten or twenty miles. This technology is the fruit of rapidly increasing computer power, which is used to compensate for the complex distortions inherent in the water medium that in the past, made acoustic communications far less than reliable. Given a reliable link, a submarine can receive the UUV's output in more or less real time, and it can command the UUV on the basis of that output. At the very least, that ought greatly to accelerate any mine reconnaissance conducted by the UUV, since it need not return for readout and reprogramming.

However, the potential of a UUV with a solid data link back to the operating submarine would seem to be far greater. Probably many readers will be aware of 'Manta', a concept developed by the US Navy's Underwater Weapons Center, in which a big UUV carries the submarine's torpedoes, and fires them as directed.

The main disadvantage of the link as currently envisaged is that it is not covert. In theory, then, a submarine using a link gives away its location. However, it is possible to imagine an intermediate transmitter/receiver, the use of which would conceal the submarine's position. It is also possible to imagine a submarine laying a fibre-optic network with regularly-spaced transceivers. The submarine could communicate covertly with a transceiver along a short nearly vertical (i.e., not multi-path) path; the receiver would radiate the less covert signal, so that it would not be traceable back to the submarine.

A second important communication improvement, already in service, is a high-capacity satellite link. Assuming that a submarine on some forward reconnaissance mission collects valuable data, she still needs some way to send it back to potential users. For that matter, if the submarine is to use 'Tomahawk' effectively, she needs some link that can provide detailed flight data. Again, this already exists in the form of a satellite link. As in any other sort of radio, the satellite link suffers from the important operational limitation that an antenna (larger to increase gain, hence data rate) must protrude through the surface.

If the submarine is to operate in crowded littoral waters, then the situation around her is likely to be quite complex, and she needs any possible aids to 'situational awareness'. Current efforts in data management seem to be solving the problem of assembling a usable tactical picture. That is evident in accounts of new submarines such as the 'Astute' and 'Virginia' Classes of submarine. Quite obviously there is a long way to go, and it will be a major challenge to design submarines with open enough architecture to accept computer improvements to be expected over their thirty-year lifetimes. If Moore's Law is to be believed, computer power doubles every 18 months; so, in 18 years, computer power should increase by a factor of about 4,000; in thirty years, by about a million. There is an added complication. Current submarines have one-shot reactors: they are not to be refuelled during their lifetimes. Refuelling is the time to cut open a submarine and make major changes, such as the installation of a new data bus or new computer consoles. Without it, change is inherently somewhat limited; at the least, the architecture must be very carefully chosen so that it is open enough to likely change.

Two sensor developments seem worth mentioning. One is the electro-optic mast, which replaces the periscope. From the point of view of the designer, it has the important virtue that it need not penetrate the pressure hull. Moreover, the image need not be viewed directly under the mast, so that the designer enjoys far more flexibility in internal arrangement. Some optronic masts are already in service. The step beyond is to place the optronic sensor in a pod, which can be connected to the submarine well below by an optical fibre or even by the acoustic link described above. All of this is quite aside from the virtues of inserting the image from the sensor into the submarine's command system, and thus of eliminating the usual quick spin of the periscope. Presumably these virtues become far more valuable in littoral waters.

Another point is more speculative. Submarines currently depend on either the acoustic emissions of the target or on their own emissions (active sonar). Enormous effort goes into improving the signal to noise ratio, hence into buying larger arrays and more powerful signal processors. One might note, however, that people generally see not by using searchlights (or by looking for other peoples' searchlights), but by using the ambient light reflected off objects. There are already passive radar systems, in prototype form, which use ambient electromagnetic radiation in this way; after all, the amount of such 'light' generated by any populated area is enormous. Some years ago EDO, an American company, suggested using acoustic 'light' in just this way. The idea seems not to have gone anywhere, but surely it is worth reviving as processors become more powerful, and as arrays become larger.

One might even imagine a submarine setting up such an array in shallow water, and processing its output. After all, we constantly complain about the vast amount of ambient noise in littoral areas; why not use it for a positive purpose? Incidentally, the EDO proposal was for mine detection, but the idea surely has a wider application.

All of this having been said, the long-range nuclear submarine of the future will surely face small diesel or hybrid submarines on their own territory. Because she will be large, and because she will have access to higher power, she will be able to deploy remote vehicles, perhaps even remote sensing nets, in her own support. Her independent vehicles may also be very effective decoys, forcing an enemy's submarines to show themselves. It also seems arguable that greater internal volume and more power will equate to more computers and operators, hence to better 'situational awarness', particularly since most Third World operators seem to concentrate more an anti-ship than on anti-submarine operation. A larger submarine does present a larger sonar target (though anechoic coatings may make up for that), but she also has larger sonar apertures, and she may have access to much better signal processing.

For littoral operations, the advent of UUVs and of mini-submarines for special forces seems to suggest that standard operating practice will be to stand offshore and probe remotely. Submarines may even launch devices inshore and leave and return to pick them up. Any such operation inevitably capitalises on the internal volume of the submarine. As in any other warship, larger is generally not too much more expensive, because shipbuilding steel is cheap. Given fixed power output, speed does decline with size (lengthening a surface ship reduces wave-making resistance, but that does not apply to a submarine), but on the other hand a larger submarine is, at least now, easier to silence (that would probably change with all-electric power).

It certainly is true that shallower water is more dangerous; the larger the submarine, the easier to get into trouble. However, with nuclear power there is probably a practical lower limit to size (the French seem to think that their current attack submarines are below it), and there is probably little point in staying much below 10,000 tons.

The most important point is for submarines to maintain multi-purpose capability. The world situation now is just too ambiguous for specialisation, but submarines are likely to last through some radical future changes.

NOTES

*   This paper reflects the author's own opinions, and should not necessarily be taken as reflecting those of the US Navy or of any other organization with which he has worked or currently works.

1   For more details of US submarine evolution after 1945, see this author's *US Submarines Since 1945* Annapolis: Naval Institute Press, 1994. For about five years I have been engaged in a parallel project on the development of British submarines.

2   The US Navy has a deployable array system, ADS, but deployment takes time (weeks) and is anything but covert, hence cannot benefit a submarine operating as a precursor to a larger operation. There may be submarine-deployable systems, either in service or under development.

3   The economics is tricky. The Royal Navy abandoned diesel submarines because of the excessive cost of running two parallel logistics and training lines. Diesel submarines are clearly less expensive to build, and if export customers pay the full price of both their own craft and of ones for the Russian Navy, the logistics argument may not be terribly compelling. As the Russians are forced to cut numbers, however, the cost of two rather than one logistics trains may suddenly seem rather high.

4   The original requirements for the computer system conceived for HMS DREADNOUGHT emphasise the underwater escort mission as, incidentally, did contemporary plans for BQQ-2 on board USS THRESHER. These concepts also required the equivalent of underwater data links. Contemporary US documents make it clear that the Royal Navy pioneered the direct support role

5   Unfortunately nearly all Cold War reconnaissance operations cannot be discussed openly; it is difficult, for example, to say just how important they were. It seems likely that many were mounted to obtain the signatures of Russian submarines, since from the 1960s on virtually all of NATO ASW was based on detailed signature information, used in Lofar and its derivatives. It is not clear to what extent Soviet submarines were trailed other than to obtain acoustic intelligence, or to what extent reconnaissance involved collecting Soviet radio or radar signals (submarines were clearly equipped for this purpose).

PART IV

THE ROYAL NAVY & OVERSEAS SUBMARINE FORCES

17

The United States Navy Submarine Service

Donald Tarquin

I am honored to represent the United States Navy's Submarine Service at this celebration of the centennial of the Royal Navy Submarine Force. These centennial celebrations are truly significant events in both countries. For the vast majority of our citizens, it provides their first insight into the accomplishments of a very small, but extremely potent, effective, efficient, and highly successful, part of our armed forces. I believe this visibility is critical in both Britain and the United States where budget battles determine the future strength of our defence capabilities. This occasion provides us with a great opportunity to inform and educate the public and relate the story of the 'Silent Service'.

This chapter will adress the partnership that the Royal Navy and the United States Navy Submarine Services have enjoyed over the past hundred years. I firmly believe that this partnership is the strongest and most effective bond that any branch of two countries' armed services enjoys. However, having researched and looked closely at the historical events and reflecting on my own experiences with the Royal Navy and, in particular, the Royal Navy Submarine Service, I have a couple of problems writing on that subject. The biggest problem is the classification restrictions of this forum and the fact that, on my retirement ceremony in 1984, I pushed the 'erase button' on my memory bank and instantly removed everything I ever knew about submarine operations.

And therein lies a problem; to speak of a 'partnership' without covering operations is like taking a shower without getting wet. It is simply not possible to do it effectively. I propose, instead, to provide a few insights that I picked up in the course of my career that may be of interest.

My naval career was focused on sea duty. In fact, I hold the dubious honour of having the longest continuous tour of sea duty in modern U.S. Navy history. At least, this claim has never been challenged. It lasted 24 years, from the grade of Ensign to Captain, without a tour ashore. People on active duty today cannot understand how or why this happened. The answer was that, in the sixties and seventies, there was a critical shortage of submarine trained officers of my vintage; the opportunity for sea duty was, therefore, ever present and I was a willing participant. When my final sea tour, as a Submarine Squadron Commander, completed, I was sent to the Pentagon to get my ticket punched in that arena. I learned quickly that shore duty was not my cup of tea, so I opted to take early retirement. The point of this story is that my experience with the Royal Navy is entirely operationally oriented.

My initial exposure occurred in the late sixties, as Executive Officer of USS STURGEON in the Submarine Development Group in Groton, Connecticut. As is well known, the Development Group had a Royal Navy Liaison Officer who handled Submarine Tactical Development for the entire Submarine Force. STURGEON did a lot of work in this area since she was the lead ship of a new class and, at that time, the most capable US attack submarine ever built. In my humble opinion, a 'Sturgeon' Class submarine was superior to its successor, the 'Los Angeles' Class, but that is another story. It was during this tour that I learned about the outstanding tactical expertise and professionalism of the Royal Navy Submarine Service. It was an eye-opener for me, who, at that time, thought there was no one else in our league. I learned this not only from the British Liaison Officer, but also from operations conducted jointly and information exchanged on operational matters.

I went from STURGEON to the Sixth Fleet Staff in the Mediterranean where I served as Anti-Submarine Warfare (ASW) Officer for over two years. In this billet, I worked on a daily basis with British Submarine Officers both in Naples on the NATO staff and in London. We were dealing with approximately 15 to 20 Soviet submarines in the Mediterranean continuously. It was an exciting period, very professionally rewarding, and gave me a much broader outlook on ASW than I previously had.

After five years in command of both an SSN and an SSBN, I had the very best job that a post-CO could ever hope for – that of 'Teacher', or as we call the position, PCO Instructor. It was during this tour that I got a look at how 'Perisher' was conducted and saw some of the differences in emphasis that our two submarine services had. I propose to comment on those differences, since I am no longer in uniform and therefore no longer accountable for so-called 'indiscretions'.

It is generally accepted that Admiral Rickover and his successors have held that a submarine officer be engineer-qualified on each submarine assignment. The Royal Navy took a different position and maintained an engineering duty specialist on board each submarine while focusing on the officer's eligiblity for command on tactical and seamanship experience. During my tour as 'Teacher', I learned to appreciate better the British approach over the American approach. Recalling that, during my career, nuclear submarine officers were in critically short supply, it was important to keep every eligible officer in the rotation. As a consequence, there was no selectivity and, therefore, every candidate I had in PCO training went on to command. There were some, not many, about whom I had serious doubts about passing.

The tendency in these cases was for the PCO to face aft where he perceived the emphasis seemed to be. But to enhance the war fighting capability of the boat, the Commanding Officer had to face forward. I felt this was a basic fundamental – but in some cases, it was not to be. I must say that today there is selectivity at each level of progress from Department Head to Executive Officer to Command and this selectivity is surely providing the best and most qualified officers for command. So, perhaps, my problem with the philosophy may very well be moot at this time. I should also add that I have the highest admiration for the way the Royal Navy's 'Perisher' course is run. I can see why the Royal Navy gets such highly qualified officers to command their submarines.

I would like to say a few words about force levels, both British and US I believe both Submarine Services feel strongly that total submarine assets are below the comfort level. Operating tempo is high in the US Navy because the demands and obligations have remained constant, or even increased, as force levels have steadily decreased. The US Navy is suffering in terms of morale and retention, and the outlook is not optimistic. The demands and expectations remain high and yet the number of SSN's is still dwindling. The fleet and unified Commanders-in-Chief have argued strong cases for higher submarine force levels but the politicians reply that it is not affordable.

The United States is currently authorising the acquisition of one 'Virginia' Class SSN a year and it does not look as though this rate will change in the near or distant future. Here in Britain, the SSN20 program was being debated before I retired and the 'Astute' program which finally resulted is only now in its early build stage. We all know that these low build rates will not sustain the force levels that are needed in our fleets. The current level of funding ship construction in both countries is inadequate to support the required force levels. Nor is it adequate to keep skilled construction workers fully occupied in the submarine building business. It is as simple as that. Somehow, the message needs to be broadcast that this situation must be rectified. History has taught us that only through strength in both our armed forces will peace be sustained. Why must we have to relearn this lesson again?

In conclusion, I offer a sea story, one of my fondest memories of joint US/UK submarine relations.

In 1976, my first command tour was coming to a close. USS DRUM, a late model 'Sturgeon' Class, had just completed a very strenuous 70-day operation and pulled into Subic Bay for a port visit. We parked behind a British SSN, which, as I vaguely recall, was HMS VALIANT. Apparently, it was her last day in Subic and, upon our arrival, an invitation for a joint dining-in was received. We accepted, but I was unable to attend as I had to brief my boss on our just-completed operation. The rest of the wardroom, however, with the exception of the Duty Officer, participated. It was held at the Quonset Huts, dubbed the 'Submarine Sanctuary' where both submarines' officers were housed during their visit.

To make a short story long, I completed my business late in the evening and proceeded to the Sanctuary, expecting to enjoy an after-dinner drink with the two wardrooms. When I arrived, I saw about 20 grown men in white service uniforms, in a row, on their knees, led by the British Commanding Officer in the van, singing "Heigh Ho, Heigh Ho. It's off to Olangapo...." They snaked out the Sanctuary door and my officers were not seen again until the following afternoon – each suffering a great deal from the effects of the previous night's festivities. HMS VALIANT got underway that morning with the skipper on the bridge looking fresh and wide awake, as if he had a full night's rest. That was truly impressive!

Let me end by extending my sincere condolences and those of all submariners of the United States Navy, past and present, to the families and friends of the Russian submarine KURSK and to the Russian Submarine Force. We may have been competitors, but we are also comrades-in-arms and we feel your loss. Thank you for this opportunity to contribute to this splendid celebration. It has been a great honor.

18

The White Ensign beneath Russian Waters

Igor Kozyr

I am not sure whether the younger generation of submariners in Russia and Great Britain are aware of the intricate relations between the Submarine Services of our two countries over the past hundred years. It is even doubtful whether those involved in one or other historical event could at the time have anticipated its future impact on the evolution of the relations between the two fleets and nations. In the search for historical accuracy, we often come across a chain of paradoxes that regularly appear throughout the history of both the Russian and Royal Navy Submarine Services. Over a relatively short historical period, we have, alternately, been either friends or enemies. But we find ourselves, on the eve of the hundredth Anniversary of the Royal Navy's Submarine Service as good friends, recalling first of all our combat fraternity born at a time of struggle against German aggression. And we recently experienced that close friendship again in the common concern of our seamen during the rescue operation of the Russian submarine, KURSK.

Russia, like many other countries, met the arrival of the 'Silent Service' at the turn of the nineteenth and twentieth centuries and was cautious in its early prognosis of the submarine's combat abilities in contemporary naval warfare. Initially, the role of this new sea combatant was considered best suited as a coast guard, for the protection of naval bases or performing patrol duties. Submarines were often considered as a sort of active minefield with only small advantages over those mentioned above. At the same time, however, thanks to the efforts of subsurface navigation enthusiasts in the fields of submarine design and warfare, Russia soon took a place alongside the world leaders in this new technology.

Before the First World War, the General Staff of the Russian Imperial Navy prepared a plan to introduce submarines into the Baltic and Black Sea fleets and the Siberian Flotilla. The basic elements of that plan were incorporated in a so-called 'Small Shipbuilding Program' of 1912. Under than plan, at the Saint Petersburg and Revel (Tallinn) shipyards, 18 new 'Bars' Class submarines were ordered and 12 more added at the Black Sea yards. The first completed boat was not expected to enter service until 1915. Russia's limited industrial capacity, especially in the field of motors, nautical optics, and electronics, was insufficient to meet the demands of this ambitious program.

By the beginning of World War I, the Russian Baltic Fleet had only eleven old boats in service. These had very poor combat qualities for operating either under or on the surface. The only boat considered modern and up-to-date was an 'Akula' ('Shark') submarine, launched in 1911. Her patrol endurance was rated at two weeks, and her fuel capacity gave her a cruising range on the surface of 1,000 miles. Her storage capacity for lubricating oil, however, took up most of the boat's free space, including the torpedo loading area, with oil canisters and bottles. Moreover, its design exposed an unprotected rudder and a medial screw propeller that was often damaged when navigating in the shallow Baltic waters.

Without waiting for a request from the Russian Command, the British Admiralty decided to deploy three submarines into the Baltic Sea after the Naval Staff had taken into account the sequence of events in that area, on the one hand, and German operations in the Northern Sea on the other. They were also concerned with the more 'vigorous' activities of the German Navy in the Baltic theatre and had a special interest in the naval base in Kiel that was being used both for training exercises and battle ship refitting, and as a base for submarine operations.

The Royal Navy submarines E-1, E-9 and E-11 were chosen for this duty, but only two of them (E-1 and E-9) succeeded in breaking through the German blockade and arrived safely at the Russian naval base at Libau, at the end of October 1914. The following year, 1915, HM Submarines E-8, E-18 and E-19 carried the colours of the Royal Navy to the Baltic. Later, in 1916, the decision was made to send four more 'C' Class submarines into the Baltic (C-26, C-27, C-32, C-35). Because the Baltic straits were blocked by German naval forces at that time, the submarines made the journey on board merchant freighters to Archangel. From there, Russian barges transported them along the Dvina and Suchona Rivers, through the ancient sluices of the Mariinsky channel into Lake Ladoga. From there, they continued to St Petersberg, which by then had been renamed Petrograd because of the 'German' sound of its old name.

Before the second half of the 1915 campaign, the three 'Bar's Class submarines (BARS, GEPARD and VEPR) were commissioned British submarines with each having a Russian liaison/navigation officer on board. It was left to them to carry the main burden of war duties against the enemy's supply lines and communications. This is confirmed by figures shown in Table 1.

TABLE 1

RUSSIAN AND BRITISH SUBMARINE ACTIVITY DURING THE 1915

Average:	Patrols (Days)	Coast guard action (days)	Reconnaissance missions (Libau)	Active missions (Days)	In harbour (Days)	Torpedo attacks (average)	Used torpedoes (average)
small Russian submarines	7.6	13.4	0.5	4.0	169	1.6	3.4
large Russian submarines	8.5	10.5	6.4	19.0	80	1.5	5.0
British submarines	7.6	8.6	6.0	41.2	88	6.6	8.8

BALTIC CAMPAIGN

During this period of the war, Russian submarines were also handicapped by poor torpedo equipment supplies and an unsatisfactory method of firing torpedoes (fan shaped with an Angel aperture of 5 to 10 degrees). The Russian Naval High Command did not manage to overcome these difficulties until the beginning of the 1916 campaign, after which time Russian submariners achieved ever better results than their British colleagues. Nevertheless, the British Royal Navy Submarine Forces made a significant contribution to Allied successes during the war at sea in the Baltic. In particular, the most distinguished service was that of HM Submarine E-19, which took part in Baltic Sea operations from September 1915 onwards and completed 17 war patrols. Her gallant crew has to their credit eleven enemy ships, sunk, damaged, or taken as prize.

In October 1915, the British submarine E-8 sunk the German battle-cruiser, PRINZ ADALBERT, (9,000 tonnes displacement), which subsequently turned out to be largest naval ship ever to be sunk by a submarine in Baltic waters. It is an irony, however, that HMS VICTORIA (1,095 tonnes), should have been torpedoed by the Soviet submarine PANTERA in 1919, and became the largest warship ever sunk by a Russian or Soviet submarine throughout its entire history.

'C' Class submarines were not able to record any notable successes in the Baltic Sea, though their presence, as well as their high combat activity, played a role in the battle of Moonzund in October 1917. This was the engagement when the Baltic Fleet managed to frustrate the German Naval Command's plans to occupy the Bay of Riga and then break into the Finnish Gulf. The Commander-in-Chief of Naval Forces in the Bay of Riga, Rear Admiral Bachirev, thus put an end to any further German intentions in that area.

The most industrious combat units were the 'C' Class British submarines, of which only the most favourable comments can be made. All orders were carried out by them not only with distinction, but also with dedication to their naval duties.

The poor state and readiness of the Russian Submarine Forces, however, as well as need for improvements in the submarine programme, came as no surprise to the Russian Command. A week before the outbreak of the First World War, a conference was held in which commanders, flag-officers and flag-specialists discussed the role of submarines in a future war and came to the conclusion that submarines would considerably reinforce the Russian Fleet's combat capabilities. The proposition to build thirty new submarines was acknowledged to be a fundamental requirement. Further calculations by the General Staff of the Russian Navy produced even more precise figures of the number of submarines needed by the Russian Imperial Navy. They were as follows: the Baltic Fleet needed 41 boats; the Black Sea Fleet, 34; and the Pacific Fleet, 40. According to these calculations, the Russian Imperial Navy required, in total, 115 boats. Taking into account those already under construction, an additional 45 submarines needed to be built.

The necessity of transporting submarine sections by railway to the Far East, where they would be assembled, made the situation even more demanding. The submarine shipbuilding program was approved in September 1914, but was only expected to be completed in 1920 because submarine construction lead time took between two and two and a half years for the Russian shipyards to complete. This would not meet the Navy's requirements in time of war. The Naval Command, therefore, had to appeal to Great Britain for help. With the assistance of the 'Noblessner' Company, Russian naval officials petitioned for credit to purchase a number of submarines abroad.

The commission well served the commercial interests of the Company for it received a contract to procure 28 submarines, each costing four million rubles. At the time, 'Noblessner' had close business relations with the Holland Company in the USA, who had indicated that it was ready and able to build a number of submarines for two and a half million rubles each. 'Noblessner' then simply redirected its order to the USA, and in the process received 42 million rubles in pure profit for its efforts.

The British government answered her ally's request by providing the necessary credit and granted Russia the right to order a number of' Holland' Class submarines. As the USA was not allowed by law to sell submarines to a belligerent power, the first stage of submarine construction was carried out in Barnet, Canada, not far from Vancouver. Separate sections were then transported to Vladivostok, in the Russian Far East, by sea and from whence they were taken by railway to Petrograd and Nikolaev. There, the submarines were assembled and fitted out with their instruments and armaments. In accordance with the first contract, the Electric Boat Company had to build eleven submarines, five of which were destined for the Baltic Fleet and the remainder for the Black Sea Fleet. All the submarines were given the abbreviation 'AG' (American, G(H)olland). The Baltic submarines were given additional numbers 11 to 15; their sister ships in the Black Sea in their turn were given numbers 21 to 26.

A second Russo-British agreement provided six more submarines for delivery to Russia, including three for the Arctic Ocean Flotilla. However, they were destined to remain under American colours. From the Spring of 1917, a number of 'AG' Class Baltic Submarines were assembled as the 4th Submarine Detached Division and sent to Hanko. These submarines, which were ready for the beginning of the 1917 campaign, completed several patrols. One of them, AG-14, perished near Libau, having most probably hit a mine on the 6th of July 1917. With the crew died her Captain, Senior Lieutenant Anton von Essen. He was the only son of Admiral Essen, who was at the time Commander-in-Chief of the Baltic Fleet, a post he had held since the beginning of war. Before Anton von Essen was appointed to command the AG-14, he had served for some time as liaison officer on British submarines operating in the Baltic Sea, particularly on HM Submarine E-9, for which he had been awarded an Honorary Distinguished Service Cross.

Because of revolutionary foment in the Imperial Russian Navy, these new boats soon lost their fighting quality. Furthermore, they also placed British submarines in some danger. On April 3, 1918, the Russian submarines were at risk of being captured by the Germans having been sighted not far from Gange. As a consequence, the submarines AG-11, AG-12, AG-15, AG-16 and the tender OLAND were scuttled by their crews and sunk.

Crewmen from the Division managed, however, to escape to Helsingfors (Helsinki) whereupon they joined the crews of other Russian submarines based there. Most of them took part in the famous 'Ice Run' of the Baltic Fleet. During this incident, 'AG' Class submarines E-1, E-9, E-18, E-19, C-26, and C-27, and C-35 of the Royal Navy Submarine Service, were also scuttled and blown up by their crews on Sveaborg ride. This heroic saga, coupled with rapturous epithets to the sailors' valour and selflessness, were included in all the Russian textbooks on the history of Navy. It now appears from recently released documentary sources, that the Soviet government was bound by a secret agreement with the German General Staff not to retain the ships of the old Imperial Russian fleet.

However, Captain of 1st Rank Schastny, who took command of the Baltic Fleet and led the operation, was shot after the standard incrimination of having taking part in a counter-revolutionary plot, his name being for a long time buried in oblivion. It is stated in certain monographs that Schastny had copies of documents he received from the British Naval Command that contained information about the secret negotiations between the Bolsheviks and German General Staff. They had been found in his briefcase when he was arrested.

The Holland submarines that were put into service in the Black Sea were not only to last longer but also were to play a dramatic role in the complicated relations between the Allies. The first three, namely AG-21, AG-22, and AG-23, were commissioned into the Russian Navy in March 1917, though AG-21 only entered service in 1918. Together with other submarines, she was berthed in Sevastopol but was unable to leave for Novorossyisk when German expeditionary corps marched in and occupied the city. For some time, she was at the White Navy's disposal, but as Antanta troops marched into Sevastopol the British command moved in and captured all the Russian submarines. To eliminate any possible threat from Soviet Naval forces in April 1919, all the submarines were towed out to sea and sunk. AG-

22, however, was completed after some effort by White Army personnel, whereupon she took an active part in the Civil War mainly as a patrol ship and also for reconnaissance duties. With all the other ships of the White Navy, AG-22 left Sevastopol and made for Constantinople. From there, they sailed to Bizerta, Tunis, which became the final base of the remnants of the White Russian Navy.

In its turn, the Red Navy did all it could to finish building AG-21 as soon as possible once it had been seized in the Nikolaev docks. No sooner had the Soviet Red Banner been hoisted over the submarine on the 22nd of September 1920 than a note from the British Government followed on the 26th of September with the sharp diplomatic warning that British ships had been ordered to sink the submarine on sight. Furthermore, the British had set up a sea blockade along the Black Sea coast from Novorossiysk to Tuapse. The Communist Party leaders discussed the supply problems for the only Soviet submarine in the Black Sea whilst, at the same time, every effort was made to complete the construction of submarines AG-25 and AG-26.

The United Kingdom government's order to sink every Soviet submarine also extended to the Baltic Sea. The final note of undersea war in the Black Sea was sounded when AG-23 participated in the Sevastopol blockade, and made ready to torpedo any ship that had on board evacuated regiments of the White Army under the command of General Wrangel. The commander of the Soviet submarine, equipped with captured British torpedoes, was instructed to attack only those ships bearing the St. Andrew ensign. However, in accordance with the strict conditions of the French authorities, all such ships were declared to be French property as compensation for the cost of Allied supplies to the White Army during the Civil War from the 13th November 1920. For this reason, the Soviet skipper was able to avoid committing fratricide.

In 1928, AG-21 was raised from the sea bed where she had been for nine years. The submarine joined the Soviet Navy in 1930, but during tactical exercises she collided with a destroyer and sunk to the bottom with all hands. After two days, the crew succeeded in surfacing the vessel due to a special feature of the Holland's design, namely an 'air cushion' which saved the lives of nine crewmen. When repaired, the submarine returned to active service.

In spite of their advanced age, and with the exception of submarine A-11 (former AG-23) which had undergone a thorough refit and was held in reserve, the Holland submarines A-2 (AG-24), A-3 (AG-25), A-4 (AG-26) all played an active part in World War Two combat operations. Each completed 17, 19, 15 and 12 war patrols, respectively. A-3 perished in 1943, but A-5 operated successfully until 1944, notwithstanding the heavy damage she sustained during one of her wartime patrols. The submarine was awarded the 'Red Banner' Order for her distinguished service.

There is, however, one sad episode in the naval history of the Civil War and Russo-British relations. Nevertheless, the event is of great significance in the history of the Soviet Navy. Towards the end of 1918, Great Britain was actively supporting the young Baltic Republics in their struggle for independence against the Red Army. Royal Navy ships made an unexpected appearance in the Baltic Sea and succeeded in capturing two Soviet destroyers, the SPARTAK and the AVTROIL, on 25th-26th December. The poor technical condition of the two ships and the low professional skills of their new 'revolutionary' command, effectively guaranteed an easy victory. Later, both ships joined the Estonian Navy and at the beginning of 1930 they were sold to Peru.

It is worth noting that the money raised from that sale was spent in England on the construction of two new submarines, the KALEV and the LEMBIT. They served in the Red Navy after the Soviet regime was established in the Baltic. KALEV had served as a minelayer in the Soviet Navy for just over four months before she perished at the end of October, 1941, probably in the mine field near Naisser Island.

LEMBIT, sailed under the command of Hero of Russia (which he was awarded posthumously in 1995) Captain of 3rd Rank Matiasevich, who subsequently became one of the most successful submarine commanders in the Red Navy. The submarine was awarded the honorary name of 'Red Banner Order Ship'. She sunk in total twelve enemy ships, including three with torpedoes, five ships totalling 10,961 tonnes displacement, and four warships by mines.

Returning to the events of the Civil War, on the 23rd of May 1919 a detachment of the Royal Navy's 7th Submarine Flotilla with its tender, the LUCIA, arrived in Revel (Tallinn). The Flotilla was under the overall command of Captain Martin Nasmith, one of Britain's most experienced submariners and famous for sinking the Turkish battleship BARBAROSS HAIREDDIN. The 7th Submarine Flotilla consisted of the medium class submarines E-27, E-40, L-12, L-16, and L-55. Among the officers were many who had served in the Baltic Sea operations in 1915-1917. The L-12's commanding officer, Rolland Blaslock, when First Lieutenant of E-1, had taken part in the famous attack on the German dreadnought MOLTKE in the Bay of Riga in 1915. L-55 was under command of the E-9's former First Lieutenant, Charles Chapman. Soon after their arrival, the submarines began to patrol along the Soviet Russian coasts.

The first combat contact with a Red Navy ship was made on the 26th of May, 1919. It was made by the L-16 that had earlier tried to sink the Soviet destroyer AZARD. Nevertheless, the Red Baltic Fleet started this campaign having first selected its most ready and best trained units. In spite of repeated attempts to attack Soviet destroyers in the Kaporsky Bay area, the British submarines failed to record any successes. On the 4th of June, HM Submarine L-55 tried to torpedo AZARD, which was patrolling the area. The destroyer avoided the submarine's two torpedoes and then counter-attacked. The submarine, after one torpedo salvo, dived to a secure depth and kept her conning tower well below the surface. A shell from the first salvo from AZARD hit the L-55's conning tower. The L-55's attempt to escape below the surface was met with a massive explosion caused by one of the mines of the British anti-submarine barrage that had been laid against Soviet boats. The stricken submarine went to the bottom with her crew of 42.

In subsequent combat episodes, submarines from both sides were occasionally involved. For example, on 26th of July the Soviet submarine PANTERA simultaneously attacked two British submarines, the E-11 (which replaced the lost L-55) and the E-40. Because of the bad technical state of torpedo warfare, both Soviet torpedoes from the first salvo failed to work and immediately sank. The E-11 was able to avoid the next salvo, though only with great difficulty. On 1st September, a Royal Navy Submarine Detachment was replaced with the 'H'-type submarines under the command of Max Horton, who later became a famous Admiral during World War Two. The 'H' Class submarines remained at sea until January 1920 and were tasked to prevent the Red Baltic Fleet from attacking the Baltic republics.

In 1926, a submarine was accidentally found on the sea bottom in Koporsky Bay by Soviet minesweepers. At the time, they were sweeping the British, Russian and Soviet minefields from the 1914-1920 period abandoned in the area. The lost submarine proved to be a timely discovery because it coincided with the time when the USSR was about to begin a new naval shipbuilding programme, with submarines given a top priority. At the time, Soviet shipbuilding was facing major difficulties and most shipbuilding facilities were engaged in the process of rebuilding their industrial capacity. The industry lacked in particular the technical knowledge and skill for research and development in the theory and practice of submarine navigation. There was also an acute lack of qualified specialists, most of whom had either perished in the Civil War or had emigrated from Russia. Aware of their limitations, Soviet specialists were, however, quick to learn from, and to adapt, foreign experience in the field of submarine design and development. At the time, it was extremely difficult to get the needed technical information because of the West's economic and political blockade of Soviet Russia.

The opportunity to be able to examine a submarine that was thought to be the best in her class was a stroke of good fortune. In July 1928, after thorough and detailed preparation, a Special Expedition on Underwater Works started operating in the Koporsky Bay. Despite the severe storms and the existence of mines, one of which was responsible for the sinking of the Soviet rescue ship, KOMMUNA, the L-55 was successfully raised to the surface on August 11th, and towed to one of Kronstadt's docks. Chairman of the USSR Revolutionary Military Council Voroshilov, Commander-in-Chief of Red Navy, Muklevitch, and Commander-in-Chief of the Baltic Fleet, Victorov, were the first to inspect the submarine.

On August 14th, when the sea water had been drained away, work began on cleaning out the submarine's compartments. In the course of that work, the remains of the 42 British sailors were found in the silt. The bodies were placed in coffins, but because diplomatic relations between the two countries had not been restored, the procedure of returning the remains of the crew to their homeland proved difficult. As the Soviet authorities refused to let a British warship enter Kronstadt's harbour, the task was entrusted to a specially chartered Swedish steamer, the TRURO. The negotiations with Soviet Russia for the return of the British crew were conducted with the assistance of the Norwegian Ambassador, acting as intermediary. The TRURO then sailed for Revel (Tallinn). The bodies of the crew of L-55 were then transferred to HMS CHAMPION. They were then conveyed to the United Kingdom under escort of four British submarines.

Russian shipwrights fully restored the L-55 and in the Autumn of 1930, the submarine successfully passed all her commission tests. However, the constructors and submariners were somewhat disappointed because they were unable to reach the surface speed of 17 knots as stated in *Jane's Fighting Ships*. Another disappointment was that her working depth was only 50 metres and, as a result, she did not have any significant advantage over the latest Soviet 'D' Class submarines. Nevertheless, Soviet engineers and specialists examined L-55 carefully to try and discover any significant technical innovation. Their assessment of the submarine's technical state turned out to be contradictory. Some found nothing of any importance; others, however, agreed with Aksel Berg, Chairman of Naval Science and Technique Committee Section and future famous academician and admiral, who considered that the L-55 was of great significance to Soviet submarine designers. He argued that it would be prudent to delay the development of some submarines in order to install certain technical features contained in the British boat. Berg's judgment was probably influenced by his wartime experience when he served as a liaison officer on one of the British boats in the Baltic during World War One.

The examination of the L-55 was reflected, and reincarnated, in the design of the first Soviet submarine minelayer, LENINETS. For example, she had the same distinctive hull shape and light contours as the 'English lady'. This hull form improved stability and simplified manufacture and construction. In August 1931, amid the usual festive ceremony of colours, she was commissioned and assigned to the Baltic Fleet Submarine Forces. The decision what to name the boat was discussed at the highest level; at the time, political connotations were considered extremely important to the Soviet Naval Command, for which reason the submarine retained her original name, L-55 - for "imperialistic aggressors' education". No alterations were ever made to the design of her heavily damaged (an unusual feature for Russian boats) conning tower.

After a short time, the submarine, as a first of Class, was assigned to test new radio and electronic equipment for submarines. She was also frequently seen on the Neva River during naval parades. According to Captain of 1st Rank Constantine Egorov (who is still living in Saint Petersburg), who served on L-55 in 1936, she was considered to be a technically reliable submarine with strong artillery and torpedo armament. Her distinctive feature was a wide use of hydraulics in auxillary machinery and control systems, which were advanced and some what exotic for Soviet boats. At the beginning of World War Two, the L-55 was recommissioned and used as a charge station. She remained in the Soviet Navy until January 1945, just before the Allies' victory over Nazi Germany.

Though relations between the Soviet Union and Great Britain could not be described as friendly because of their well-known ideological differences, it was in the submarine field where there was a certain co-operation and basic understanding, albeit in rudimentary forms. On the July 17th 1937, the USSR and Britain entered into a covenant under which the two countries provided each other with information on new ship developments and their entry into the naval service. Soviet Russia also bought from Great Britain echo sounders, hydro compasses and other nautical instrumentation.

On the July 15th 1941, Winston Churchill informed the US President, Franklin D. Roosevelt, that in the event of a war between Germany and the USSR, he would support an alliance with the latter. Three days previously, an instruction had been issued to the Ministry of Defence to form a military delegation, ready to be flown to Russia. Ten days later, on June 25th, a British military delegation headed by Admiral Miles arrived in Moscow. At that time, Germany had embarked on an offensive in the North, the objective of which was to occupy Murmansk in the shortest possible time. Once there, the intention was to destroy the Soviet Northern Fleet, which, though not numerous, still represented a military threat in a strategically important theatre of war.

The political leadership saw the Arctic as an important segment of a large circle peripherally drawn around Germany. Britain and the USA were concerned lest the USSR should come out of the war, so they sought to support the country in every possible way. It was only via the Arctic, the shortest available route, that this could be achieved. In case the course of events should turn out to be unfavourable, the British Navy would be tasked to prevent Soviet fighting and merchant ships from being captured by the Germans.

Severe weather conditions, a primitive infrastructure, and weak anti-aircraft defences made Soviet naval bases in this region uncomfortable for the British naval forces. Svalbard had neither defences nor the means of logistic supply. The only option was for Britain to assume offensive operations in the Arctic. With the consent of the Soviet Naval Mission in London, the Admiralty decided to send two submarines into the region so that they could operate from a naval base in Polyarny. It was planned that the primary task of the submarines would be to attack enemy shipping and to provide cover for Allied convoys. Commander Davis was appointed to the British Naval Mission in Polyarny, as Detachment Commander, and was responsible for co-ordinating the combat activities of the two British submarines operating in Soviet Arctic waters.

The first of the two submarines, HMS TIGRIS, arrived in Polyarny on August 4th. HMS TRIDENT arrived six days later. Soviet sailors welcomed the British crews heartily, but there was no time for rest. On August 11th, HMS TIGRIS left Polyarny and headed out for her first war patrol in the Barents Sea. On August 17th, a Norwegian freighter HAAKON JARL (1,480 tonnes) under German colours was sighted and torpedoed, thereby opening the combat score of Allied Submarine Forces. The submarine HMS TRIDENT then left Polyarny not long before midnight on August 16th and headed for the Norwegian coastline. After several unsuccessful days, the submarine gained her first victory, sending to the bottom the German freighter OST PREUSSEN.

A few days later, HMS TRIDENT was more than compensated, with interest, for her earlier lack of success when attacking a strongly guarded enemy convoy. Her torpedoes hit two of the largest merchant ships DONAU (2,931 tonnes) and BAHIA LAURA (8,561 tonnes). This was the most successful attack made by a British submarine in the Barents Sea throughout the war. German escorts were alerted and chased the submarine, rocking her with a string of 56 depth charges. The German submarine U 566 later attempted to sink TRIDENT on her run to her 'home base' in Polyarny, but she evaded the enemy's torpedoes, though not without difficulty.

The successes of the British submariners greatly impressed their Soviet colleagues. Before the British boats arrived at Polyarny, the 22 submarines of the Soviet Northern Fleet during the 1941 campaign had failed to sink a single enemy vessel. Soviet submarine officers were keenly interested in the details of HMS TRIDENT's war patrol, especially in learning about her tactics and torpedo firing methods. The British skippers were open and frank, sharing their experiences, and they never attempted to conceal anything, even their mistakes. It should be noted that in the beginning of the war the Soviet submariners, along with American colleagues, were keen to share information on their sharpshooters' torpedo firing experience. The lessons they received soon bore fruit. Captain-Lieutenant Bibeev was one of the first to apply the 'British' methods in his own war practice. He took over command of the D-3 after a period of training whilst on board HMS TIGRIS that was, at the time, providing cover for the Arctic convoy PQ-1 in company with the Soviet submarines K-2 and Shch-402.

The period when British submarines were operating in the Barents Sea was relatively short, from August 1941 until January 1942. During that time, they completed ten war patrols. HMS TIGRIS and HMS TRIDENT performed three patrols apiece and HMS SEALION and HMS SEAWOLF, which replaced them, each completed two patrols. It is on record that together they sunk one patrol ship and seven freighters totalling 17,547 tonnes displacement. To put these figures in perspective, and for purposes of comparison, in the campaign of 1941 Soviet submarines operating in the Barents Sea destroyed six enemy fighting ships, including a German patrol ship of 470-tonnes, three merchant ships of 6,442 tons total displacement and two Norwegian trawlers. The British submarines that operated from home bases in Great Britain sunk 20 ships of 52,498 tonnes total displacement during 1941.

There is no doubt that the British submarines who fought shoulder to shoulder with Russians sailors in Arctic waters made a significant contribution to the process of strengthening the Allied fleets' combat co-operation during a critical period of the war against fascist Germany and helped to defend Northern Russia. Despite the fact that those victories had long been erased from the official history of the Soviet Navy, they have been kept in the memories of Russian submarine veterans. And it is through the restoration of our friendly relations between Russian and British maritime communities that there are now more opportunities to know better our common heroic past.

A transfer of four British submarines in accordance with the conditions of capitulation of Italy on the September 8th 1943 is the final link in the history of combat co-operation between Russian and British submariners. Three submarines of 'Unity' Class and a fourth of the 'S' class sailed under the Soviet Navy's colours. They were modern submarines that had successfully proved themselves in combat at sea. During the 1942-1943 campaigns, the Soviet Northern Fleet had lost 19 submarines; the reinforcement of these additional four submarines was, therefore, of great importance to the Soviet submarine forces that numbered at the beginning of 1944 23 boats, of which eight had a displacement of under 300 tonnes. The best Soviet crews were selected to operate these British submarines.

Among veteran Russian submariners I have heard a story that the Soviet Naval Command established a Special Purpose Submarine Detachment commanded by the top submariners. These were, in fact, Hero of Soviet Union Captain of 1st Rank Tripolsky, who was assigned to be the Group Commander. Hero of the Soviet Union Captain of 2nd Rank Fisanovitch, took command of HMS SUNFISH (B-1). The submarine P-42 (B-2) was skippered by Captain of 2nd Rank Potapov, who completed eleven war patrols, and submarine P-43 (B-3), in her turn, was under the command of the very popular Soviet Navy Captain of 3rd Rank Kabo. Finally, submarine P-59 (B-4) was commanded by Hero of the Soviet Union Captain of 3rd Rank Iosseliany.

From April 10th 1944, all four British submarines were officially recommissioned as Fighting Ships of the Soviet Navy. On getting quickly acquainted with the new machinery, the Russian submariners then prepared to sail for Polyarny. Submarine B-1 was the first to leave Lerwick, the others following. In the course of their voyage, the submarines repeatedly detected the presence of German U-boats from their torpedo firing. On August 6th, the last unit of the Submarine Group arrived in Polyarny. However, B-1 was missing, the one that had been first to put to sea. With her, the Russian Navy lost one of its best commanders and an excellent crew.

It is believed that boat was sunk in the Norwegian Sea by an Allied aircraft. According to an official report issued by the British Admiralty, the submarine was spotted 80 miles outside the boundaries of the recommended route. On seeing the plane, the submarine dived, contrary to instructions to maintain its position on the surface. Why B-1 failed to obey these instructions remains a mystery, but from the recollections of one of the veterans, Fisanovitch, there was a degree of distrust felt toward the Allies arising from some very strange telephone calls that had been received from Dundee just before B-1's departure, warning that a delayed action mine had been hidden inside the boat.

The 'English ladies' completed only a few war patrols before the end of the war, which was by then moving Westwards. They added two more victories to the battle score of the Northern Fleet Submarine Forces; one was a freighter of 542 tons and the other an enemy patrol ship of similar displacement. German U-boats, operating against Allied convoys to Russia, represented the greatest danger at that time in the Barents Sea. The Soviet Naval Command decided to employ these former British submarines to reinforce the anti-submarine defence of the main headquarters in the Kolsky Inlet as these boats were equipped with more advanced sonar and radar systems. They did not, however, manage to spot the enemy or increase their combat score. When the war came to an end, B-2, B-3 and B-4 were kept in the Soviet Navy for several years. Then, at the end of May 1949, the boats were decommissioned from the Soviet Navy and afterwards returned to the Royal Navy, where they soon sold for scrap.

Almost fifty years were to pass after the former Allies, once united in their struggle against fascism, became divided by the Iron Curtain. Their children and grandchildren were to carry out submarine patrol duties with missiles and torpedoes aimed at each other. But even under conditions of ideological confrontation, these submariners kept their tradition of brotherhood, united in their undertaking of dangerous missions in the oceans' depths that had become a grave for many of their shipmates.

The depth and strength of that brotherhood was manifest during the recent International Submariners' Convention in Brest, France (1999) and in Saint

Petersburg, Russia (2000). That bond was revealed to its full extent when they were in the prayers and thoughts when looking for ways of rescuing the crew trapped in the submarine Russian submarine KURSK and when British submariners went to the Barents Sea with help.

We mourn together our lost friends and believe that this hard and bitter lesson will be taken into consideration not only by the maritime community but also by political leaders of all countries in the world. The ocean is a hostile space, outside human control. That is why we must combine our good will and practical efforts to avoid, or minimise, the risk of any global disaster on or under the sea. We need to create an effective international maritime rescue system (including those trapped under the surface), and to develop legislation for the international control of strategic nuclear armament.

Through the centuries, the White Ensign more than once came to Russia's assistance when she was in difficulty. British submariners performed their duties with honour carrying their colours proudly. The memory of them will stay immortal in Russian hearts. Dear colleagues, please accept our sincerest respect and gratitude as we congratulate the Royal Navy and its Submarine Centennial Jubilee. Let us hope that from now on, nothing will disturb our friendship.

19

The French Submarine Service

Jean-Pierre Barbier

It is a great privilege for me to be invited to attend and to present a paper at the Royal Navy's Centennial Celebration Conference. I can also say on behalf of the Chief of Staff of the French Navy that it is a great honour for France, for the French Navy and for the French Submarine Forces to be invited to contribute this paper on today's French Submarine Service.

The British and French submarine forces have tied relationships and close links. We in France are happy with that and are looking forward to this process continuing in the future. The first operational French submarine went to sea one century ago as well as the Royal Navy's and I think that the development and implementation of the submarine has been a great asset for both nations and a tremendous adventure for our respective navies.

My aim in this chapter is to outline what the French Submarine Service is, how it is organised, and what it is used for.

The French Submarine Force is under the command of a 2 or 3 or 4-star admiral, called ALFOST (which is the equivalent of FOSM). The French submarine forces' Headquarters has experienced a recent move from its previous home at Houilles (near Paris), where it was located for 36 years, to its new home at Brest.

ALFOST has two kinds of commands, depending on the type of the submarines: attack submarine or strategic submarine. First, he exercises full command over the ballistic missile nuclear submarines (SSBNs); that is to say he is responsible for the administrative, or organic, command over them. This means that, firstly, he is to be responsible for the maintenance of the vessels, the training of the crews and their state of readiness; secondly, he is responsible for operations, that is to say the command and control of the SSBNs at sea. The Squadron of four SSBNs are home based in Brest.

Second, in the area of the attack submarines, ALFOST only exercises an administrative, or organic, command. The Squadron of six SSNs are home based in Toulon. The last SSK in the French Submarine Service is based in Brest and she will be decommissioned next year.

Where do we come from, where are we, where do we go? These are enduring questions! By selecting a 25 year time span to the present day, I shall demonstrate the recent evolution of the French Submarine Service.

The strategic component of the French Submarine Service has remained constant and stable. The number of SSBNs is directly linked to the country's strategic and political posture as laid down by the political leadership. From one SSBN at the very beginning in the late sixties, the size increased to a maximum of five, but in recent years has now remained stable at four SSBNs.

The type of submarine, however, has changed. From the 'Le Redoutable' Class we moved to an improved variant, the 'Inflexible' type, as a consequence of an extensive refit of 'Le Redoutable' Class boats. We then built a new generation of SSBN, with 'Le Triomphant' Class of SSBN. Now, two of each type are operational. At the end of the period, France will concentrate on having four 'Le Triomphant' type SSBNs.

The size of the submarine attack component has seen more significant changes as a consequence of a dramatic reduction of the number of the diesel submarines and the introduction of the SSNs. We have now stabilised the number of nuclear attack submarines at six, each of the 'Rubis' Class. That total number of six SSNs will be maintained in the future until the new SSNs that we are starting to develop to replace the 'Rubis' Class SSNs come into service.

The decrease of the numbers of hulls (around twenty per cent less) has obvious consequences for the total personnel in the French Submarine Service.

The strategy of deterrence remains at the heart of the French national defence policy. This also lies at the core of the strategic component of the Submarine Service. The French Navy, with its SSBNs, provides the main element of the nation's deterrence. The mission assigned to the SSBN component is that it must be able to operate permanently two SSBNs at sea, if necessary. Today, this mission is provided by a force that is limited in size, but it is also one that is able to respond at a level of sufficiency after a re-evaluation of the nuclear threshold has been completed. Therefore, its format has been established at four SSBNs, with all boats of the latest generation, by 2008.

ALFOST is at the cross-roads of two chains of command for the implementation of the strategic component. As an organic commander, he is under the orders of the Chief of Staff of the Navy. As an operational commander he is also under the orders of the Chief of Staff of the French Armed Forces. It is his responsibility to give the submarines the means with which to fulfil their mission. Only the President of the Republic, however, can order the SSBN to fire its missiles.

ALFOST has under his control two main communication stations, each dedicated primarily to the operational control of the SSBNs. For obvious national security reasons, it is not possible for me to say what France's SSBNs do at sea or where they operate. I only can say a few words about the crew of the SSBN's rotational tour of duty.

After the Assisted Maintenance Period (AMP), the SSBN carries out her patrol of nine or ten weeks and returns to Brest for a Docking and Associated Mainenance Period (DAMP). The SSBNs are operated by two crews, the blue one and the red one.

Turning attention, now, to the six SSN attack submarines based in Toulon. Here we find that they are manned by two crews on the basis of a cycle of periods of maintenance and then operations at sea. That cycle allows the French Navy to have at any one time three SSNs available for missions or deployment. This translates into about 200 days of availability at sea or ashore per SSN in any one year.

The SSNs are involved in three main missions dedicated by the political power to the French armed forces: war deterrence; conflict prevention; and power projection

In the field of nuclear deterrence, the front line vessel is the SSBN, as explained above. In this field, however, the SSN provides very high value support for the SSBN's deterrent role. She also helps the surface Navy improve its technical and tactical expertise in Anti-Submarine Warfare (ASW), in training the SSBNs to defend themselves against other submarines, and ultimately in supporting and defending them. The SSN is also a very valuable asset in sea control or sea denial roles. It is worth remembering that the sea belongs to nobody, but to whoever gets there first!

In the crisis prevention role, the SSNs are also valuable assets. They have the ability to be deployed quickly and to operate far away and for long periods of time. Their stealth and quietness make them the only asset able to operate undetected in many kinds of mission, such as discreet gathering of information and intelligence or putting special forces and agents ashore, and so on.

Last, but not least, power projection is one mission in which the SSN takes pride of place. Sea control, sea denial, harbour interdiction, anti submarine warfare, anti surface ship warfare, alone or in support of a surface task force, are what a SSN can do, and does well.

In conclusion, the French Submarine Service is built around two components of limited size; but they are safe and extremely efficient in their respective fields of action.

20

Canada and the RN Submarine Service: 1915-2000[1]

Peter T. Haydon

While the Canadian Navy cannot claim a full 100-year association with the submarine, the origins of the submarine branch of the Navy date back to the First World War. It has not, however, been a continuous association; rather, it has been sporadic, invariably contentious, and always politically charged. Also, as in most Canadian military undertakings, the submarine experience reflects the 'go British-go American' dichotomy. Because the focus of this volume is on the submarine in Royal Navy service, I shall keep to that side the Canadian story. However, to make sense of it all, I have to make some reference to the American excursions. Of the various peaks and valleys in the 85-year Canadian experience with submarines, the period after 1945 is the most active and by far the most controversial; so it is on that era that I shall concentrate.

The process by which Canada recently acquired the four 'Upholder' Class submarines was intensely political and unbelievably convoluted—unless, of course, you are a student of Canadian defence policy when it all seems fairly normal. You cannot begin to understand the 'Upholder' acquisition unless you understand the decision to buy and, eventually, modernise the three 'Oberons' which they replace. And you cannot understand that decision unless you understand the history of how the Royal Canadian Navy (RCN) sought to maintain submarine target services in Canada, once the joint ASW training facility in Bermuda and Digby, NS, was closed down after the Second World War. Into this messy historical pot we must throw in the five attempts by the Canadian Navy to gain political approval for nuclear-powered submarines as well as the story of the RN's Sixth Submarine Division in Halifax. In many ways, the story of Canada's various adventures with submarines is as much a story of the trials and tribulations of the Canadian fleet as a whole, as it is of the submarines. Nevertheless, it is not difficult to draw the submarine story together.

THE IMMEDIATE POST-WAR PERIOD

The story starts at the end of the Second World War when the politically orphaned RCN struggled to stay alive and operationally relevant in the midst of a post-war fervour to disarm. The admirals desperately wanted to avoid the experience of the 1920s when the Navy was reduced to a mere token force with little more to do than preserve Canadian territorial and political sovereignty at sea against American intrusions.[2] In 1945, as the politicians forged ahead with demobilisation and disarmament plans—believing, yet again, that the 'last' war had indeed been fought—the Canadian admirals made plans for a naval capability based on a carrier task group on each coast. The strategic rationale for this somewhat strange concept was a belief that a return to a form of Imperial defence was necessary, but with an acknowledgement that there might also be a need for UN expeditionary forces.

Within this concept was a belief that the antisubmarine warfare (ASW) skills learned during the Second World War need only be kept alive as a contingency capability to be provided by the Naval Reserve. Future naval engagements, the admirals maintained, would be surface actions much in the tradition of Canadian destroyer operations in the Channel during the War. However, they acknowledged that keeping the Naval Reserve ASW expertise alive would require the services of a training submarine from time to time. So, when it came time to return the Royal Navy's 'L' and 'U' Class submarines which had provided ASW target services in Canadian waters in 1944 and 1945, serious thought was given to keeping one of the submarines, HMS UNA, in Halifax. The idea was short-lived, and by November 1945 all the submarines had gone, leaving the RCN with the problem of solving its ASW training requirement.

The prevailing view of a post-war force structure in which the carrier, the cruiser, and the fleet destroyer were dominant and in which the submarine had little place other than as a training aid for the Naval Reserve would not last long. The politicians, essentially echoing Mackenzie King's long-held belief that a "good workable, little navy" was all that Canada needed, simply would not give the Navy the money or authorise the manpower necessary to maintain such a fleet. But the winds of political change were beginning to blow and would cause the Navy to rethink its basic philosophy and embrace an ASW role.

By October 1945, the US strategic planners had identified the Soviet Union as a potential adversary and by early 1946 they were championing the potential threat posed to allied security by their submarines.[3] These early American threat assessments were almost certainly inflated and were intended to generate the support of Congress in opposing naval disarmament. At the same time, the Americans were drawing the Canadians into a bilateral agreement for continental defence. Unlike their ever-sceptical political masters, the Canadian senior officers quickly embraced the new concept of strategic planning. Political support for the naval dimension of Cold War planning would come later—more as a function of preserving Canadian territorial sovereignty from American military intrusion than as a reflection of any particular concern over Russian military threats.[4]

By early 1947, the RCN had changed its philosophy, not without a little foot-dragging, and had acknowledged, first, that its primary mission in the future would be ASW and, second, that it would be done by the RCN and not by the Naval Reserve. Predictably, the need for a training submarine rose to the top of the Navy's priority list. Initially, the Naval Staff determined that one submarine would be needed for the whole year and, based on the short loan of HMS TOKEN in the autumn of 1946, proposed to the British Admiralty that the RN might provide the necessary submarine.

The Admiralty did not agree. Instead, the RCN was told that HMS ALLIANCE could be provided for two months in the autumn of 1947 and that Canada would have to pay the operating and maintenance costs. The offer was accepted grudgingly. HMS ALLIANCE became HMCS ARTEMIS and spent the autumn of 1947 operating out of Halifax. Playing both ends against the middle, the RCN convinced the US Navy to provide additional submarine services which it did without cost largely as a function of a new bilateral defence agreement. Nevertheless, it was quite obvious to all concerned that a better solution to the ASW training problem had to be found.

FINDING A BETTER SOLUTION

The RCN had never made a secret of the fact that, although the ideal solution was to form its own submarine branch, it simply did not have the experience. In this, arguments raised in 1942-43 surfaced again: politically, operational submarines would not sell; and 'de-fanged' training submarines were unlikely to attract many volunteers.[5] In 1948, manpower and money were further constraints. With this in mind, there was really no option but to go cap in hand to the RN and ask for help. The US Navy made it quite clear that it would continue with joint ASW exercises, but could not provide anything near the level of support sought by the Canadians.

The Admiralty reluctantly agreed to provide an operational submarine for six to eight months a year, provided that the Canadians paid all the running costs; paid an increment to the British crew to bring them up to a rate of pay equivalent to the RCN; and make a contribution to the submarine's maintenance. One of the problems was that the time spent in Halifax provided no opportunities for 'pro-submarine' training; as a consequence, those services were provided at an expense to the RN's overall operational readiness. Although, both parties agreed to continue this level of support, nobody found the short-term loan arrangement satisfactory, added to which the cost was rising and the return on the investment to the RCN needed to be examined.

Discussions on how to solve the problem went on and on inconclusively. By late 1950, though, two possible solutions had emerged: either the RCN would take over two 'U' Class with ideas of being self-sufficient in about five years; or the RCN would accept a longer term - 18 months - loan period for an RN-manned submarine to be completely funded by Canada. This latter option would have required that a British submarine be taken out of reserve, manned, and sent to Canada. As the Admiralty constantly reminded the RCN admirals, it was not possible to keep on simply providing operational submarines for ASW training.

The discussions dragged on without getting anywhere. Meanwhile the RCN, itself, was busy re-establishing itself for the Cold War and needed even more ASW training. In early 1952, the First Sea Lord, Admiral Sir Roderick McGrigor, visited Ottawa and put the RN case to the Canadian Naval Board. Pressed for manpower, and with increasing commitments, the RN was not going to lend Canada any more operational submarines. The period of procrastination was over, and the time had come to find another solution.

By autumn that year, the option for the RCN to borrow and man two 'U' Class submarines had been fleshed out. The RN agreed to train the necessary personnel and, even, to lend Canada the key people to get the program running. In fact, the RCN had already started to send a few officers to the UK for submarine training and, despite the possible availability of a few ex-RN personnel in Canada with submarine experience, the task of finding enough people was a key part of the program. That is what the admirals thought at the time but they had overlooked the political factors.

As the details of the plan were drawn-up, one of the interminable *ad hoc* committees by which the Naval Staff sought solutions to their many problems, determined that the RCN needed almost 1,000 submarine days a year for training and R&D. Obviously, two 'U' Class submarines were insufficient. Nevertheless, the reluctance to take to the first step to forming a submarine branch of the RCN and doing something about the problem was still much in evidence. The British response to the ensuing Canadian request for the loan of six RN manned submarines was entirely predictable, but they did say that the RN would continue to provide one submarine a year and would help with the training and development of a Canadian submarine branch.[6]

The time had then come for the Chief of the Naval Staff (CNS), Vice-Admiral 'Rollo' Mainguy, to pose the question to his political masters. Explaining that the loan and re-activation of two 'U' Class submarines, at a cost of around three quarters of a million pounds plus another million in annual personnel and operating expenses, would do much to resolve the RCN's ASW training problem, Mainguy recommended that the Minister of National Defence, Brooke Claxton, approve the plan. Predictably, Claxton baulked. In his reply to Mainguy, he asked whether or not NATO could provide submarine services, whether the Army and Air Force would agree to such a costly and high priority program, and whether the RCN could actually provide the necessary people without paying off surface ships. These were perfectly fair questions but they also indicated a political preference for not forming a Canadian submarine branch. Claxton also knew that the other two Services were generally opposed to the creation of a submarine branch.

After yet another round of high-level discussions, it was decided that Claxton would write to the British Minister of Defence, Lord Alexander, to clarify the concept. Although this seemed a blatant expression of distrust of the RCN's planning ability, it reflected the Canadian political dislike of changing defence policy in a way that might lead to public criticism: the Mackenzie King philosophy of a "good workable, little fleet" was still alive and well despite the demise of its creator. Though the politicians had reluctantly accepted aircraft carriers and submarines - especially operational submarines – they were not thought to be acceptable within that time-tested political philosophy.

After an exchange of correspondence between the two Ministers, Mainguy was duly sent to London where, in May 1954, he was able to reach a compromise. There would be no Canadian submarines. Instead, the RN would provide two more submarines, making a total of three, on eighteen-month deployments in Halifax for which the Canadians would pay the operating and one-third of the refit expenses, as well as provide two and a half submarine crews. The deal was accepted by the politicians and after nearly a year of fine-tuning, the Sixth Submarine Division was established in Halifax. The 'Heads of Agreement' as it became known raised many problems for both the RN and RCN in reaching concurrence. Among the more predictably contentious issues were:

- Control of the submarines in time of crisis or war. In the end, it was agreed that they would revert to RN control. (In fact, the October 1962 Cuban Missile Crisis was the only test of this provision);
- conditions of service. This was mainly concerned with how much of a pay increment RN personnel serving in Halifax would receive and whether they could bring their families;
- the level of technical support to be made available in Halifax, where the RCN tried to provide as little as possible and the RN get as much as possible; and
- how to administer, and admonish, RCN people serving in RN submarines.

The first draft of RCN personnel to undergo submarine training in the United Kingdom left Canada in November 1954. It consisted of two officers and 46 men ranging in rank from Chief Petty Officer to Able Seaman. They were joined later by another four officers and another 118 men in January 1955. In view of the potential difficulties integrating people of two very different navies, particularly where the RCN had gone to great lengths to create its own identity after the Second World War, the initial training and integration of the Canadians into RN submarines went remarkably well under the circumstances.[7]

On 19 February 1955, Commander W.T. J. Fox and a handful of other RN personnel arrived in Halifax to begin establishing the Division in preparation for the first of the submarines. HMS ASTUTE and HMS AMBUSH arrived that spring and were joined by HMS ALDERNEY later in the summer thereby starting a rotation that would last until 1966 when the RCN brought its own 'Oberon' Class submarines to Halifax.

Fox did a superb job in establishing an operating cycle that gave the RCN as much experience as possible while preserving enough time for the submarines to conduct pro-submarine exercises and do the very necessary maintenance. The value that the RCN got from these submarines was considerable. Not only did they have a qualified submarine planning staff to help schedule some of the more complex exercises, but with three operational submarines they could also do an enormous amount of training, including some basic familiarisation. That the RCN was able to run complex ASW operations was a huge boost to their training. The concept finally developed into the formation of a RN submarine squadron in Canada, and was clearly the right one at the time; on their own, and with smaller submarines, it is very doubtful whether the RCN would have progressed so far, so quickly.

Although squadron operations settled down quite quickly, it soon became apparent that the demanding operating schedule was exacting a heavy toll in terms of minor defects and additional maintenance time was needed to keep the submarines seaworthy. It also became obvious that the three submarines could not provide the number of days of ASW training the RCN originally hoped for. Rather than the anticipated 196 days a year (a 55 percent activity rate), the submarines were only able to provide between 165 and 180 days. Other than defects, two factors contributed to the drop in availability: longer time on passage to get to good operating areas; and the adverse weather that so often plagued the Western North Atlantic.

All things considered, it seemed for a while as if the RCN had found a workable solution to the ASW training problem. But as we all know, nothing about military planning and defence policy should ever be taken for granted.

IMPROVING THE SITUATION

Even though SM6 seemed to be working well, a number of other problems emerged, some immediate and some longer-term. In hindsight, it would be easy to accuse the RCN of creating some of these problems themselves.

Despite the relative strength of the bilateral continental defence structure, Canadian naval priorities in the early Cold War had a distinct Atlantic bias. The end of the Korean War, the Soviet detonation of a thermonuclear device in 1953, and the resulting shift in NATO strategy (promulgated in MC48 of November 1954) led to a re-appraisal of Canadian naval policy. One of the long-standing problems that had to be faced was that of ASW training for the West Coast fleet. The occasional training provided by US submarines was not enough; a better concept was needed. The Americans quickly made it clear that they could not help, and the suggestion that the RN provide a fourth submarine to be stationed on the West Coast was quickly rebuffed.

However, the option for the RCN to take over an older submarine, and man it, was left open. The same option was available for a US submarine. The American option was eventually taken and in 1961, HMCS GRILSE (formerly USS BURRFISH) was commissioned. An off-shoot of this process was that the Canadian submarine community became divided between those who supported the 'American way' and those who preferred the British approach. It went deeper than just the preference for equipment; it also manifested itself in training and operating concepts and would come to a head when setting up the First Canadian Submarine Squadron in 1966.

Another problem, entirely self-induced, was the 'on again, off again' love affair with nuclear-powered submarines. It all started with a study of ASW systems conducted by the Naval Staff in 1957 which concluded that submarines were the best ASW systems and that nuclear-powered submarines were better than any others at this task. In a heartbeat, the RCN technical community seized the initiative and started looking at the feasibility of building and operating nuclear submarines in Canada. Their study quickly acquired a high profile and involved the Americans because the 'staff solution' was the USS SKIPJACK. I would want to say that practical considerations were overlooked in the process, but the technical study paid little attention to such things as manning, communications, rescue, and interoperability. The operational plan was that SSNs would replace the ageing destroyers.

When presented to the Naval Board, the SSN study was received politely but somewhat sceptically; the cost of the proposal was just too high for the naval budget and the political climate was not right for the necessary funding increase. Anyway, the associated personnel problems were too great at the time to warrant serious consideration. Nevertheless, the concept was kept alive as a long-term consideration. More importantly, it was used as the catalyst for beginning the process of establishing a true Canadian submarine service. The concept of Canadian SSNs surfaced again briefly in 1961 with the ill-timed and unrealistic study of future force requirements undertaken by Rear-Admiral Jeffry Brock. It emerged yet again in 1964 and 1966 as the Navy struggled to create a politically acceptable force structure during the tumultuous years of the Hellyer reforms. And it would re-surface once more as part of the 1986-89 defence policy review.

It would be easy to categorise the RCN admirals as slow learners on the basis of their various 'affairs' with nuclear-powered submarines. Obviously, it was a concept that was doomed to failure politically, especially with the Liberal Party in power. The Tory *inter-regnum* of 1957-63 may have opened the window slightly but not really wide enough to let an SSN program through. However, what the 1957-63 window did provide was an opportunity to look at Canadian submarine requirements in general.

In June 1960, following the rejection of the SSN proposal, a committee was formed to look at 'conventional' submarine requirements. It established that the RCN needed nine submarines—six on the East Coast and three on the West—to meet all its training and operational requirements. The value of the ASW submarine was not questioned; rather, it was assumed to be a logical concept that Canada should adopt. The report contained an interesting comparison of British and American submarines and their respective suitability for the RCN. The conclusion was that if price was the dominant factor then the RCN should buy 'Oberon' Class submarines from Britain; if not, then the American 'Barbell' Class was more suitable because of system compatibility, especially if they were to be built in Canada. This was an interesting shift in thinking, reflecting the dominance of technical considerations rather than operational and personnel factors.

By August, a proposal was making its way through the political system recommending that six 'Barbell' Class submarines be built in Canada and that they replace six old, wartime surface escorts. Submarine requirements and the various options for meeting them were discussed in a series of meetings and exchanges of correspondence at the highest levels for the next 12 months. Eventually, in January 1962, consensus was reached that Canada should acquire nine submarines: three 'Oberons' as the first step in establishing a Canadian submarine service followed by six 'Barbell' Class, to be built in Canada, to provide the main component of the new service. However, this plan was dropped quickly following a powerful and damaging intervention by the Vice-Chairman of Defence Research Board stating that he thought building 'Barbells' made no political sense and would merely leave the government open to public criticism of spending money on obsolete equipment. All of a sudden, nine submarines became three 'Oberons', and the necessary negotiations with the British began. Two things had to be worked, the sale of three 'Oberons', and the extension of the SM6 Agreement until the 'Oberons' entered Canadian service.

In April 1963, the Tory government fell and was replaced by the Liberals who appointed Paul Hellyer as Minister of National Defence. It was as if all that had gone before was suddenly null and void. Hellyer demanded a rationalisation of virtually every military program in a determined effort to make significant cuts in the defence budget. After much further discussion, Hellyer agreed to support the submarine program, and in November 1963 made a public statement that the acquisition of three 'Oberons' would go forward "subject to satisfactory completion of negotiations with the British government". After lengthy and frequently frustrating talks, that apparently included *quid pro quos* for British spending in Canada an agreement was reached that covered the building and "Canadianisation" of three 'Oberons'. All that remained to be done was to work out a schedule for exchanging the SM6 submarines in Halifax for the 'Oberon's as they were accepted into Canadian service.

HMCS OJIBWA arrived in Halifax in February 1966, initially becoming part of SM6, replacing an RN submarine. She was followed by HMCS ONONDAGA in the summer of 1967, and HMCS OKANAGAN in late 1968. In July 1966, SM6 was closed down and replaced by the First Canadian Submarine Squadron under the command of Commander Ed Gigg. The last RN submarine, HMS ACHERON sailed for Britain on 3 May 1967. A lengthy chapter of Canadian submarine history thus came to an end. Some would say that it ended with a whimper rather than a bang as it indirectly acknowledged that the RCN's involvement with submarines would remain passive with the submarines providing training services rather than being ASW platforms as the admirals had once hoped. Once again, though, things would change.

GETTING BACK INTO THE ASW BUSINESS

When the Canadian 'Oberons' were built in the late-1960s they were already approaching obsolescence: the hull design and many of the systems dated back to the 1950s. But as training submarines—which was their intended function despite attempts by their officers to retain full operational proficiency—they were ideal. As far as the government was concerned they had been bought as training submarines and training submarines they would remain. It was acknowledged though that they had a defensive capability should the need arise, and thus had self-protection weapons and long-range surveillance sonar. But they were not considered effective ASW platforms; this would come later as a result of a major mid-life modernisation.

The fleet's overall ASW capability declined in the 1970s through a fatal combination of political indifference, tight budgets, and the inability of the Naval Staff to push shipbuilding programs to the forefront of the defence program. It therefore became increasingly difficult to meet SACLANT's force goals at a time when NATO was actually looking for a bigger commitment. Not surprisingly, Canada was quickly being seen as a weak link in NATO. Something had to be done.

A major fleet modernisation program was out of the question; in fact it would be another decade before any new ship entered service, and the replacement maritime patrol aircraft program was bogged down in a political morass. In the meantime, two stop-gap programs to improve fleet ASW capability were approved. One program, the Destroyer Life Extension (DELEX) Program, saw the command and control, long-range sonar, and electronic warfare capabilities of the destroyers upgraded so that the ship-helicopter ASW team was credible within a NATO formation. This was started in 1977 and continued until 1979. Under the other program, the Submarine Operational Update Program (SOUP) which ran from 1980 to 1985, the three 'Oberon's were upgraded and given a full ASW capability. A key point was that the programs were relatively inexpensive and thus would not require full political review.

The justification for the submarine modernisation was stated to be that the "Canadian 'O' Class submarines are now approaching that point where non-maintainability of their equipment plus a rapid increase in the threat, combine to dictate an urgent need for this operational update. The potential remaining life of this submarine class makes such a modernisation economically attractive."[8] From a political perspective this was a good thing to do because once the modernisation program was approved, the submarines could be offered to SACLANT as ASW assets to off-set the declining capability of the escorts and the maritime patrol aircraft. What it meant for the submarine community was that they were no longer just 'clockwork mice'.

Rolled into the modernisation program, but for obvious reasons not publicly stated, was a distinct change in Canadian naval policy. Building on some rather open-ended wording in the *1971 Defence White Paper* about the need to move to more versatile and multi-purpose naval forces rather than focusing on ASW, the rationale for Canadian submarines was changed.

> *Submarines make an effective contribution to the combat capabilities of a balanced maritime force because of their unique characteristics. In peacetime, as well as during periods of tension or conflict, deterrence is a very real requirement for the Canadian Forces. Due to their versatility, covertness, cost-effectiveness, and general purpose nature, submarines are most effective deterrence assets. They are particularly effective at Anti-Submarine Warfare, Anti-Surface Ship Warfare, Covert Surveillance, Intelligence Gathering, Special Operations and Mine-laying Operations. They also provide realistic training for other ASW forces.*[9]

Although only proposed formally to government in 1986 the program had existed within the Naval Staff for several years waiting for the right political moment. What is important about the replacement program is that it legitimised the modernisation program of the late-1970s by seeking to replace the 'Oberons' with the same sort of ASW submarine the government had roundly rejected in 1963.

Interestingly, the old numbers returned. Instead of just three submarines on the East Coast, the new plan called for twelve—seven on the East Coast and five on the West—as the minimum number needed to meet NATO and national operational requirements as well as provide training support. The intended tasks included operations in Arctic waters as well as in waters under NATO control and in the Gulf of Alaska. Although the initial replacement plan envisaged a fleet of diesel-electric submarines, the possibility of incorporating some form of air independent propulsion was included. Without specifically saying so, the door was also left open for a nuclear option.

THE NUCLEAR OPTION – AGAIN!

As long as the Liberal government of Pierre Elliott Trudeau remained in power, new submarines, let alone more submarines with greater capability, were out of the question. However, the election of Brian Mulroney's Conservatives in 1984 was seen as an opportunity to press ahead with the submarine program. The Tories had come into power with a pro-defence platform that had the 1983 Report of a Senate Committee as a framework upon which to build a new defence policy. Because the

Senate supported the acquisition of a new submarine fleet it made sense for the Naval Staff to table the 'Oberon' replacement program.[10]

Going back to square one, the new *Statement of Requirements* detailed the need for Canadian submarines for both training and ASW operations. The initial rationale was that they would be used in ASW operations, frequently as part of a sub-air team with an MPA, and as part of advanced surveillance screens. In this they were an integral part of Canada's NATO commitment. Although this tasking did not require a nuclear-powered submarine, it was clearly stated that nuclear-powered submarines had unlimited flexibility and were thus a better way of doing the job. Hence, the early concepts for the replacement submarines included longer-term requirements for an air-independent propulsion system as the means of increasing capability. Another important assumption was that only a full-size nuclear-powered submarine could operate freely in the Arctic.[11]

When Bob Coates had to resign as Minister of National Defence in early 1985 as a result of some 'inappropriate behaviour' while visiting the Army in Germany, he was succeeded by Eric Nielsen who continued the 'de-Liberalisation' of Canadian defence policy. In a briefing session on the capital program, Nielsen was introduced to the submarine replacement program. He quickly endorsed it; NATO wanted it and it made sense if one was attempting to build a balanced fleet along the lines suggested by the Senate in 1983. However, he observed that it might be worth looking again at the nuclear option, especially the smaller SSNs being built by the French—the 'Rubis' Class. This innocent remark—it was not political at that stage because Nielsen was not sufficiently well briefed to understand the deeper issues or to be able to make the link between Canadian-controlled SSNs and the Arctic sovereignty issues—set in motion a complete new study paralleling the naivety and false expectations of the earlier nuclear submarine studies.

Nicknamed the 'Nielsen Study', it was almost entirely comprised of technical staff none of whom had operational submarine experience. As with earlier studies, the engineers charged ahead with a feasibility study for acquiring six 'Rubis' Class submarines without really thinking about the operational aspects. Even though some work was done on patrol cycles and deployment areas (including to the North Pole) little was done about communications, manning, safety, or operational interoperability with the British and Americans. For some reason these were seen as secondary considerations to the technical feasibility. Here, the study team made exactly the same mistake as their predecessors: they failed to hoist in the fact that nuclear submarines required not only a comprehensive concept of operations but also a complete and very expensive infrastructure. However, by early 1987, some of these areas were beginning to be taken into consideration, albeit reluctantly as the real cost factors came to light and the financial realities of the concept came home to roost.

As a result of Nielsen's interjection in the submarine replacement program, which was probably misread by the Naval Staff, the whole concept of the submarine replacement program took on a new life. All of a sudden unfamiliar statements started to creep into defence documents. For instance, one document stated:

> *One of the most challenging tasks for the Commanding Officer of a Canadian submarine would be to conduct offensive operations in the vicinity of Soviet SSBN bastions or mining operations near ports such as Polyarnyy and Petropavlovsk. To carry out such missions, the Canadian Submarine would have to penetrate through the entire spectrum of the Soviet ASW threat.[12]*

To conduct the full spectrum of tasks envisaged by the new statement, which included anti-SSBN patrols, barrier operations, surveillance patrols, and special operations, it was estimated that 12 submarines would be needed. As Canadian submarines would operate in all three of Canada's oceans, the need for enhanced dived capability was established but without specifically mentioning nuclear power. This concept essentially put pay to any ideas of working with the USN within a co-operative framework and committed Canada to going it alone underwater. It was the most isolationist policy yet proposed and completely out of context with the years of Canada-US defence co-operation. It should not have been a surprise that the Americans did not greet the plan enthusiastically when finally made public in the *1987 Defence White Paper*. The Canadian insistence on the SSN program was hard to understand unless put in a political context; in brief, it had more to do with Arctic sovereignty than North American strategic ASW.

Information about the proposal to build nuclear-powered submarines was 'leaked' to the press and the defence community well in advance of the *1987 Defence White Paper*. The government was surprised by the vehemence of the opposition to the plan. Unlike the usual 'guns or social programs' argument, the plan provoked a veritable storm of criticism over the actual need for that capability and over the international signals going 'nuclear' would send. And it was not just the disarmament groups; the opposition came from a wide range of Canadians and played well to the traditional Canadian nuclear paranoia. The program was so controversial initially that even the most stalwart supporters had trouble explaining the rationale. The publication of the *White Paper* in the summer of 1987 only intensified the public debate. Meanwhile both the British and the French actively pursued the contract, offering the 'Trafalgar' and 'Ametheste' Class SSNs, respectively. The Americans did not enter the fray, but were obviously involved through the technology transfer implicit in the British proposition.

By 1988, however, the criticism had subsided, leaving the field to only a few determined opponents. A public opinion poll, if they are indeed reliable indicators, produced figures showing that the majority of Canadians were not opposed to the program. For a while it looked as if it would happen.

The cancellation of the SSN program in April 1989 for 'economic' reasons was a relief despite the outburst of anger at the time.[13] The various Canadian SSN programs have, unfortunately, been aberrations. A consensus exists on what comprises a realistic Canadian naval force— it has always been there in one form or another. It should be 'balanced' in terms of its capabilities but not overtly 'offensive', and it can contain a few submarines for training, surveillance, and defensive tasks. The SSNs obviously fell outside that consensus. In time, nuclear propulsion may again become fashionable and politically acceptable. But until an overall marine nuclear propulsion program can be implemented, any future notion of SSNs should be viewed with suspicion.

THE LONG ROAD TO THE 'UPHOLDERS'

With the nuclear option once again closed, the Naval Staff returned to a 'conventional' replacement programme and re-started the process of defining requirements, identifying the contenders, and waiting for the right political moment to re-submit the programme. The end of the Cold War brought with it another bout of the traditional, and short-lived, disarmament euphoria. The Gulf War and the realisation that the collapse of the Soviet hegemon brought with it a host of messy quests for self-determination soon made it evident that military and naval forces were still needed. In Canada, this quickly become political with extensive implications on force structures, with a marked preference for 'peacekeeping' missions. For the Navy, the eight destroyers originally traded off in the late 1980s for the SSNs vanished from the long-term plan. The fleet would be smaller in the post-Cold War era. The question was whether or not the submarines would survive the restructuring process.

A change of government in 1993 saw the return of Liberals and a promise to rationalise Canadian defence policy in the hope that the defence budget could be reduced significantly. A public defence policy review, spearheaded by a Special Joint Committee of Parliamentarians and Senators, was started in early 1994. The first salvo, fired by the Canada 21 Council, an *ad hoc* group of military minimalists, not only wanted to convert the Navy into glorified coast guard but, predictably, wanted to 'eliminate' the submarine capability altogether. Their grounds were that it, and the whole ASW capability, was entirely a function of the Cold War and no longer necessary or appropriate in the new world order.[14] The naval community, uniformed, retired, academic, and other supporters, quickly returned fire with a series of well-argued position papers, editorials, and public statements discrediting the Canada 21 Council's views. The public debate was on, and lasted some eight months during which the naval case steadily gained ground. Much to the delight of the naval community, the new Defence White Paper issued in November 1994 opted for an essentially *status quo* navy and, more importantly, endorsed the need to replace the ageing 'Oberons' with the following:

> The Special Joint Committee on Canada's Defence policy found that submarines could conduct underwater and surface surveillance of large portions of Canada's maritime areas of responsibility, require relatively small crews, can be operated for roughly a third of the cost of a modern frigate, and work well with other elements of the Canadian Forces. It also recommended that, if it should prove possible in the current environment of military downsizing around the world, to acquire three to six modern diesel-electric submarine on the basis that they were demonstrably cost-effective (i.e., that could be managed within the existing capital budget), then the Government should seriously consider such an initiative. The United Kingdom is seeking to sell four recently constructed conventional submarines of the 'Upholder' Class, preferably to a NATO partner. The Government intends to explore this option.[15]

This was a remarkable statement under the circumstances. Decried as a betrayal by the disarmers and a significant part of the print media but welcomed with relief by the naval community, the new policy made the point that Canada's maritime dimension had to be taken seriously and could not be idly dismissed. Unfortunately, White Papers are seldom binding commitments to a course of action: the submarine programme had further gauntlets to run.

It took a while to get going, but eventually the political system was prepared to look seriously at the 'Upholder' option. As so often happens, it required a return to square one and a re-justification of why Canada needed submarines. Despite the positive tone of the *White Paper*, political scepticism remained and many in government were convinced that the end of the Cold War had eliminated the need for 'offensive' capabilities such as ASW. The rationale presented in May 1995 was based on operational requirements for:

- surveillance of national waters;
- retaining an broadly-based underwater warfare capability within the collective security environment especially with the United States;
- training for both Canadian and allied forces, particularly those of the United States; and
- leverage with allies for intelligence and information sharing concerning submarines.

Without a lot of additional explanation, this was a tough sell, politically. However, when put into different words, the document began to make more sense. "Submarines have several distinct advantages of government policy, both nationally and internationally. They may be prepositioned in an area of interest. Overtly or covertly, they enjoy an unparalleled degree of freedom of action and independence. Finally they can be easily withdrawn without diplomatic cost or commitment."[16] What makes sense militarily, however, seldom makes political sense. Not surprisingly, the 'Upholder' option was off to a slow start.

Implementing the new defence policy, especially the submarine programme, would prove to be very difficult and as controversial as the policy process itself. By mid-1995, it was acknowledged that talks were being held with British authorities on how to strike an acceptable deal. Reports that a price of $800 million, that included some *quid pro quos* covering the use of Canadian bases for UK Army and Air Force training was bandied about. Also, there were reports of savings of some $200 million by getting rid of the 'Oberons' and switching to the newer and less-costly 'Upholders'. The Cabinet dithered on the package, obviously unable to reach consensus and troubled by the 'submarines or social programmes' campaign launched by the opponents of the plan. There were also reports that the British were about to close the window on the deal and offer the submarines to Portugal.

In short order, there was a public debate in the media on whether Canada actually needed submarines. "The economic and military argument for buying submarines now is unconvincing." the ever-sceptical *Globe and Mail* stated, and continued, "We cannot afford them and do not appear to need them - however attractive the price."[17] Rather than put pay to the matter, as the *Globe and Mail* may have hoped, the Editorial sparked an intense exchange from coast to coast that focused on operational rather than financial aspects of the programme. Navalists expounded the virtues and versatility of submarines while the disarmament community branded them as relics of the Cold War with no function in the 'new world order'. The debate continued through the autumn and into the winter and took on a new dimension as parliamentarians were lobbied by both sides. The Cabinet remained divided and indecisive, much to the frustration of all, including the UK Defence Liaison Staff in Ottawa.

Even with a Cabinet shuffle to bring in the new year, 1996, the submarine programme remained politically stalled and the media set a death watch. The *Globe and Mail* again attempted to bring closure to the issue by burying the submarine programme in favour of the more popular and less controversial search and rescue helicopter and armoured personnel carrier programmes. "Submarines," the paper opined, "for their part, have had their day. We no longer need them, and in the context of our military situation, we can no longer afford them."[18] Predictably, this brought about another wave of responses and fresh justifications from the naval community and, strangely, some glimmers of hope from an over-heated rumour mill that a deal was imminent. Yet, the programme remained stalled in Cabinet, but there was speculation that the Prime Minister himself was refusing to consider a submarine deal.

At the same time, the intensely controversial public enquiry into the Somalia Incident (in which a rag-tag Canadian Army unit, which should not have been let out of the country, killed two Somali civilians in March 1993 and was followed-up by an attempt to cover-up the incident) redirected and consumed the media's energies. As a result, public attention was drawn away from submarines and other defence acquisitions onto the Somalia scandal and the ensuing fiasco of the Enquiry.

By June 1997, at the end of the Enquiry and two Defence Ministers and two Chiefs of Defence Staff later, submarines were back on the agenda.[19] The problem with new Ministers, at least in a Canadian context, is that the staffs invariably have to go back to square one each time. This can also happen when a new Minister travels and is asked questions he or she cannot answer. The submarine programme was one such programme. When Doug Young, the new Minister, went to the United Kingdom at the beginning of 1997 the subject of the submarine acquisition was naturally raised. At the time, he apparently made the observation that "the Navy must be able to provide a compelling explanation of why Canada needs to maintain a submarine service."[20]

That explanation was quickly provided and the programme continued to move ahead at a snail's pace much to the continued frustration of all. The direct lobbying of parliamentarians and Senators continued but without much evident success. One small break-through occurred in February when the results of an opinion pole indicated that public support for replacing the 'Oberons' was strong - 68 percent in support versus 12 percent opposed. It began to look as if the 'submarines or social programmes' argument was indeed a charade engineered by the disarmament groups. This was still not enough to break the political log-jam.

Throughout all this the British government had not been able to sell the four 'Upholders' and so it was clearly in their best interests to attempt to come to some arrangement with the Canadian government. For the rest of the year a considerable number of people on both sides of the Atlantic and at many levels, some surprisingly high, worked very hard to find a package that would be acceptable to the Prime Minister, his advisors, and Cabinet. This also involved the Americans and the programme was discussed by the Permanent Joint Board on Defense (PJBD) whose minutes were delivered personally to the Prime Minister. By this time, the package was such that to decline the offer would have made Canada look unbelievably stupid. As the official announcement of 6 April, 1998 said:

> The project includes $610 million for the acquisition and $140 million for project-related costs. It includes the cost of crew training, simulators, spare parts, Canadian modifications, and project support. To maximise savings and value for Canadian taxpayers, the project involves an innovative eight-year, interest-free, lease-to-buy agreement in which Canada's lease payments will be 'bartered' for the ongoing use of Canadian training facilities by the British forces at Canadian Forces Bases Wainwright, Suffield, and Goose Bay.[21]

In the end, everybody's interests were served.

- The Navy had four replacement submarines for the obsolete 'Oberons' at a price that met the intent of the 1994 *Defence White Paper*.
- The acquisition was politically acceptable to the Liberal Party of Canada.
- The British were finally rid of the submarines and without facing problems of technology transfers that might have had American dimensions.
- The Americans were happy because they would have continued access to a diesel-electric target submarine for littoral operations and they also had access to a submarine that could operate in shallow waters in support of joint and combined operations.

That it took so long to accomplish was almost a function of Canadian politics. But for the entrenched dislike of submarines by many senior Liberals - people who essentially perpetuated the minimalist naval policy of William Lyon Mackenzie King and saw Canada in 'continental' rather than 'maritime' terms. That the governing Liberal Party was obsessed with public opinion did not help. They, as did many of their predecessors, believed that the media was a fair representation of public opinion when, in reality, the public debate on issues such as military procurement is held between elites and not the general public. Submarine acquisition thus forms an excellent case study of the near-Machiavellian machinations of Canadian defence policy.

CONCLUSION

The future promises to continue the high political profile 'enjoyed' by Canada's submarine community as there are several issues as yet unresolved. These can be summarised by a series of questions:

- Will political forces demand that women serve aboard Canadian submarines; submarines are, after all, the last bastion of the all-male military—other than Roman Catholic priesthood of course?
- Will the money be found to pursue the AIP option and thus give submarines a better under-ice capability? This, I suspect, will once again be a function of the level of political interest in the Arctic.
- Will the submarines survive another round of defence cuts? Without a strong base of public support, the new submarines will always be vulnerable unless they can be shown to give a better return on investment than other vessels.
- Will the Navy be able to 'man' the submarines in a climate where retention is low and morale fragile?

Looking back, what are the key points about the complex saga of the Canadian submarine branch? Clearly, the overarching fact is that submarines are politically contentious and the Navy has always had to struggle to keep them in the inventory. Roles have been changed, to the point at one stage of trying to sell the requirement for submarines on their ability to conduct fisheries patrols! Frankly, under a government obsessed with 'soft' power and Pearsonian peacekeeping, traditional naval capabilities, such as those inherent in submarines, are difficult to sell. Perhaps the Arctic will be political once more. This has invariably helped the naval cause, especially for submarines but not necessarily nuclear power. Unfortunately, one has to wonder how much longer that struggle to retain a Canadian submarine capability can be maintained. It is, as I said earlier, enormously vulnerable politically.

In all the comings and goings of the Canadian submarine branch over its 85-year history, and since 1945 in particular, the Royal Navy has been its mentor. Stern at times, particularly when Canadian admirals tried to get more than was realistic, and generous at other times, such as when the post-war RCN struggled to meet the international role set for it its political masters. I think Canada may have pushed the British tolerance and generosity to the limit over the 'Upholder' deal.

Perhaps, the 'Upholders' represent the maturing of a Canadian submarine service. Perhaps this is the point at which Britain lets the 'youngster' finally fend for itself! If so, it can only be hoped that the Canadian Navy can and will meet the challenges of the years ahead. In this, it will be the relationships with the politicians that ultimately determine the fate of the submarines. In this, though, gaining public support will be major factor.

The old Chinese adage about living in interesting times has certainly applied to Canada's experience with submarines, and I see no reason why this will change. The future will indeed be interesting.

NOTES

1   The documentary basis for this paper comes mainly from three archival collections. The first is the former RCN files on "UK Submarines" (PAC, RG24, Acc 83-84/167, Volumes 3923-25, File No. 8375-SS); the second is the Canadian Naval Staff files held by the Directorate of History and Heritage (DHH); and third the "Naval Program" files in the Raymont Collection (73/1223) also held by DHH.

2   See James Eayrs, *In Defence of Canada: From the Great War to the Great Depression* Toronto: University of Toronto Press, 1964 especially Chapters IV and VII, and G.N. Tucker, *The Naval Service of Canada* (Volume 1: Origins and Early Years) Ottawa: The King's Printer, 1952 Chapters 14 and 15.

3   Michael A. Palmer, *Origins of the Maritime Strategy: American Naval Strategy in the First Postwar Decade* Washington, DC: Naval Historical Centre, 1988, also various minutes and documents of the Canada-United States Permanent Joint Board on Defense (PJBD) - PAC, RG24, Vol. 8067, File NSTS 11270-15-1.

4   Although Churchill's "Iron Curtain" speech of March 1946 did not go unnoticed in Ottawa, the American assessment of the likelihood of a clash with the Russians was not generally supported. In fact, for much of the Cold War, Canadian and American political views on the Soviets and on communism generally differed.

5   Minutes of the 105th meeting of the Naval Staff on 13 July 1942. However, this did not preclude members of the RCN volunteering for service in RN submarines during the war. In fact, 22 Canadian officers served in RN submarines, two of whom rose to command: LCdr F.H. Sherwood and Lt. J.A Cross. For more information see, J. David Perkins, The *Canadian Submarine Service in Review* St. Catherine's: Vanwell, 2000.

6   The amount of background material on this subject is huge, much of it is well summarised in the background papers and minutes of a meeting in November 1953 between Rear-Admiral G. Bernard, Deputy Chief of Staff at the Admiralty, and the Canadian Naval Board. (Minutes of the Naval Board for 16 November 1953 and files in PAC, RG24, Acc 83-84/167, Vol. 3924, File 8375-SS (series)).

7   The RN continued to train men for Canadian submarines until the mid-1960s when a small school was established in Halifax. Officers were trained in England until the 1980s. A relatively small number of officers and men were also trained by the US Navy, primarily for service aboard HMCS GRILSE and her successor HMCS RAINBOW.

8   Statement of Requirement "Submarine Operational Update Program" of November 1977.

9   Statement of Requirement "Canadian Submarine Acquisition Project (M1837) December 1986, para 102.1.

10   The 1983 Report of the Senate Sub-Committee on "Canada's Maritime Defence" endorsed the value of the submarine in a modern navy and supported the view that Canada should maintain a submarine capability but specifically rejected the notion that Canada should build its own nuclear-powered submarines despite the changed strategic importance of the Arctic (p. 51). Yet, they strangely advocated that Canada attempt to work out a deal with an ally to either patrol the Arctic for us or let Canada have access to nuclear submarines to conduct Arctic patrols.

11   See Commander E.J.M. Young, "Submarines for the Canadian Maritime Forces" *Canadian Defence Quarterly*, Summer 1986, 25-36.

12   Statement of Requirements "Canadian Submarine Acquisition" Project (M1837) December 1986.

13   See William L. Dowdy, "The Canadian Navy: Torpedoed Again", *Armed Forces and Society* Vol. 16, No. 1, Fall 1989, 99-115.

14   The Canada 21 Council, *Canada 21: Canada and Common Security in the 21st Century* Toronto: Centre for International Relations, University of Toronto, 1994, 64.

15   Canada, National Defence. *1994 Defence White Paper* Ottawa: Minister of Supply and Services, 1994,47.

16   DND briefing note "The Upholder Option" of May 1995. Obtained through Access to Information.

17   *Globe and Mail* Editorial, 2 August, 1995.

18   *Globe and Mail* Editorial, 13 February, 1996.

19   The two Chiefs of the Defence Staff were essentially victims of the Enquiry as was David Collenette, the Defence Minister when the scandal broke. The other Minister, Doug Young, lost his seat in the 1997 federal election. This very brief note here is, in fact, far too simplistic for this enormously complex issue, but we do not have time to go into it in any more detail. The essence of the incident and the troubled Enquiry can be gained from two books: David Burcuson, *Significant Incident: Canada's Army, the Airborne, and the Murder in Somalia* Toronto: McClelland and Stewart, 1996 and Peter Desbarats, *Somalia Cover-Up: A Commissioner's Journal* Toronto: McClelland and Stewart, 1997.

20   Letter of 17 February 1997 (MARC: 11900-1(Comd)) from Rear-Admiral G.L. Garnett, Commander Maritime Command, to Vice-Admiral L.E. Murray, Acting Chief of the Defence Staff.

21   Department of National Defence News Release NR-98.018 of 6 April, 1998.

21

The Norwegian Submarine Service

Solveig Krey

HISTORY AND DEVELOPMENT

The Norwegian Submarine Service was established on the 28 November 1909, when HNoMS KOBBEN, Norways first submarine, was commissioned. The four first submarines were German and named 'A' Class.

An anecdote to how the very beginning of The Norwegian Air Force was founded shows that a submariner played the key role. The first officer on board KOBBEN, Lieutenant Dons, became the pilot on board the aircraft 'Start' and was the first Norwegian pilot to fly a Norwegian airplane. Dons went through a short basic training in Germany and he bought one aircraft from Berlin. He crossed the Oslofjord on the 1 June, 1912. So, a Norwegian submariner was the first pilot in Norway and this event was the foundation of 'Det Norske Flyvevæsen', the very first beginning of the Norwegian Air Force. Submariners have the will and the flexibility to take challenges and tasks and do something about it right away!

The 'B' Class submarines were built in Norway after WWI. These six submarines replaced the 'A' Class and were in service until 1940-1943. When Norway was invaded in 1940, both the 'A' and 'B' Class submarines were in service.

During WWII, the Norwegian submarines operated from England. The submarine B-1 was incorporated in the British 7th Submarine flotilla and stationed at Rothesay on the West coast of Scotland. She was used to educate Norwegian submarine crews. The British 'V' Class submarines were taken into the Norwegian submarine service during the war and the years after the war. They were given Norwegian names and were called the 'U' Class. The commanding officers and the crew members were Norwegian and they went through their basic training in England. The procedures on board were based on the British. The submarines played an important role during the war as they carried out offensive patrols off the Norwegian coast.

The submarine VENTURER (later UTSTEIN) carried out a most unusual and also successful attack. She torpedoed the submerged German submarine U 864 in the Fedje area North of Bergen in February 1945.

In February 1943, the submarine UREDD was going to make a landing with six men from the Norwegian Resistance south of Bodø in the northern part of Norway. She came from Lerwick (Shetland) and went through a German minefield in Fugløyfjord and was lost. In 1985, one of our minesweepers found the wreck and on the 13 of March 1986, the wreck was declared a war grave. The Norwegian Submarine Service took the initiative to look for UREDD. One monument is placed on land not far away from the area.

Another one is placed at Haakonsvern naval base in Bergen with the names of British and Norwegian crew members and men from the Norwegian Resistance 'Kompani Linge' inscribed on it. Each year Norwegian submariners remember what happened to UREDD and her crew at a memorial ceremony.

After the war, the Submarine Service returned to Bergen and Norway. From 1946 to 1954, the main base for the submarines was in Trondheim. Since 1954, the submarines have been based in Bergen.

In the sixties, a fleet renewal programme was carried out, partly financed by the USA, aiming to replace most of the WWII legacy with modern naval units. As a part of this programme 15 submarines of the 'Kobben' Class were acquired from German industry.

Already in the mid seventies, a new submarine programme was initiated intended to replace the 15 'Kobbens' with 12 modern submarines by the end of the eighties. Facing a possibility of having to half the submarine force, the Norwegian Authorities decided to procure six new submarines of the 'Ula' Class and to use the rest of the available funds to modernise six of the 'Kobben' Class. In addition, three 'Kobben' Class were modernised and sold to Denmark. Norway had a balanced submarine force of 12 boats at the beginning of the nineties. Norway's submarines have played an important role in the anti invasion scenario but after the end of the cold war, we do not focus so much on anti invasion any more. In the future, the submarines will probably be used more in surveillance and, hopefully, in international operations.

CURRENT STATUS

All submariners are on board voluntarily. This has been the case since 1909. The Submarine School at Haakonsvern Naval Base in Bergen educates and trains all the submariners. The first submarine attack trainer was purchased from Britain in 1946. Escape procedures are taught at the Diving School. We have good experiences with increased training in simulators. At the Submarine School there are attack trainers, a technical trainer and a steering trainer. This year it has been decided to reduce the total structure by two submarines. If enough funds cannot be made available in the future for a new submarine programme, the force could be further reduced. Over a 15-year period, the Norwegian submarine force can be in the situation to be reduced to less than half of its original size. Today six boats are under command, two 'Kobben' and four 'Ula' Class. From next August there will be no 'Kobben' Class under command.

The Norwegian submarines are all named after Norwegian lighthouses. They are conventional and constructed to operate in the northern part of Europe. The 'Ula' Class can conduct patrols up to 40 days. Normal operations last from one to three weeks. With the old 'Kobben' Class we operated close to the coast because of the sensors and torpedoes. But the modernised 'Kobben' and the new 'Ula' both received improved sensors and torpedoes. Torpedoes are fired at longer distances and we operate more in open waters further from the coast than before. Of course we practice both inshore operations and special operations. The 'Ula' Class with a towed array on board will improve the sensors further.

The 'Kobben' Class has a displacement of 572 tons and is 48 metres long. They have a crew of 21 members and are armed with 8 torpedoes (6 TP 613 and 2 Mk 37). They have been modernised from the original 'Kobben' Class.

The 'Ula' Class is 60 metres long and has a displacement of 1,150 tons. They are two compartment boats and have a crew of 21 members. The torpedoes are German DM2A3s and there are 14 on board. We have had problems with the flank array on board and have decided to replace it with a towed array.

25   The improved 'T' Class Submarine HMS TALENT (1945)

courtesy BAe Systems

26   The French Submarine RUBIS that laid 525 mines in WWII (1945)

courtesy BAe Systems

27   The 'A' Class Submarine HMS AMPHION (1945)

courtesy BAe Systems

28   Attack Teacher Training (1945)

courtesy RNSubMus

29   The 'Ex' Class HMS EXPLORER (1954)

courtesy BAe Systems

30   The 'Porpoise' Class Submarine HMS PORPOISE (SO1) (1956)

courtesy BAe Systems

The aim is that all submarines shall have a minimum of 1,800 hours at sea per year. The Norwegian Navy, however, has experienced problems keeping the submariners in the service and to man the positions in the submarine service ashore. It is a great challenge to keep both enough personnel and especially those with long experience on board. Reduced defence budgets are also a challenge concerning giving the submarines satisfactory time at sea.

Women can serve on board, it was opened up in 1985. On the 11 September 1995, Lieutenant Commander Solveig Krey became the first female Commanding Officer of a submarine in the world when she commissioned HNoMS KOBBEN.

OPERATIONS AND CO-OPERATION

The basis of Norway's submarine training, procedures and operations was made during WWII. It adopted the British approach and started with the Norwegian submarine HNoMS UREDD which was commissioned in 1941. Since then, for almost two thirds of the time, the Norwegian Navy has had submarines and has operated and trained their crews in a similar manner to the British.

Today, the Norwegian Navy trains and educates its commanding officers in Norway. Up to the 1990s, we had candidates at the British 'Perisher' Course. But when England ceased to operate conventional submarines, it was decided to educate all Norwegian submarine commanding officers in Norway. The Netherlands, United Kingdom and Norway today are co-operating with the Submarine Commanding Officer Qualifying Course (The 'Perisher' Course). They discuss how to improve their courses and how to make the most of their resources. Norway needs to look into the others' experience concerning the tactical use of towed array. Danish officers have taken part in the Norwegian 'Perisher' Course and an officer from the Netherlands has also graduated from it.

Watch officers from Denmark and Sweden use Norway's periscope trainer at the Norwegian Submarine School. Swedish officers also use the technical trainer for snorkelling procedures and when practising the steering console.

Norwegian submarines participate with at least one submarine in each JMC (Joint Maritime Course). The Submarine Service co-operate with British Defence Evaluation and Research Agency (DERA) concerning Stingray-firings and tests at the BUTEC range in Great Britain.

From 2001, Norwegian submariners will also participate in exercise FOST (Flag Officer Sea Training) which takes place in the Channel. Earlier they took part in these exercises, but they have not participated since the 1980s. This is a payment for British frigates taking part in the Norwegian "Perisher".

Norwegian submarines are now included in the STANAVFORLANT for shorter periods when they are operating in the seas of Northern Europe.

In 2000, for the first time, a Norwegian submarine was deployed to the Mediterranean to take part in an exercise. This was also to demonstrate that Norwegian submarines were able to operate in Southern waters during the wintertime. The main problem for Norwegian submarines operating in these temperate waters is the temperature: there is no air conditioning on board and the cooling system for the batteries is not good enough.

In 2000, a MOU (Memorandum of Understanding) was signed between the United Kingdom, France, Turkey and Norway concerning a NATO Submarine Rescue System.

Norway exercises with both Britain and Sweden on submarine rescue in addition to the exercises Sorbet Royal. Consequently, Norwegian crews are very familiar with the LR5 and the URF.

THE FUTURE

At a time where defence budgets are limited, it is difficult to maintain the necessary size, and improve the capabilities, of submarine forces for many of the smaller navies. This also applies to Norway. National developments in this area are very expensive and acquiring used submarines or existing designs could well prove to be unsatisfactory, especially with respect to unique requirements derived from new operating concepts.

The question is how the necessary size of the Norwegian submarine force can be maintained and how new capabilities can be acquired at the lowest possible cost, given the reduced defence budgets and the competition with other important defence assets. Results from a common feasibility study indicate that Denmark, Sweden and Norway can acquire affordable modern submarines through a joint procurement programme, based on a common set of requirements.

After two years of pre-feasibility studies, a permanent project group was established in 1997, called the Viking project group. It was tasked to carry out a feasibility study aimed at harmonising the national requirement for new submarines for Denmark, Sweden and Norway. Although the three nations are neighbours and historically closely related, there are marked differences in their respective national requirements. For example, their operating areas are very different, especially in respect of water depths and area coverage.

Their differences have been overcome, however, and almost all of the requirements have been harmonised. The most important agreement is probably the common diving depth that allows for the design of one pressure hull and hence one common base for a submarine concept. The only remaining significant differences are with the Norwegian's requirement for longer endurance and higher speed.

The 'Total Project Document' assumes four submarines for Denmark, two for Sweden and four for Norway. None of the nations has decided to procure new submarines. Based on the documentation forwarded after the feasibility study phase, the three nations will decide whether or not to continue to the project definition phase. A new important milestone for decision on further co-operation is in 2002, after a parliamentary agreement in Norway and Sweden on their future military force structures. The objective is to start production in 2005, after a corresponding settlement in Denmark.

Norway's future submarine force structure is under evaluation; whatever the outcome, submarines will remain important to Norway's defence and security.

22

The Origins and Development of the Indian Submarine Service, 1967 – Present Day

Raja Menon

We are an old country but a young state and that about describes our Navy too. The modern Indian Navy all started with a naval plans paper written in 1948, appropriately numbered ONE which aimed at a balanced force of two aircraft carriers, 12 destroyers, 14 frigates and eight submarines. The operational tasks of the new navy were as yet undefined, but the Commonwealth connections were strong. For those who remember the nature of Commonwealth tactical exercises in the 1950s, surface and anti-submarine warfare scenarios dominated. The maritime defence of India was a brand new subject in New Delhi, since this had always been the headache of the Flag Officer, C-in-C Far Eastern Fleet in Singapore during the days of Empire.

Not surprisingly, early Indian maritime thinking was obsessed with the 'SLOC preservation' theme, but our sea lines of communication (SLOCs) at the time were too small to substantiate a pro-naval argument. As a result, it was not difficult for a parsimonious government to knock submarines off the list when pruning the Indian Navy's wish list. There were other bigger factors waiting in the wings to act against the Navy. The first was the Kashmir problem, which focused the attention of the politicians on territorial integrity as being synonymous with national defence. The other was, of course, the war with China over the boundaries with Tibet. This war further reinforced the territorial preoccupation of New Delhi. Ministers were often heard saying in their constituencies that defence policy essentially meant that not one inch of India's soil would be surrendered.

With such a simplistic concept of national security, it was difficult to work in the idea of a submarine. Nevertheless, the Commonwealth connection came in useful after the Chinese invasion of 1962 when the first batch of officers and men were sent to HMS DOLPHIN to join the submarine basic course. I was in the second batch that went there in 1965. We had no submarines of our own to serve in, and all we had seen of submarines were the old 'A's and 'T's which came across to India once a year from Singapore for our 'pinging' practice.

The Indian government suggested that we would like to buy our first boats from the UK, but the yards were busy fulfilling orders for 'Oberons' from the Australian and Canadians and we were offered an 'A' Class submarine. The government refused and sent a delegation to the former Soviet Union, which, of course, offered anything within limits. This first transaction was the beginning of our long association with shipyards in Russia, Poland and the Ukraine. All this was not without its amusing side effects. I had become a regular watch-keeping officer in the old HMS TALENT and we were the clockwork mouse for fleet work-ups and took part in the odd NATO tactical exercise. My status suddenly became uncertain, but the commanding officer and I came to a sensible arrangement that, if we closed Soviet warships or trawlers, which we often did, I would change watches with someone else. On one occasion the exercise was called off owing to a large number of Soviet snoopers somewhere North of Ireland. A few years later, commanding my own boat and working up in the Baltic with Soviet instructors on board, we had to abort the exercise owing to severe NATO interference. I remember being amused at the time, and am still amused at the number of other mirror images we have witnessed in our time.

Our first impressions at the time of transition to the 'Foxtrots' was of superior engineering, but of rather uneven standards and indifferent electronics; but, most disturbing, was the absence of any concept of an action information organisation or system. This philosophical difference in the manner of handling tactical situations persists to this day. A hard core of eight executive and six technical officers trained in the UK were to guide the destinies of the new Submarine Service which came into being with the commissioning of the first boat at the end 1967. Those who did not get their command in the first commission got them two years later. Four boats were acquired in four years but we suddenly found that we had to man the staff, naval headquarters, training schools and dockyards. Memories of the first years are of endemic personnel shortages, except in the submarines which were terribly overcrowded as we tried to train enough submariners to cope with the shortages.

An early decision made by naval headquarters was to separate the Eastern stream of ships (as they were called) from the Western stream, for ease of maintenance and logistics. At about the time of commissioning of the first submarine we started building our first series of major war vessels, the 'Leanders', which were based on the West coast, while the Soviet acquisition ships were on the East Coast. It would be dishonest to say that the Navy did not undergo an ideological rift as a result. The Western school accused the Eastern ships of being powerfully armed but not knowing what was going on. The Eastern school countered this by saying that there was no point in knowing what was going on if one could not do anything about it, referring to the lower density of armament in the Western origin ships.

In the Submarine Service we found the Indian Ocean much easier than the Atlantic to work in. The seasonal layers were strong and often quite absurdly close to the surface. Young submarine commanding officers often demolished the fleet in tactical exercises but had to be careful to pull their punches in the battles of the debrief. Barely had the first four boats been acquired when the Bangladesh war was upon us, in 1971. Looking back at it from a purely submariner's point of view it was a perfect nightmare and the reasons I shall come to shortly. At the outset, the pioneers had decided to accept whatever was good in the Soviet system and graft it to what we had learnt in the UK.

So, we had the rigorous work up and inspection procedures of the Soviets with the British methods of submarine attack, tactical handling, squadron organisation, and base support. None of us had had any experience in politico-naval matters as yet. The oldest submarine officer was 35. We learnt that maintaining submarine presence off enemy shores, the declaration of exclusion zones, measures to prevent mutual interference, the Rules of Engagement in the Precautionary Stage and targeting instructions to commanding officers were serious politico-military subjects in which we were relatively inexperienced. As they say, however, one probably learns more from doing badly than from doing well.

As the first submarine officer to have undergone the Indian staff course and our first 'perisher', for which we made up the rules as went along, I remember sitting with a blank notebook having been ordered to write the first submarine operating and tactical instructions. One of the great lessons of our 1971 war was that it was impossible to use only four submarines and affect the strategic purpose of the war in any way; it was a lesson that did not go unnoticed by Gorschchov during his visit to Delhi in 1972. He quickly cut all the red tape. As a result, we acquired four more 'Foxtrots' in three years, some of us having to go back to Riga once again. Looking back on the number of years in Russia, perhaps the most challenging were those weeks spent in Leningrad at the Frunze Academy discussing tactical theory.

In the meanwhile, our decision to set up an entirely new naval base at Visakhapatnam on the East coast had fallen behind schedule and submarine refits had begun to pile up, partly aggravated by their bunched acquisition. It also became clear that if we wanted to become independent for submarine construction, as we had for surface ships, we needed a separate agreement with someone who would include a design as well as a technology transfer package. At this stage, most of our dockyard staff were terribly hesitant to work on the pressure hull. For this, we went on a world tender in 1977 and finally short-listed Kockums of Sweden and HDW of Germany to construct submarines in India. The contract was won by HDW under some circumstances that were to cause problems later. But I was satisfied ever since I had been sent across from a British submarine in Portland to a new German submarine being worked up by FOST to instruct them in the time bearing plot. I had come away staggered by the technical refinements they had built in and thought it the most impressive submarine I had visited in Europe at the time.

There were three teams that went to Germany. One was for the transfer of building technology, another for submarine design, which went to IKL in Lubeck, and the third was an overseeing and naval work-up group. I headed the technology transfer group, but in retrospect the programme that benefited the Navy the most was the design group at Lubeck. It was they who went on to establish the permanent submarine design team in Delhi. Most of us who spent those years in Germany came away with many permanent values on such things as quality assurance, quality control, industrial and workshop practices and industrial planning. Most of the submariners in senior positions were, by then, experienced and had some understanding of the different submarine cultures in the UK, the Soviet Union and Europe. The German experience, with the choice of equipment from anywhere in the world, and the challenges of interfacing them with other sensors and weapons was another benefit which now resides with the weapons, equipment and sensors electronic establishment in Delhi.

While the Service was being set up, a most interesting interface was the human interface, particularly two aspects of it. One was the response of naval personnel to the Submarine Service, and the other was the official career interface between submariners and the general service. The first, that is the attitude of naval personnel to the Submarine Service, has been indicated by the volunteer response. This has not entirely been financially motivated, as was first thought. There was also a substantial difference between having enough volunteers and having the best volunteers. It became clear that regular cadet entry career officers in the upper percentile would volunteer for the intangibles like career prospects, early command and glamour, but would only be put off by poor pay. The sailors who in the Indian Navy serve for a minimum period of 15 years would volunteer essentially for better pay, provided the end of service qualification equated well with job prospects in the civilian market. These were momentous discoveries distilled out of a decade of fiddling with personnel policies.

The question of absorbing submarine officers going over the top was initially an equally contentious issue. The qualifications for the top slot in the Navy runs through the criteria appointments of area command, fleet command, successful captain's command and a successful commander's command. The submarine service often released an officer into the general service after a submarine command to fend for himself and, in the early years, this resulted in avoidable casualties. It was 23 years after we started the Service that a submarine officer attained fleet command, and 27 years for a submariner Chief of the Naval Staff to take office.

But to get back to force levels; the German boats began to come into the service in the mid eighties and, being state-of-the-art, created a tactical impact immediately. To old time 'Foxtrot' submariners, it was a revelation that a submarine could be dived without yelling and screaming, but their greatest impact was their extraordinarily high availability and their designed resistance to the high corrosion of tropical waters. These boats were designed specifically for India and one of the unusual features has been the rescue sphere. This rests on top of the only pressure-tight bulkhead in the boat, has access from either side and is capable of taking out the entire crew. There were dissenting views in the Indian Navy about the wisdom of surrendering 27 tons of ballast and the penalty paid in carrying that weight through the life of the boat, but this is probably a controversy with no final answer.

The local building of the HDW boats set in motion a fresh offer from Russia for the 877 EKM otherwise known as the 'K' Class at substantially lower prices. The purchase of eight of these was meant to replace the 'Foxtrots', or 'Fs' that began to be decommissioned every two years. All 'Fs' are expected to be decommissioned by the year 2003. The manufacture of the HDW boats was stopped partly because the strong DM had raised the rupee prices to unaffordable levels and partly owing to some other controversies.

In the meanwhile, the country acquired on lease for three years from Russia, a nuclear submarine. There is, as is well known, sufficient literature in the media about the Indian nuclear submarine. Official sources have denied that such a project exists, but this is a stand that is unavoidable owing to the technology control regimes that do not always follow any predictable logic. India's nuclear energy programme is extremely broad-based and the production of a 190 mw submarine reactor should not pose a problem. Also, international regimes such as the Non-nuclear Proliferation Treaty (NPT) and Missile Technology Control Regime (MTCR) do not have any bearing on a country manufacturing its own nuclear powered submarine.

But the fact is that India has operated under some kind of a technology denial regime for two decades, ever since it exploded a nuclear device in 1974 and followed it up with tests in 1998. The nuclear submarine project has undoubtedly been hit by having to run it in a clandestine manner; but India is committed to the belief that in this century an ocean-going Navy without a nuclear submarine would be unable to affect even the internal military politics of a country, not to speak of the external dimension. This policy also naturally assumes that the country's nuclear deterrent will shift underwater, as have the arsenals of Britain and France. In that sense, I do not think any new variations of nuclear strategy have been discovered in India.

The country, the Navy and the Submarine Service benefited greatly from being open to Eastern and Western streams of technology, submarine building and the way in which submarines are manned and fought. But when I look back at the 31 years that the Indian Submarine Service has been in existence, there is the great excitement and nostalgia of being pioneers. But there is also the remembrance of the relative innocence with which officers in their thirties and forties were required to negotiate the future of the Service with the other institutions of government. I certainly remember the fight for submarine pay. It was one Lt. Cdr. and a Lt. versus the government of India, who wanted to know what pay the other navies received. We ourselves were surprised at the enormous variation between one navy and another, but we kept the UK figures out of the paper as they were the lowest at the time! However, the government asked for only the UK figures, and that was what we eventually got.

At the end of these thirty years, which is a short period, I do not know whether this qualifies us as the youngest Submarine Service. The impression that comes most to mind is the great disparity in literature between the tactical and strategic levels of operating submarines. At the tactical level, the standards of submarine training is rigorous everywhere. Indeed, the effort in terms of inspections and qualifications is probably the highest in any branch of the Navy. There is no shortage of material on how to train a submariner, a submarine or even a squadron of submarines. At this level, it is my observation, and I may be wrong, almost all literature dries up. How does one use or deploy not a submarine, or a squadron, but an entire submarine service? In other words, how does one wage a submarine campaign. Of course, there are some historical narratives, but they contain little analyses and certainly there is very little that has been written by the practitioner – like for instance Hezlett's excellent book.

23

Development and Roles of the Argentinean Submarine Service

Guillermo J. Montenegro

INTRODUCTION

The history of the Argentinean Submarine Service reveals that it has had only limited contact with its Royal Navy counterpart, in spite of strong ties that have existed between Britain and Argentina for more than a century and in spite of the fact that British yards, or the Royal Navy, were significant warship suppliers for the Argentinean Navy over the same period.[1] Furthermore, there were many instances of Argentinean Navy personnel attending a great number of training courses in the UK.

EARLY ATTEMPTS

The Argentinean Submarine Service came to life between the late 1920s and early 1930s. The oldest records of submarine projects, however, go back to 1811. In those days, Buenos Aires had revolted against Spanish rule and was being effectively harassed by Spanish naval forces sailing out of Montevideo who fought on the Loyalist side. An American, named Samuel William Taber, offered the Buenos Aires Government a project of a submarine with the intention of attacking Spanish men of war in Montevideo. Except for the project having been mentioned in Buenos Aires Goverment records, as well as an attempt to test the device, there are no further details on Taber's proposal.[2]

The Wars of South American Independence came to a successful conclusion in 1824. In spite of naval actions taking place during the foreign and civil wars that involved Argentina up to the late 1860s, there is no further trace of submarine projects.

A few years later, in early 1870s, tension was mounting between Chile and Argentina due to their countervailing claims to Patagonia. The bulk of this border dispute was solved by a Treaty between Chile and Argentina that was signed in 1881. Unfortunately, the wording of the Treaty left some issues open and tension between the two countries increased again in the early 1890s. This started an arms race in which the two Navies played a significant part. It was in this context that a submarine proposal was made by an engineer, Jorge Bolthauser, who submitted his ideas to the Argentine Navy in 1891. Nothing, however, came from the project and, again, there is no available data. Almost at the same time, another engineer, Teobaldo Ricaldoni, devised a second submarine project and a successful scale model was built. However, when the time came to build the actual submarine, financial constraints precluded it. In addition, it should be recognised that, in those days, submarines were regarded as little known, experimental, unsafe devices, even by the leading Naval Powers.

The dispute between Chile and Argentina was settled when both countries agreed to solve their differences and asked the British Crown in 1902 to arbitrate between them.

SOUTH AMERICAN SOUTHERN CONE NAVAL RIVALRIES[1]

A few years after the Chilean - Argentinean settlement, the Southern Cone countries were again to become involved in another naval arms race. In 1904, Brazil decided to start a significant naval expansion programme, which took final shape in 1906. This naval buildup included two 'Dreadnought' type battleships, two light cruisers and ten destroyers to be ordered from British yards.

Argentinean reactions to the Brazilian buildup were mixed. As usual, there were the 'hawks' - advocating a similar expansion for the Argentine Navy - and the 'doves' - who perceived no danger and saw no need to support the high cost of a naval build-up. After a long and heated debate, an Armaments Procurement Act was passed by the Argentine Congress in 1908. On the Naval side, the Act authorised the acquisition of two battleships, six destroyers and twelve torpedoboats. In fact, two battleships were ordered - to be built in American yards - as well as twelve destroyers - four from Britain, four from France and four from Germany. Chile followed her neighbours and, in 1910, ordered two 'Superdreadnoughts' and six destroyers from Britain.

Brazil and Peru led the way to submarine development in South America. The Brazilian Navy ordered its first three submarines from Italy, which were commissioned in 1913. Peru received two boats from France in 1912-13. These two countries, therefore, were the only ones to be operating submarines in South America at the outbreak of World War I.

The First World War was to have a significant influence on Chilean and Argentinean naval programmes. Argentina got her two battleships, but only four out of the twelve destroyers had been delivered before the outbreak of the War. Chile fared even worse. The two 'Superdreadonughts' still being built in Britain, and the six destroyers, were taken over by the Royal Navy. One of the battleships became HMS CANADA and was delivered to Chile at the War's end. The second 'Dreadnought' was converted into an aircraft carrier and commissioned in the Royal Navy as HMS EAGLE. Five of the six destroyers were finally commissioned in the Chilean Navy after the end of the War. As a compensation for HMS EAGLE, Britain transferred five submarines to Chile and a sixth boat was purchased by the Chilean Government. Thus, the Chilean Submarine Service became the third in South America.

Even when World War I was still in progress, Argentinean naval leaders became decidedly interested in submarines as a necessary new acquisition for the Navy. Intellectual support was given by the writings of several naval officers, of which *Intereses argentinos en el mar*, by Segundo R. Storni deserves special mention. In a Mahanian-inspired work, he dealt thoroughly with Argentinean maritime interests and the ways of protecting them. When defining the need for an Argentinean immediate naval expansion, he asked for six submarines.[3]

In spite of the appointment of a civilian as Navy Minister in late 1916 - an unusual development in those days – the Minister actively promoted the argument that submarines were an essential requirement for Argentina in his annual reports to Congress, because of war experience and also because "all the South American countries who have a Squadron" had submarines in commission.[4] On 12 August, 1918, the Executive sent to Congress a Naval Procurement Bill which, among other requirements, asked for funding for 20 submarines. Unfortunately for the Navy, this Bill was never enacted.

At the same time, consideration was given to train future submariners. In 1917, four lieutenants were sent to the U.S. Naval Submarine School, New London, in order to qualify for submarine duties.[5] After finishing their course, they served for several months on board US submarines. Again, in 1918, another group of three Argentinean lieutenants followed the same way.

THE FIRST SUBMARINES

The aforementioned interruption in the naval build-up that had been authorised under the Weapons Procurement Act of 1908 was a great frustration for Argentinean naval leaders. As previously stated, there had been an attempt to correct this state of affairs by way of the never-enacted Bill of 1918, but this only served to add to the sense of frustration.

In October 1922, a new elected government took office in Buenos Aires. The general perception among the Navy was that the Argentinean Navy was in a position of relative inferiority vis à vis the Brazilian and Chilean navies. As a matter of fact, there were mirror perceptions in Brazil, and Chile was experiencing an increase in tension in her relations with Peru, due to an unsolved territorial issue. Moreover, from the Argentinean viewpoint, there was news about planned Brazilian and Chilean naval expansion.

The newly appointed Navy Minister, Admiral Manuel Domecq García, ordered work on a study of Argentinean naval requirements, given the then Southern Cone situation. Garcia's study stated that, in future, the Argentinean Navy could only count on the most recent acquisitions, i.e. the battleships and the four German-built destroyers. An interesting consideration contained in this study is that it pointed out the likelihood that rival buildup predictions were going to be difficult. His argument was based on the financial instability of Southern Cone countries and because the bulk of the Southern Cone countries' economies rested almost exclusively on primary products, whose prices could experience significant variations from one year to the next.

This study identified three steps for a future naval buildup, which may be referred to as 'minimum', 'acceptable', and 'desirable'. These involved increases in numbers of units to be requested. First, six submarines of 750/900 tons surface displacement were considered the 'minimum' requirement. Building costs per ton were taken into account and British submarine building prices were used as one of the sources taken into account when reaching an average figure.[6] As may be imagined, financial realities led to the enactment and effective fulfillment of a naval programme not too dissimilar from a 'minimum' one.

Later on, in March, 1923 the Navy Minister appointed a Board to define staff requirements for the destroyers and submarines then under consideration for the Argentinean Navy. This Board delivered its Report in July, 1923. In the section on Submarines, the Report defined two basic types for the Argentinean Navy, a 'Medium' submarine of 550-680 tons and an 'Ocean' submarine of 800-1000 tons. An interesting feature of this Report, in the item headed 'habitability', it mentioned the Royal Navy Medical Corps as having recommended the need to look carefully after submarine crews' welfare, both at sea and in harbour. In addition, the Report defined Mar del Plata as the best location for the Argentinean submarine base. There was also a draft of the future Submarine Service organisation, as well as some hints about crew selection, extra pay, extra allowance for food, etc.[7]

The Argentinean Navy asked foreign yards for sketch designs and prices for several types of warships in 1924 in order to figure out the funds that would have to be asked from the Congress. There was considerable interest in the foreign yards that submitted projects for cruisers, destroyers and submarines. The four main British yards that answered the Argentinean's request for submarines were Armstrong, Vickers, Cammel Laird and Beardmore.[8]

The Naval Procurement Bill was sent to Congress in mid-1925. An explanatory introduction by the Executive underlined the submarine's cost-effectiveness for a minor naval power such as Argentina. In addition, it stated that the shore facilities in Mar del Plata - the prospective submarine base - were going to be kept to a minimum in order to ease the financial burden in the coming years. The Navy Minister sent also to the Legislature a rather extensive report, in which he depicted naval needs in detail. On the Submarine section, this report emphasised 'classic' submarines' advantages, including a special mention of their deterrent value. Typical submarine roles were also stated in this same report.

The Bill was enacted in late 1926,[9] after a long and heated debate. It authorised a considerable amount of money for those days, about £15,000,000, to be spent over ten years. In addition to improvements in shore facilities, ships authorised were three cruisers, six destroyers, six submarines and two surveying vessels. There was a considerable interest in foreign yards, which submitted tenders for cruisers, destroyers and submarines.

In November, 1926, the Navy Minister appointed another board designated as 'Comisión Preliminar' (Preliminary Board), to analyse and grade the information supplied by the builders. In January, 1927, this Board reported to the Navy Minister, favouring British yards for building the destroyers, but did not express any special preference in the case of the submarines.

On the submarine section the report emphasised that the choice should be based on existing submarine designs and built by well reputed yards in order to ensure their successful performance in the Argentinean Navy.[10] In February, 1927, the same Board submitted another report in which it insisted on procuring already built, proven submarine designs.[11]

As a result of the tender selection process, two cruisers were ordered from Italian yards, three destroyers from Britain, two existing destroyers from Spain - very similar in design to the destroyers ordered from the British yards - and three submarines from Italian shipbuilders.[13] These first submarines were named after Argentinean provinces each being given a name beginning with the letter 'S'. These were, the SANTA FE (S-1), SANTIAGO DEL ESTERO (S-2) and SALTA (S-3).

The arrival of the three submarines in Buenos Aires, on 7 April 1933, was a major occasion. The President himself attended the welcoming ceremony and even the former President, Alvear, who had served between 1922 and 1928, sent a letter to then retired Admiral Domecq García - his former Navy Minister - commenting on the submarines' maiden voyage from Italy. It read, "Results of these units' transit is highly satisfactory. This has underlined the crews' efficiency when handling sophisticated equipment, as well as good hardware performance, and the soundness of choosing this type of submarine".[14]

Later on, the submarines were sent to their assigned base in Mar del Plata - about 250 miles South of Buenos Aires - which still is the Submarine Service's home port. The submarines arrived in Mar del Plata on 3 September 1933, which is commemorated as the birth date of the Argentinean Submarine Service. Shore facilities in Mar del Plata, however, were scarce, so the old armoured cruiser, BELGRANO was used as depot ship until 1947.

Initially, submarine instruction and training was performed on board the depot ship, with first hand, on-the-job training on board the submarines. Later on, permanent shore facilites were built in Mar del Plata in the late 1940s, which also led to the establishment of a regular Submarine School.

EXPANSION ATTEMPTS

On 9 September 1941, the Argentinean Congress enacted a naval expansion programme which authorised the purchase of six submarines[14]. The reasons for this acquisition of submarines were again their cost-effectiveness and their deterrent value, as well as the planned replacement of the three boats already in service. The roles outlined for submarines were the 'classic' ones. As might have been expected, these were the early days of World War II, and there was no prospect at all of finding a suitable supplier. Post-war attemps to increase the number of Argentinean submarines in commission proved unsuccessful, so the original boats were the only operational ones right up to the mid-1950s.

THE AMERICAN INFLUENCE

'Salta' Class boats rendered 25 years of good service in the Argentinean Navy, but by the mid-1950s it was evident that their days were over. In additon to wear and tear over time, their sensors and fire control systems were decidedly outdated. This led to the decommissioning of the last unit of this Class in early 1959.

In the late 1950s and early 1960s, the US Navy exercised a strong influence over the South American navies and had a deep interest in enhacing their ASW readiness. This set of circumstances led to the transfer of Fleet type submarines to several South American navies, who were to perform primary duties as sonar targets. The Argentinean Navy received two American boats, which kept the names of the older ones but with a different hull number: they were named the SANTA FE (S-11) and SANTIAGO DEL ESTERO (S-12). These units rendered excellent service until 1971, when they were decommissioned. In spite of the ASW emphasis, Argentinean submariners managed to perform an extensive amount of training in other, 'proper', submarine operations.

Argentinean perceptions were that US Fleet-type submarines had a rather restricted combat capability. This was mainly because of their obsolescence and their limited torpedo stock. This led to Argentina drawing up plans to buy European submarines and/or build them in Argentina, but with European assistance.

It cannot be clearly ascertained whether or not the Argentinean attitude triggered it or whether, perhaps, it was just a coincidence, but a little after the first Argentinean contacts with prospective European builders, the U.S Government authorised the transfer of two 'Guppy' Class submarines to the Argentinean Navy. Both boats were commissioned in 1971. Financial and personnel availability issues then led to the aforementioned decommissioning of the Fleet type boats. Again, the 'Guppy' submarines kept the same names as their predecessors, but again with different hull numbers: SANTA FE (S-21) and SANTIAGO DEL ESTERO (S-22).

FURTHER DEVELOPMENTS IN LATE 1960S

In the late 1960s, the Argentinean Navy began to think over what could be the 'right' future submarine for their needs. It was then that the British 'Oberon' Class appeared to be the obvious choice. They were a proven design, - 28 of them had been or were being built for the Royal Navy, Canada and Australia - and surface and submerged performance appeared to be good, as were their sensors and weapons systems. As part of the preliminary deals, HMS OPPORTUNE was sent to Mar del Plata in 1967 in order to be evaluated by the Argentinean submariners. She gave an excellent impression, and the visit, which included several days at sea, was regarded as a success.[15]

Again, in early 1969, a British Task Group came to South America, and perfomed combined training operations with several regional navies, the Argentinean included. Two British submarines were part of the Task Group, HMS OTUS and HMS NARWHAL. They came to Mar del Plata, where they spent several days, and they had on board both in port and underway some Argentinean submariners, both as liaison officers and as observers.

In the meantime, among several offers for building surface ships and submarines for the Argentinean Navy, the German firm IKL submitted its 209 design, which was being built at the time for Greece and Turkey. After a careful examination of each individual project, the Argentinean naval leaders decided to order two type 42 destroyers from Britain and two 209 boats.

Both 209 submarines, which were named SALTA (S-31) and SAN LUIS (S-32), were built in Gemany in two sections and then shipped to Argentina. There, both sections of each individual ship were welded together and their systems connected. SALTA and SAN LUIS were commissioned in 1974. Of them, SALTA is still in service.

A little after the commissioning of the 209 boats, the Argentinean Navy began considering a replacement programme for surface vessels and submarines, taking into account that it was to be impractical to keep US-built destroyers and submarines in service after the mid 1980s. In the case of submarines, staff requirements called for an increase in range, weapons carrying capacity, and transit speed. The German project, TR-1700, duly fulfilled these staff requirements, and two boats were ordered from German yards. In addition, as part of the same deal, Thyssen Rheinstahl was commissioned to give support to the Argentinean Navy to build a submarine yard in Buenos Aires, in which it was programmed to build four additional TR-1700 submarines. The German-built boats were given the names SANTA CRUZ (S-41) and SAN JUAN (S-42). The first one was commissioned in 1984, and the second in 1985. They are all currently in service.[16]

The Buenos Aires yard was built, and the first submarine was laid down in 1983. Unfortunately for the Argentinean Navy, the new government that came to office in late 1983 regarded local submarine building a very low priority, and, after some years of hesitation, the project was abandoned.

CRISES AND CRISIS ESCALATION

In parallel with the aforementined replacement/expansion plans, there was a serious deterioration in Chilean-Argentinean relations after mid-1977, because of a dispute around the Beagle Channel/Cape Horn area followed by a period of sustained increasing tension from mid-1977 until late 1978. At the end of 1978, the crisis set in motion preventive deployments of military forces on boths sides. Argentinean submarines then in commission, SANTA FÉ (S-21), SANTIAGO DEL ESTERO (S-22), SALTA (S-31) and SAN LUIS (S-32), were part of the naval deployment in or close to the crisis area. Fortunately, Pope John Paul II offered to mediate between both parties, and his offer was accepted. After long negotiations, the issue was settled by Treaty in 1984.

The next crisis came in March, 1982, and, regrettably, it did escalate into war between Britain and Argentina. The crisis started in mid-March, 1982, because of an incident on South Georgia/Isla San Pedro in the South West Atlantic. After several crisis moves and countermoves, the Argentinean Government decided to land military forces on the East Falkland Islands/Isla Soledad. The landing took place on 2 April, 1982. The British Government reaction was swift: in addition to referring the case to the Security Council, it announced that a Task Force was going to be sent to the South Atlantic to retake the Falkland/Malvinas Islands by force if no settlement was reached before its arrival. The following events are a well known story. The British forces recaptured South Georgia/Isla San Pedro in late April, 1982, and on 1 May, 1982 they began military operations in the Falklands/Malvinas area. British forces succeeded in taking full control of the islands on 14 June, 1982.

War against Britain took the Argentinean Navy by surprise. Coincidentally, the most modern Argentinean vessels in commission were British built type 42 destroyers; one of them, SANTISIMA TRINIDAD, had in fact just returned from extensive trials in Britain in late 1981, and Meko 360 class destroyers - then being built in Germany - had as a special requirement that their propulsion plant was to be based on Rolls-Royce Olympus and Tyne turbines to give them common logistics with type 42 destroyers.

The Argentinean Submarine Service was no exception to this state of affairs. Two of the boats deployed in the late 1978 crisis were not available or had a limited perfomance: SANTIAGO DEL ESTERO (S-22) had been decommissioned as scheduled in late 1980, and SANTA FE (S-21) was approaching the end of her useful operational life (an overdue battery change was not regarded as cost-effective, because of her age and general condition). One of the 209 boats, the SALTA (S-31), developed a series of defects that precluded her operational deployment during the conflict.

In spite of her limitations, the SANTA FE took part in the Argentinean landing in East Falkland/Isla Soledad by carrying commandos who landed in the surroundings of Port Stanley in the early hours of 2 April, 1982. Later on, upon returning to Mar del Plata, the SANTA FE was ordered to carry supplies and specialist personnel to South Georgia/Isla San Pedro. She was able to get into Grytviken and land men and equipment, but she was succesfully attacked by British helicopters when leaving Grytviken. She was forced to return to harbour, where she was captured in a damaged condition and later sunk by the British.

SAN LUIS (S-32), the remaining 209 submarine, was deployed to the Falkands/Malvinas area. When in transit to her patrol area, she experienced a serious failure in her main fire control system, but she was ordered to carry on, in spite of this limitation. She conducted two sound bearings attacks on British surface ships in which she fired one wire guided torpedo against each. No evidence has been found to check the results of the first attack, but the second torpedo, launched after getting into a good fire control position, could have been a success, but for the target towed torpedo decoy.[17]

FINAL REMARKS

As the reader may know, Argentina's history along the Twentieth Century has revealed serious political and economic troubles from time to time: a World War in which she was not on the victor's side; strained relations with the leading hemispheric power from the mid 1940s until the late 1980s; a war with Britain in 1982; and periods of recurrent tension in Southern Cone relations.

As a part of the Nation, the Argentinean Navy has paralleled the ups and downs of Argentina during the century. As may be expected, the Submarine Service has been no exception. As a matter of fact, the Submarine Service came to light in times when the Argentinean Leadership perceived an adequate balance of Military Power in the Southern Cone - Naval Power included - as an essential capability for national security. This environment has significantly changed today.

Looking into the future, there is ample evidence that suggests that no expansion of the Argentinean Submarine Service can be predicted. The end of the Cold War, a significant improvement in relations among the Southern Cone countries, improvement in British-Argentinean relations, and tight budgets underline this argument.

However, the cost-effectiveness of the submarine as a weapon system, and its value as a deterrent will continue to be significant considerations when outlining the future Argentinean Navy. In addition, current realities show that an effective control of the Exclusive Economic Zone (EEZ) requires an assortment of platforms and vessels to face increasingly larger and increasingly sensor-sophisticated intruding fishing fleets. In short, power realities give cause for optimism for the future of the Argentinean Submarine Service.

NOTES

1 For instance, ten out of the ten destroyers commissioned in the Argentinean Navy in the interwar years were built in Britain (and the remaining two were Spanish built to a British design), the first Argentinean aircraft carrier was the ex-HMS WARRIOR, and the first guided missile desstoyers were RN type 42 ones.
2 Carranza, *Campañas Navales*, Vol 1, pp. 151-154.
3 Storni, *Intereses argentinos*, pp. 103-104.
4 *Memoria Anual del Ministerio de Marina 1916-17*. (Buenos Aires: Ministerio de Marina, 1917), pp. 17-18. South American navies who had submarines in those days were the Brazilian an the Peruvian ones. The Chilean Navy was on its way to acquiring its first submarines.
5 These were part of a batch of ten naval officers who were sent to the United States. Of the remaining six, three served on battleships and three went to the Naval Aviation.
6 *Estudio comparativo sobre Poder Naval Sud-Americano 1923*
7 Section "Submarines" of report dated 19 July, 1923 from the board appointed to define staff requirements for destroyers and submarines.
8 "Antecedentes sobre pedidos de precios - Año 1924".
9 Act Nr. 11378.
10 Informe N° 2 de la Comisión Preliminar, p. 29.
11 Informe N° 3 de la Comisión Preliminar, p. 9.
12 In addition, remaining funds authorised by the 1926 Naval Procurement Act allowed the building of seven RN 'G' Class destroyers for the Argentinean Navy in British yards, in mid-1930s.
13 Letter from Former President Alvear to his Navy Minister, dated 16 april, 1933, *Archivo Alvear 2.*, pp. 280-281.
14 Act Nr. 11290.
15 The author was liaison officer to HMS OPPORTUNE on that occasion. I sailed on board her from Mar del Plata to Buenos Aires, and served as a makeshift River Plate pilot, except for the actual entrance in Buenos Aires. I was even nicknamed the 'spare Jimmy'.
16 SANTA CRUZ is currently (September, 2000) undergoing a mid-life refit in Brazilian yards. SAN JUAN is scheduled for the same work in the coming years.
17 David Brown in *The Royal Navy and the Falklands War* (pp.155-157) depicts this event. He states that the target was HMS ARROW, in which the towed torpedo decoy was retrieved badly damaged.

24

The South African Navy's Submarine Service

Anthony N. Howell

INTRODUCTION

The majority of South Africans believe that their country's entry into the world of submarine operating Navies began in 1969 when the first 'Daphne' Class submarine was launched. Very few know of the false starts, which preceded this historic occasion.

As early as 20 September 1919, the British Colonial Secretary, Lord Milner, sent a telegram to the Governor–General of the Union of South Africa, Earl Buxton, offering for sale a number of vessels, including submarines, which had become available as the Royal Navy was being reduced after WWI. It was proposed that six to eight 'L' Class submarines be stationed in Simon's Town with fifty percent manned at any one time. Imperial officers and ratings would crew them and train RNVR (SA) personnel. Bureaucratic haggling seemed to follow and this all came to naught.

SOUTH AFRICAN SUBMARINERS IN WWI AND WWII

The South African Navy was officially founded on 1 April 1922 so did not participate as a Navy in WWI. However, three South Africans serving as officers in the Royal Navy and one in the Royal Naval Reserve lost their lives while serving in British submarines during that war.

WWII was a different matter with South African ships and personnel participating fully. South Africa did not have submarines, of course, but a total of 30 officers and ratings served as submariners with the Royal Navy.

Prior to April 1941, only Royal Naval personnel were permitted to serve in Royal Naval submarines. A seconded South African RNVR Officer, Lt A.H. MacCoy, was one of the first volunteers accepted and became the first South African Officer to command a submarine when he was appointed in command of HMS SEABORN and later HMS UNRUFFLED.

THE DECISION TO ACQUIRE SUBMARINES

In terms of the 1957 Simon's Town Agreement between the United Kingdom and the Union of South Africa, a modern South African Navy was to be created for the protection of the Cape Sea Route in conjunction with the Royal Navy.

In the mid 1960s the SA Navy consisted of two 'W' Class Destroyers with Wasp helicopters, three Type 12 Frigates, ten 'Ton' Class Minesweepers and two Boom Defence vessels. Efforts to acquire three submarines began in earnest. Some of the contenders at that stage were the USA, Britain, France and the Netherlands. It was reported in a UK newspaper that South Africa had ordered three 'Oberon' Class submarines at the cost of R26m. It is believed that a shipyard in the UK had even commenced construction at its own risk when the deal was stopped by the UK government.

Eventually an order to supply three 'Daphne' Class submarines was signed with France by the then South African Minister of Defence, Mr P.W. Botha, in April 1967. This was the first time in its history that the SA Navy had embarked on a project that was not under the wing of the Royal Navy. The Royal Navy continued to support the SA Navy at that stage. I personally spent two weeks training in HMS AMBUSH during exercises off the Cape of Good Hope in 1969.

Up to this stage, the SA Navy was very much an 'off-shoot' of the Royal Navy and shared most of the customs and traditions. The acquisition of French submarines brought a new culture into the Navy. Submariners even started eating their cheese before the sweets!

Construction of the submarines took place at the Dubigeon–Normandie shipyard in Nantes on the Loire River. On 18 March 1969, South Africa's first ever submarine was launched. The occasion was used to announce the three names: SAS MARIA VAN RIEBEECK, SAS EMILY HOBHOUSE and SAS JOHANNA VAN DER MERWE. These names were recently changed to SAS SPEAR, SAS UMKHONTO and SAS ASSEGAAI (the second and third also mean 'Spear' in Xhosa and Afrikaans, respectively). The 'EMILY', as she was then known, was launched on 24 October 1969 and the 'JOHANNA' on 21 July 1970.

The first crews were selected from volunteer serving naval personnel. Psychological tests had been developed by the National Institute for Personnel Research (NIPR) after a number of psychologists had joined a RN submarine for a two-week trip. These crews were divided into three groups and sent off to France to learn the 'black art' of submarining, all in a foreign language. The training was achieved in an incredibly short time and, after the normal standby build, trials and workup, the submarines returned to South Africa. The first arrived on 13 May 1971 and the last on 19 June 1972. The South African Navy then tackled the formidable task of building an operational submarine capability. A submarine base and refit facility was built from scratch, fortunately before the days of budget cuts.

OPERATIONAL HIGHLIGHTS

The brand new flotilla realised that they still had a lot to learn and set about their task with enthusiasm. Exercises were held with the surface fleet, Shackletons of 35 Squadron, as well as submarine versus submarine.

The first real test of skill came in 1973 when a large Royal Navy force, led by HMS TIGER and including the SSN, HMS DREADNOUGHT, exercised off the Cape for ten days. The small 'Daphne' Class submarines acquitted themselves exceptionally well. The local submariners had matured and become experts in their home waters.

At that stage the Royal Navy was using a tactic which meant that the submarine was effectively used as an independent VDS. She would transmit on her active sonar for a period and then run fast and silent before transmitting again. She became an exceptionally easy target for the small and very quiet 'Daphne'. I believe that this tactic was reconsidered after this exercise.

A second Task Group led by HMS BLAKE and including the SSN, HMS WARSPITE soon followed with similar results.

However political pressures were increasing; on 16 June 1975, the Simon's Town Agreement was cancelled and by the end of 1975, all opportunities of exercises with other Navies had disappeared, not to reappear until 1994, after the first democratic election in South Africa. Since then the submarines have exercised with many Navies and although they are now over 30 years old, they have done exceptionally well and have proved that they are still a force to reckon with.

During the years of isolation, the submarines warfare proficiency was kept at a high level exercising with its own forces, the three Type 12 ASW Frigates and the Shackleton LRMP aircraft. However, by the mid 80s, both had disappeared and the submarines were left on their own. The crews may have lost anti surface warfare skills but they have become expert in shallow water operations.

It was not only exercising opportunities that were lost, but also all training opportunities. All training, from basic courses to Officer Commanding level had to be locally developed. The first Submarine Officer Commanding Course (SMOC), based on the RN 'Perisher' and French course, was run in 1978. A total of nine courses have been run for 26 South African and 14 foreign candidates. Seventeen of the South African candidates were successful. When the latest course was run in 1998, we were fortunate enough to once again have foreign Navy participation in the form of a Nimrod LRMP, HMS CORNWALL and RFA OAKLEAF as well as a French Atlantique.

LOGISTICAL HIGHLIGHTS

It is one thing to own and 'drive' submarines but it is another to operate them in the full sense of the word. In other words to support them fully including refitting and modernising them.

Each of the three submarines has been refitted locally four times. The refits have taken a little longer than the French for two reasons: expertise is not as abundant and with only three submarines the refit duration has been adapted to ensure a constant workload on the dockyard. With a four-year operational cycle and a two-year refit cycle one submarine is always in dockyard hands.

The first victim of sanctions was the combat suite. Equipment not only became obsolete, but spares were also unobtainable. The Navy teamed up with local companies and an indigenous combat suite was developed. The second generation suite is now being fitted and should be at sea before the end of 2000. The shore ops room and control centre simulators have also been upgraded.

NEW SUBMARINES

In 1976, it was announced that South Africa would acquire two additional 'Agosta' Class submarines from France. Building commenced, standby teams and instructors were sent to France. The latter returned to South Africa and commenced training the crews for the new boats which even received names, SAS ASTRANT and SAS ADVENTUROUS. However, politics intervened once again and the sale was embargoed on 10 December 1977. The first of the two was launched four days later and they were later both sold to Pakistan.

The submarines were ageing and spares were becoming more and more difficult to obtain, even after sanctions were lifted. However the priority was still to regain a blue water surface combat capability.

The South African Navy has been planning for many years to replace the Type 12 Frigates. The Staff Requirement was written long before the last Frigate was taken out of service in 1986. The long term acquisition plan was to replace the Frigates by 1998 and the submarines by 2005. This meant that the submarine project would have to commence in 1998/99. At the RNBAEE in September 1995, it was suggested to Vice Admiral R.C. Simpson-Anderson, the Chief of the South African Navy that South Africa should consider the four 'Upholder' Class submarines which had become surplus to the Royal Navy's requirements. This seemed an excellent opportunity and a team was sent to inspect the boats. Although the 'Upholders' were not exactly what South Africa required, they are excellent submarines and it was too good an opportunity to miss.

They were much larger than the 'Daphnes', required more crew and a number of facilities such as synchro lifts and repair sheds would have had to be altered.

One thing led to another and to cut a long story short the 'Upholder' opportunity led to South Africa being offered a 'basket' of equipment from a number of countries which became known as the 'strategic packages'. Besides the 'Upholders', France and Spain offered the 'Scorpene', Sweden the A19 'Gotland', Italy the S1600 and Germany the Type 209-1400 Mod. Canada woke up to the real threat that they might lose the 'Upholders' to South Africa and committed to purchase them early in 1998. On 18 November 1998, the South African Cabinet approved the procurement of three Type 209-1400 Mod submarines from Germany along with four Patrol corvettes, maritime helicopters, light utility helicopters, fighter trainers and fighters.

Negotiations commenced and on 3 December 1999, the contracts were signed. On 12 July 2000, the first payment was made and the project has begun in earnest. Two 'Daphnes' will be kept operational; mainly to train crews, until the 209s arrive back in South Africa from mid 2005. New challenges lie ahead but at least South Africa's submarine capability is assured for the next 30 years.

WHY SUBMARINES?

I have just discussed our new submarine programme. I would like to conclude by giving the logic behind why the South African Navy has submarines at all and what their roles and tasks are. To place this in context, it is important to highlight the challenges and opportunities facing South Africa in the future.

First, it is critical for South Africa to operate to create a positive regional context - particularly in the eyes of the global investor community. We are a large African power, but in a relatively impoverished environment. Sub-Saharan Africa has a combined GNP of $300 billion - the same as Belgium. 43% of this figure comes from South Africa; 11% from Nigeria. But whereas Belgium's population is just 10 million, Sub-Sahara-African's 48 countries have a combined population of 600 million. We have a tremendous task to provide responsible, stabilising leadership in this context.

Second, we need to link up with like-minded partners, not just in our region, or to the North, but also among the bigger powers in the 'South' - such as Brazil, Argentina, India, Korea, Indonesia and Australia, all of which possess a submarine capability. Intra- and inter-regional partnerships are a stepping stone towards global participation and competitiveness.

Third and finally, in the light of these two points, we have also to be aware of our own socio-economic weaknesses and challenges, such as the need for poverty aleviation and the related challenge of skills creation and retention necessary for any modern (or modernising) society - particularly one so affected by the HIV-AIDS pandemic. One in five South Africans is today estimated to be affected by HIV.

With these challenges in mind, I believe that submarines make a small navy credible and that they form a crucial part of any well-balanced Navy. The SA Navy has built up a small but efficient submarine capability. With the 'Daphnes' coming to the end of their lives the decision had to be made as to whether to continue operating submarines or not. If the capability were lost, it would be extremely costly to restart, if at all possible. The decision to maintain the capability was based on the classic roles and tasks that submarines fulfil: anti-surface, anti-submarine, strategic surveillance or intelligence gathering and special operations. Primarily, however, they are the country's ultimate strategic deterrent.

South Africa has a coastline of some 3,000 km and a EEZ area of just under 2m km², including the area around Prince Edward and Marion Islands, some 1000 nautical miles to the South East. But it is not only this area that the South African Navy has to patrol or at least monitor. Our neighbours to the North of us, both West and East, also have large EEZs but very meagre naval resources. Our future lies in regional co-operation and for many years the South African Navy will have to take the lead. Three conventional submarines are hardly sufficient but they provide a core of expertise, which can be built on, if ever required, and a deterrent none the less.

PART V

SUBMARINE DESIGN, CONSTRUCTION & SUPPORT

25

Submarine Construction, Technology and the Future

Bill Oliver

SUBMARINE BUILDING AT BARROW

Most people will be familiar with the role that BAE SYSTEMS has played in the history of the submarine in the United Kingdom. The Barrow shipyard, operating previously under a variety of names (GEC Marconi Marine, VSEL, Vickers, Vickers Armstrong), has designed and constructed most of Her (or His) Majesty's submarines and has, of course, supported the creation of major platforms for the UK's nuclear deterrent. It has also built many submarines for countries across the world.

One hundred years on, it is interesting to note than the submarine is still an integral part of the Company's core business. The programme we are currently undertaking is the 'Astute' Class submarine project and, beyond that, we look forward to new underwater technologies and new ways of working with our customers, both in the UK and around the world. In a world where, sadly, overall marine engineering capabilities are perhaps shrinking, BAE SYSTEMS nevertheless remains committed to its interest in submarine design and construction.

THE PAST AS PROLOGUE

Earlier chapters have covered much ground historically in terms of the Royal Navy's Submarine Services and its record in peace and in war. The next few chapters, by contrast, will be looking to the future, to what BAE SYSTEMS and the submarine industrial base is doing today and tomorrow; to current and new technologies and to how these have emerged from the past.

It is in paying due respect to the Submarine Service's past that I have stolen a couple of apt quotes from a pamphlet I found on a visit to the Royal Navy's excellent Submarine Museum at Gosport.

> *"The submariner has created his own type of officer and man with a language and tradition apart from the rest of the Service"* .... *(Rudyard Kipling, 1915)*

And, probably, the most famous quote, and one that has been cited already by Commander Tall (above):

> *"Great deeds are done in the air and on the land; nevertheless, there is no part to be compared to your exploits*..... *(Winston Churchill, 1943)*

But, lastly,

"The crews of submarines captured should be treated as pirates and hanged".... (Admiral Sir Arthur Wilson, 1901)

Clearly, you cannot win them all!

The Company has been, and is, a special part of Britain's naval and shipbuilding heritage. We must build upon the considerable achievements of the last century to determine where the future will lie.

WHAT DOES THE FUTURE HOLD?

In terms of the Royal Navy, I would like to examine the current 'Astute' Class submarine programme and look beyond it for hints as to where submarine design and construction is going. What is different about 'Astute'? What are the things in design and construction terms that we are doing differently for 'Astute' from that which went before?

First of all, there is the customer. The Royal Navy's requirements are changing; clearly there is a change in the threat and, as has been outlined in previous chapters, the scope and theatre of operations of the Navy's boats will be different. There will be a greater range of weapons carried in today's and future submarines, in order to provide greater role flexibility.

The way in which the customer wants to do business is radically different. 'Smart Procurement' is a continuing initiative with which the contracting community has to come to terms. The phrase 'faster, better, cheaper' has been much quoted in this context.

It is also understood that contractors will have to work as part of a team with Customer One (The Royal Navy) and Customer Two (The Ministry of Defence Procurement Agency). The MOD has created, within its own operation, the concept of the Integrated Project Team (IPT). It wants to discharge a lot of the work and most of the responsibility for procurement programmes by engaging a prime contractor (along with the whole of the supply chain) in its effort to create more efficient defence products.

Another highly significant change is the desire to think about how the boat will be maintained, operated and supported throughout its service life, even before design has begun.

Very simply, when 'Astute' is compared with previous classes of nuclear powered submarine (SSN), innovation is the watchword. The boats have to be built cheaper and faster than ever before. In order to do that, all of the major contractors involved have to do some clever thinking. They have to think carefully about how and when to build these boats, what the build sequence will be, and how to break down the design into 'buildable' constituent parts.

To this end, it is necessary to modularise as much as possible in order to generate efficient production working. A vital tool in this enterprise is the 3D Computer Assisted Design Model, with full space/volume management capability, which is linked to an electronic database for the submarine. By these means, BAE SYSTEMS will manage the hugely complex data-sets that lie behind the design of the boat.

BEYOND 'ASTUTE'?

What lies beyond 'Astute'? At present, it is not yet clear how many 'Astute' Class boats there will be; but there is always the prospect of the future attack submarine (FASM) coming next in line. The size and shape of these submarines will of course be determined by technical requirements; but of equal importance will be the matter of unit cost and operating cost. The number of 'Astutes' and FASMs will be dependent upon the comparative cost of new build versus the operational cost of the Royal Navy's existing boats.

There are other things to consider, of course. There are many technological developments to take into account, of which the primary one must be the choice of propulsion system. 'Astute' is nuclear powered, but there are a lot of other considerations and options to be borne in mind. A more general question, and one which applies to all parts of the customer and supplier community, is the fundamental need to maintain our submarine industrial base to support these desired products.

Increasingly, contractors who are engaged on submarine design and construction have to have a full systems engineering and integration capability and not be just designers or builders. The industry has to work in partnership with the Ministry of Defence, in partnership with other contractors, and perhaps, in partnership with companies throughout Europe. The way in which the submarine business operates has changed, and will continue so to do.

THE CHALLENGE

In order to progress, we must define the challenge which lies ahead.

Ever aware of our industry's fascination with three-letter acronyms, I have extracted revenge by inventing one of my own. Summarising all that is described above, I would suggest that the theme underlying this part of the book should be 'AFT' (Affordability, Flexibility and Through-life Support).

The means by which we in the industry achieve all of these requirements will be derived from the new approaches and technologies that are detailed in subsequent chapters.

'AFT', then, is an encapsulation of the essential challenge that lies behind the theme of Submarine Construction, Technology and the Future.

26

The UK Submarine Industrial Base:
An Economics Perspective

Keith Hartley

INTRODUCTION

Much is known about submarines, but less is known about the submarine industry that designs, develops, builds, repairs and maintains them. The UK Submarine Industrial Base (SIB) is an unexplored part of the wider UK Defence Industrial Base (DIB). It provides a case study for assessing a series of policy issues of relevance both to the SIB and to the UK DIB. This chapter considers three issues: first, the problems and costs involved in retaining the UK SIB as an example of the challenges facing the wider UK DIB; second, the profitability of non-competitive defence contracts, where profits provide firms with inducements to remain in the industry. Until July 1994, UK nuclear submarine contracts were typically non-competitive (this changed with the 1994 competition between VSEL at Barrow in Furness and GEC-Marconi for the Batch 2 ,'Trafalgar' Class SSN); and third, the future prospects for both the UK DIB and the SIB with the rider; will a UK SIB survive the next twenty five years?

RETAINING THE UK DIB: A CASE STUDY OF THE UK SIB

Following the end of the Cold War, the UK DIB has been faced with gaps in both development and production work, together with small production quantities. Reductions in UK defence spending have resulted in the cancellation of new programmes, delays in existing projects, the 'stretching' of programmes, fewer new projects, and smaller orders for new equipment and for spares. These changes have impacted on UK defence industries resulting in job losses, plant closures, mergers, and exits from the industry.

The UK SIB illustrates these problems. From the late 1950s to the early 1990s, the UK SIB had an overlapping workload on nuclear and conventional submarines. Typically, during this period, production rates for UK submarines averaged about one-per-year. During the late 1970s and early 1980s, the UK SIB expanded to support the 'Trafalgar', 'Upholder' and 'Vanguard' programmes that for a period of time were running in parallel. Facilities and skills developed for the 'Trafalgar' programme were used and further developed on the 'Upholder' and 'Vanguard' programmes. The 'Trafalgar' Class of nuclear attack submarines (SSNs) started in the late 1970s and involved work on seven boats, all built by VSEL. Also, from the early 1980s to the late 1990s, the 'Vanguard' Class of four ballistic missile nuclear submarines (Trident SSBNs) provided further work for the UK SIB: they were also all built by VSEL (acquired by GEC in 1995). Similarly, over the period 1983 to 1993, the 'Upholder' Class of conventional submarines (SSKs) was built by VSEL (first of class) and its subsidiary, Cammell-Laird. For peaks in production, firms hired temporary workers and used sub-contractors for parts of the hull structure.[1]

The long-run trend has been towards a smaller UK submarine fleet. In 1945, the Royal Navy had a fleet of 142 submarines. By 1950, numbers had fallen to 61 boats and in 1956 at the time of Suez, the Royal Navy had a fleet of 47 submarines. During the Falklands War in 1982, there were 32 submarines (16+12 SSN + 4 SSBN); and in 1990, when the new UK defence policy, 'Options for Change', was announced, there were 32 submarines, but with a changed 'mix' of conventional and nuclear boats (11+17 SSN + 4 SSBN).[2] Following Options for Change, it was announced that, in addition to 'Trident', the UK planned to retain a submarine fleet of about 16 boats, of which 75% would be nuclear-powered. Orders for 'Upholder' were reduced from ten to four boats and, in 1993, it was announced that by 1995, the Navy's submarine force was to comprise 16 boats, all nuclear-powered. The 1998 Strategic Defence Review announced a further reduction to a total of 14 boats by 2006 (ie. 4 SSBNs and 10 SSNs).

In the early 1990s, UK submarine production rates were expected to stretch out to one submarine every 18 to 24 months. In fact, after the 'Trafalgar' Class of SSNs (7 boats) which started in the late 1970s, the next SSN is the 'Astute' Class (formerly Batch 2 'Trafalgar' Class or B2TC). Feasibility studies started in 1991 and the competition between GEC-Marconi and VSEL for the B2TC were held between July 1994 and June 1995. In 1995, GEC acquired VSEL and jointly operated VSEL and Yarrow as GEC-Marine. In December 1995, GEC-Marconi was selected as the preferred bidder for 'Astute' and after lengthy negotiations, the firm was awarded a prime contract in March 1997. The original in-service date was December 2001, but this was revised to June 2005. The 'Astute' contract is for three boats and support for a total of eight submarine years at an estimated total cost of £1961 million (1998/ 99 prices:).[3] There are options on a further two boats at a unit production cost of £508 million over the planned 5 boats.[4]

After 'Astute', the next SSN will be the Future Attack Submarine (FASM) scheduled to be ordered in 2008. As a result, the UK SIB is faced with an unprecedented gap in design and production work. There will be a gap of eight years between the end of detailed design work on 'Astute' and the start of detailed design work on FASM. Further complications might well arise if FASM is delayed by one year and possibly up to three years. What are the implications of these gaps in design and production work for the future of the UK SIB? Unlike other UK defence industries, there are no exports of nuclear submarines to provide work during 'troughs' in Royal Navy orders.

ISSUES FOR UK SIB

Gaps in design and production will have an impact on those skills and facilities that are unique to submarine design, construction and integration. An assessment of industrial impacts over the 'Astute' to FASM time-scale requires that the UK SIB be defined and identified. This creates an immediate problem since there are no published data on the UK SIB (e.g. via the Standard Industrial Classification and Census of Production). The following questions need to be addressed:

1   Which are the major suppliers at various levels in the supply chain? The original prime contractor for 'Astute' was GEC-Marconi (Marconi 'Astute' Class Ltd) with its main sub-contractors being GEC-Marine/VSEL at Barrow

(platform); Rolls-Royce Marine Power at Derby (nuclear propulsion); Strachan and Henshaw (weapon handling and discharge); Racal Radar Systems and Thomson Marconi Sonar (combat systems). Mergers and acquisitions have resulted in major changes in ownership. British Aerospace acquired GEC-Marconi to form BAE SYSTEMS; Strachan and Henshaw is part of the Weir Group; and Racal is part of Thomson-CSF Racal.

2 How has the UK SIB responded to any previous 'downsizing'?
3 Which are the key critical skills and facilities for nuclear submarines; and which skills and facilities are specific to submarine design, construction and integration?
4 How can these key skills and facilities be retained for FASM (including possible delays)? Can these key skills and facilities be retained by transfer to other work (e.g. surface warships; civil work); or can they be shut down and re-started in 2008 and at what cost and how quickly can they be re-started?

THE UK SIB

The submarine sector is part of the UK warship industry. Since 1975, this industry has experienced major changes in its size, structure, ownership and performance. The UK shipbuilding industry was nationalised in 1977 and the warship builders formed the warship building sector of British Shipbuilders (BS). Under state ownership, Barrow specialised in building both conventional and nuclear submarines. At this time, the major warship builders were Cammell-Laird, Swan Hunter, VSEL, Vosper Thornycroft and Yarrow. In early 1986, the warship building industry was privatised. Privatisation resulted in GEC acquiring Yarrow Shipbuilders of Glasgow in 1985. Vickers Shipbuilding and Engineering Ltd (VSEL) was privatised in 1986 after it had acquired Cammell-Laird (Birkenhead). At the time of privatisation, the remaining UK warship yards were Swan Hunter (Tyneside: a management buy-out) and Vosper Thornycroft (Southampton).

Since privatisation, there have been major changes following the end of the Cold War. VSEL ceased shipbuilding at the Birkenhead yard of Cammell-Laird; Swan Hunter exited the naval market following its losing the LPH contract to VSEL (HMS OCEAN); and in 1995, GEC acquired VSEL (after a take-over battle between British Aerospace and GEC). A further major change occurred in 1999 when British Aerospace acquired GEC-Marconi (Defence Division) which then became part of BAE SYSTEMS. In 2000, BAE SYSTEMS owned Marconi Marine (VSEL), Marconi Marine (YSL), Marconi Astute Class, Marconi Naval Systems and Underwater Weapons, as well as Kvaerner Govan on the Clyde (which was sub-contractor for VSEL for the hull work on HMS OCEAN).

By 2000, the remaining UK warship builder was Vosper Thornycroft at Southampton (with a planned relocation to Portsmouth in 2003). Thus, in 2000 there were two major UK warship building companies operating three yards at Barrow, Glasgow and Southampton. The Barrow yard is the only UK yard with a submarine-building facility and the only one capable of building large surface warships (e.g. aircraft carriers); Yarrow specialises in frigates; and Vosper Thornycroft has specialised in minesweepers, minehunters, corvettes and fast patrol boats.[5] In addition to the specialist warship builders, there are a number of UK commercial shipbuilders with the capability of constructing naval support ships and of participating in any move to the 'modular' construction of warships and submarines (e.g. Appledore Shipbuilders; Harland and Wolff).

The UK SIB has experienced similar major changes. Since the late 1950s, the UK has built and operated both conventional and nuclear submarines. There have been two classes of conventional submarines, namely, the 'Oberon' Class which were ordered and delivered over the period of the late 1950s to the early 1960s, followed by the 'Upholder' Class which were ordered over the period 1983-86 and delivered between 1990 and 1993. Conventional submarines were built by Cammell-Laird, Vickers Shipbuilding, HM Dockyard, Chatham, and at Scotts, Glasgow. The 'Upholder' Class was built by VSEL (first of class) with the remaining three boats built by Cammell-Laird (a subsidiary of VSEL).

The UK's experience with building the 'Upholder' Class of conventional submarines is an example of the costs, time and problems encountered by Cammell-Laird in re-entering submarine production after a gap of some 20 years. Cammell-Laird estimated that it could build each boat in 4 to 4.5 years: in the event, the time from contract award to delivery ranged from 5.5 to 6.3 years. Cammell-Laird experienced problems in recruiting experienced welders and this was reflected in a degradation of performance and quality. Overall, it has been concluded that Cammell-Laird achieved a successful submarine production programme that showed that conventional submarine production could be re-constituted after a gap of several years. However, this re-constitution required core knowledge and personnel with the necessary submarine expertise provided by VSEL [6]

In addition to conventional submarines, the UK has built and operated two types of nuclear submarines, namely, nuclear attack and ballistic submarines. All SSNs were built at VSEL, Barrow ('Dreadnought'; 'Valiant' and 'Churchill' Class; 'Swiftsure' Class; 'Trafalgar' Class; 'Astute' Class). Two classes of ballistic missile submarines have been built, namely, the 'Resolution' Class built from around 1964 to 1968 (Polaris missile:4 boats) and the 'Vanguard' Class (Trident missile: 4 boats) built between the early 1980s and the late 1990s. Work on the 'Resolution' Class was shared equally between Cammell-Laird and VSEL, whilst the 'Vanguard' Class were all built by VSEL.

The end of the Cold War resulted in major job losses at VSEL. By 1990, VSEL employed 13,000 people at Barrow on nuclear submarine work (out of a total labour force of 14,500 people), plus a further 2,500 people employed at Cammell-Laird on conventional submarines. In 1993, VSEL re-entered the surface warship market when it was awarded the LPH contract. By 1994, VSEL employment had fallen to some 5,800 people and the company had decided to end naval shipbuilding at Cammell-Laird.[7]

THE SIB: A UNIQUE UK DEFENCE INDUSTRIAL CAPABILITY

The UK SIB is unique in the following respects:
1   It specialises in one product, namely, nuclear submarines;
2   There is only one buyer of its product in the form of the UK Government (Royal Navy);
3   There is only one supplier (i.e. with a submarine building facility): BAE SYSTEMS Marconi Marine (formerly VSEL);
4   There are no exports of nuclear submarines: hence, the industry is a case study of the costs and problems which arise for a UK defence industry which is wholly dependent on domestic orders;
5   Small-scale orders. By 2000, the requirement for 'Astute' was three boats with options on two more boats;
6   Nuclear submarines are high technology equipment. Special skills are needed for their design and construction. Nuclear attack submarines are designed to operate under water at great depths for long periods; they have to operate quietly; they carry a range of weapons; and they have to provide a safe environment for the crew living close to a nuclear reactor;

7   The industry is characterised by major entry barriers resulting from the
    requirement for a nuclear site licence. Over the FASM time-scale, nuclear site
    licences are available at Barrow (which is licensed to install and commission
    the power plant); at Derby where Rolls-Royce Marine Power is licensed for
    the manufacture of the steam-raising plant (core factory and recovery plant);
    and at Devonport where Devonport Management (DML) Ltd has been
    designated the future sole refit and refuelling site for all Royal Navy nuclear-
    powered submarines (SSNs; SSBNs). Whilst Devonport is licensed to
    commission and refuel nuclear submarines, it is not equipped to build
    submarines (Rosyth also has a licence to refit nuclear submarines, but
    Devonport has been designated as the future sole refit and refuelling site for
    RN nuclear submarines). The requirement for nuclear submarines creates
    major barriers to entry, as well as constraints on competition and
    international collaboration;

8   The unique features of nuclear submarines require some 'key' skills. These
    comprise designers experienced on submarines; specialised teams needed for
    loading the reactor into the hull; nuclear design staff for the reactor; and the
    skills needed to retain the nuclear site licence for the core facility, construction
    and for re-fit (as required by the Nuclear Installations Inspectorate).

9   Nuclear submarines also require highly specialised facilities that have no
    alternative use (e.g. core factory; testing facilities);

10 Lengthy time-scales for development and production. 'Astute' was ordered in
    March 1997 and the first boat is due to enter service in June 2005 (over 8
    years). It can require 7-10 years to develop a new reactor and 18 -24 months
    for the assembly and production of each reactor.

11 A buy-British policy for nuclear submarines and warships. Traditionally, it
    has been Ministry of Defence policy to procure warships only from UK
    companies and this policy was confirmed with the decision to build the Royal
    Navy's new aircraft carriers in the UK.[8]

SOLUTIONS TO GAPS IN THE FASM TIME-SCALE

The gap in design, development and production work between 'Astute' and FASM
will create problems for the UK SIB in retaining its key submarine design skills, its
key nuclear skills and dedicated facilities and the necessary nuclear site licences.
Two responses are available: first, a market solution where firms are left to 'solve'
the problem on the basis of commercial criteria; and, second, state intervention
where the Ministry of Defence intervenes to 'solve' the problem.

Faced with an order gap, private profit-seeking firms will seek commercial
solutions to the problems of retaining key skills and facilities. Firms can transfer
resources to other work such as other defence or civil work within the company.
For BAE SYSTEMS, examples include work on Royal Navy surface warships (e.g.
frigates; Type 45 destroyers; aircraft carriers; Ro-Ro ferries); and staff at Rolls-Royce
Marine Power might be used on RR aero-engine work. Other possibilities include
the 'temporary loan' of nuclear staff to other nuclear firms (e.g. Devonport
Management Ltd, (DML); the Atomic Energy Authority (AEA); British Nuclear Fuels
Ltd (BNFL); university research departments); or, rather than retaining specialist
design skills 'in-house', such skills might be 'bought-in' from specialist design and
consultancy firms located in different parts of the UK or elsewhere (via computer
networks and links).

Nonetheless, there remains a core of staff and facilities that are highly specialised
and can be used *only* for submarine work. Their retention for the FASM project
requires Ministry of Defence (MoD) policy action. A 'do nothing' option by MoD

risks the loss of these core skills and facilities from the UK SIB and profit-conscious private firms with share-holders to accommodate might choose to exit the industry. This is not to suggest that the MoD should intervene to support the UK SIB: it simply highlights the risks and consequences of a 'do nothing' policy.

If MoD decides to intervene to support the UK SIB over the 'Astute'-FASM gap, it has a number of policy options, including:

1   Order another 1-2 'Astute' boats, with additional design inputs for modifications and upgrades, thereby providing work for submarine designers and for the nuclear reactor facility;
2   Ending the 'Astute' programme and bringing forward the FASM programme to start earlier than 2008;
3   Shut-down and opt-out of the nuclear submarine industry. Alternatively, it could shut-down and re-start for FASM. Following shutdown, the costs of re-start might exceed £300 million - and this is a lower-bound 'guesstimate'. The re-start time might be from two years to ten years, the longer time-scale for the nuclear expertise, always assuming that the nuclear site licences would be re-issued. A further option might be to evaluate critically the costs and benefits of lower safety requirements for the award of nuclear site licences;
4   Explore the conventional submarine option (e.g. via technology demonstrator programmes).

CONCLUSION ON UK SIB

The UK SIB is an example of a high technology UK defence industry with no exports of nuclear submarines. Current orders are for small quantities - three 'Astute' boats in late 2000 – that require an industrial infrastructure for design, development, construction and re-fit. Re-fit is required for the whole Royal Navy nuclear submarine fleet. Various industrial policy options are available to retain the UK SIB, but its retention is increasingly costly.

THE PROFITABILITY OF NON-COMPETITIVE UK DEFENCE CONTRACTS

Non-competitive contracts remain a significant component of all MoD contracts. They accounted for 25% by value of all MoD contracts in 1997/98 representing a sum of over £2 billion per year, with profits accounting for about 5-10% of the total price. The official reasons for using non-competitive contracts include a unique capability, a decision to stay with the original design team, no rights to compete, or as a matter of urgency, as in the outbreak of war. Non-competitive contracts have been used extensively in the procurement of nuclear submarines from VSEL, Barrow, Rolls-Royce Marine Power and future re-fitting and re-fuelling at DML. Profitability is also important as a determinant of firms' willingness to remain in the industry. Questions arise as to how profits are determined on non-competitive defence contracts and whether the existing profit rules need to be reformed.

Typically, competition for defence contracts is used to determine prices, including profits. However, if competition is not possible, some rules and guidelines are required to determine profits on non-competitive defence contracts. Current policy is based on the 1968 Agreement between Government and Industry. The background to the 1968 Agreement was two cases of 'excessive profits' on defence contracts that arose in the 1960s. On a SAM missile contract, Ferranti earned profits of 113% on capital against a Government target rate of 10%. At the time, the Government basic profit formula provided a rate of return of 7.5% on capital and the maximum profit rates on capital were 10% on riskless work (cost-plus) and 15% on risk work (fixed price). Moreover, before 1968, the MoD had no rights to examine a firm's costs once a fixed price had been agreed.[9]

THE 1968 AGREEMENT

The solution to the 1960s cases of excessive profits on defence contracts was the 1968 Agreement between Government and Industry. The features of the 1968 Agreement were:

1　Equality of information aimed at ensuring that both parties, the contractor and MoD were in the same position at the time of price-fixing;
2　Post-costing of individual contracts;
3　A new profit formula based on the comparability principle. It provided contractors with a 'fair' rate of return on capital defined as a rate of return equal on average to the return earned by British industry;
4　The creation of an Independent Contracts Review Board. This Board reviews the operation of the profit formula for non-competitive contracts in relation to the comparability principle; it recommends adjustment to the profit rates; and it reviews individual contracts to determine whether any refunds are required by either party for 'excessive profits' or 'excessive losses' (Review Board, 1999).[10]

THE CASE FOR REVIEWING THE 1968 AGREEMENT

By 2000, the 1968 Agreement was over 30 years old and its critics argued that it was time for change. They argued that: defence profit rates on non-competitive contracts were "too high" at a 22% return on capital on an historic cost basis in 1998/99; that the 1968 Agreement failed to provide contractors with sufficient efficiency incentives; and that Government non-competitive work was believed to be less risky than other work. Also, since 1968, there had been new developments in the financial economics literature and in the theory and practice of regulation, together with major changes in the UK defence market as a result of disarmament and changes in the size and structure of UK defence industries. A further criticism was that there was a "cosy relationship" between MoD, defence contractors and the Review Board in the light of the 'capture theory of regulation'.

A CRITIQUE OF THE 1968 AGREEMENT

There are at least five areas where the 1968 Agreement can be criticised:

1　A single formula approach is applied to all non-competitive contracts across all sectors of the UK economy. This raises questions about the selection of an appropriate Industry Reference Group for determining the target profit rate - for the application of the comparability principle. Until 1984, UK manufacturing industry was the appropriate Reference Group. Now a wider group of industrial and commercial companies is used, "operating in a fully competitive environment representing the alternative use value of capital if that capital were not deployed on non-competitive contracts.[11] Some sectors are excluded, for example, services; water; power. However, there is no single correct answer for selecting the appropriate Reference Group for comparability purposes. The diversity of alternative uses for defence contractors' resources suggests that the Review Board might provide both MoD and Industry with profitability figures for a range of different Industries rather than relying on a single Reference Group.

2   The increasing use of 'special arrangements' for 'exceptional cases. These accounted for one-third of contracts in 1997/98 and such a significant proportion of 'special arrangements' casts doubts on the continued validity of a single formula approach.

3   The treatment of risk. A limited rating of risk is used, based on a two point scale (1,0), with corresponding limits on the rewards for risk-taking. It is difficult to accept that all risk contracts have the same degree of risk and that it is not possible to introduce a scale of risk measurement. For example, all risk work is not identical; the first production contract for Eurofighter is likely to be much riskier than the tenth production contract for standard ammunition which has been in production for, say, 20 years.

4   The complexity of the profit formula. Under the 1968 Profit Formula, a target profit rate based on capital has to be converted into a rate of return on cost of production, which is then applied to estimated costs.

5   Refunds to MoD of excessive profits only arise where it can be shown that there was inequality of information at the price-fixing stage. Here, the evidence from post-costing between 1992 and 1996 showed achieved profit rates of between 15% and 143% on capital against a target rate of 18% to 19%. Refunds to the MoD between 1994 and 1996 totalled £4.9 million or 2.1% of contract value. For VSEL's submarine business, profits on sales in 1994 were some 15% against a target rate of 8% on cost.[12]

POLICY PROPOSALS

The 1968 Agreement can be modified in a variety of ways. Consider the following recommendations for change:

1   Adopt a cost of capital approach to determining the target profit rate. The cost of capital is widely used by the UK regulatory agencies and its adoption by MoD would bring the profit formula into line with policy and practice for the regulated industries (gas, electricity, rail, telecommunications and water). OFTEL might be regarded as the regulatory agency similar to the defence industry in terms of its technology. In 1997, OFTEL indicated a range for the pre-tax cost of capital for the BT Group of 9.2% to 13.4% in nominal terms and 6.1% to 8.8% in real terms, compared with a target rate of return on non-competitive defence contracts of some 21% on capital on an historic cost basis.

2   If the 1968 Profit Formula is retained, then introduce greater efficiency incentives into the Formula. This requires differential profit rates for differential risk the higher profit rates for higher risk; but there remain the problems of measuring risk.

3   New arrangements for profit sharing. The current arrangements for refunds of excessive profits to MoD following post-costing can be clarified and made more transparent. Under this proposal, an upper bound of profitability for refunds to MoD would be identified and refunds would be based on a sharing system to provide contractors with a continued efficiency incentive (similarly for excessive losses). For example, the upper band might be 1.5 times the current target profit rate and any profits above that amount would be shared, say, equally between MoD and the contractor. These arrangements would not require proof of inequality of information at the time of price-fixing.

4   Other possibilities might include a greater use of target cost incentive fee contracts; the use of outside experts to assess cost estimates submitted to the MoD; relate profit rates to cost of production rather than capital employed; and a greater use of competition in equipment procurement.

CONCLUSION: QUESTIONS FOR THE UK DIB

The defence economics problem cannot be ignored. Falling defence budgets and rising equipment costs, at some 10% per annum in real terms means that difficult defence choices cannot be avoided. Something has to go; the issue is, what goes? One option might be to abandon support for the UK DIB and import equipment ("cheaper, faster and better").

There are three questions for the UK DIB. First, can the UK afford to retain an independent industrial capability for a wide range of high technology air, land and sea systems; or, should the UK specialise in a limited industrial capability as for example keep air systems but abandon a UK SIB? Second, if the UK wishes to retain a national DIB, what are its benefits and how much extra is the country willing to pay for these benefits - an extra 10% or 20-25%? Third, does the future of the UK's defence industrial base lie with Europe? Or with the USA? Or both?

NOTES

1   HCP 369 *Royal Navy Submarines*, Defence Committee, House of Commons, London, HMSO, June. 1991.
2   Ibid.
3   HC613. *Ministry of Defence: Major Projects*, National Audit Office, London, The Stationery Office, London. 2000, pp. 68-71.
4   *ibid.*
5   Cmnd 2852 *The General Electric Company plc and VSEL plc: Report on a Proposed Merger*, Monopolies and Mergers Commission, London, HMSO, May. 1995.
6   Birkler J. et al. *The US Submarine Production Base: An Analysis of Cost, Schedule and Risk for Selected Force Structures*, Santa Monica. RAND, 1994.
7   Cmnd 2852, *op cit* 1995.
8   Cmnd 2852, *op cit* 1995, p 123.
9   See Martin Edmonds, "Government contracting in industry: some observations on the Ferranti and Bristol Siddeley Contracts" in D. Hague and B Smith (Eds) *The Dilemma of Accountability in Modern Government* London, Macmillan, 1971 pp. 129-47.
10   See, Martin Edmonds "Government Contracting and Renegotiation: A Comparative Analysis" *in Public Administration*, Spring 1972, pp 45-64,.
11   Review Board Report on the General Review of the Profit Formula for Non-Competitive Government Contracts, London, The Stationery Office, London. 1999.
12   Cmnd 2852, *op cit* 1995.

27

Submarine Design and Support : Future Developments

Harry Wyse

INTRODUCTION

This chapter will describe how BAE SYSTEMS 'Astute' Class Project provides support influence throughout the design, procurement and building phases of the submarine and how this impacts on through-life cost of ownership.

Our role in support is to achieve affordable cost of ownership. As we progress through the build process there is the requirement to give early indications, through metrics, of where we are going and predict what we expect to achieve. Furthermore, during the Contractor Logistics Support (CLS) period, we have to demonstrate what we have actually achieved against that which was predicted. During that CLS phase, we will support three 'Astute' Class SSN submarines for a total of eight boat years of operations.

This is achieved by employing Integrated Logistic Support (ILS) techniques. The approach is fully in accordance with Defence Standard 0060, but tailored specifically to the 'Astute' submarine.

By utilising Logistic Support Analysis we can concentrate on making sure that we get quick 'hits'. It is well known in industry that there are fairly straightforward targets in spares and maintenance reduction. During the design process we must show that we have properly prosecuted existing submarine class high cost drivers and have learnt, and drawn inspiration, even, from the past.

The sections of this paper cover our 'Astute' submarine programme – its specific objectives and benchmarking. Cost reduction is all very well; but it is also necessary to have a base line against which to measure progress. It is, therefore, necessary to demonstrate that future submarine support is cheaper - than what? In the case of 'Astute', BAE SYSTEMS has looked at the current Royal Navy submarine fleet from which a base-line has been established regarding maintenance and spares costs. This has not been done using anecdotal information, but hard data have been accumulated so that we can clearly demonstrate where we have been, and point to those areas where we are focusing our energy to achieve the best, and highest, return on investment. Of course, we are constructing a life-cycle cost model to predict the complete through-life cost of ownership from acquisition to disposal on all three 'Astute' submarines.

In the course of constructing and developing these cost models, we looked at the influence of support and design, and the planning and preparation for contractor logistic support. This, in itself, is a highly complex operation because we are undertaking CLS against an existing dynamic infrastructure whilst also trying to avoid duplication. The important thing is to learn from current practice and make sure that we are not standing still when faced with some of the current or potential future difficulties. This means that we have to identify those things we are good at - and perhaps what we are not so good at - in planning for in-service support.

SUPPORT OBJECTIVES

Our specific objectives concerning submarine support are to identify and resolve the high cost drivers. We then have to demonstrate that we can reduce maintenance costs. In the case of nuclear submarines, there is a real need to avoid, minimise, or at least substantially reduce docking requirements. If this can be achieved, it becomes possible to maximise underwater engineering. The requirement to undertake certain repairs whilst in dock is being looked at and analysed; and then we must design the submarine in such a way as to avoid them.

We need to optimise the supply chain where, of course, there are many initiatives being introduced at the moment. One such initiative is the so-called 'e-business'. We must also capture the opportunities being offered to improve the supply chain, for example, by using some of the techniques – such as 'Just in Time', - and Augmented Logistic Support. In all of this, we must at the same time identify what is best for the 'Astute' programme. We must demonstrate that the availability, reliability and maintainability (ARM) targets of the submarine have been achieved.

One of the biggest challenges is the introduction of electronic data management, which also includes electronic publications. We are obviously aiming for a paper-less submarine, but we well understand there are problems associated with that. Our American colleagues have adopted a 'read and rip' approach; we, however, will produce interactive electronic technical documentation, though it will still be necessary to have the ability to run off hard copies.

Finally, we need to target the cost of ownership and fully, and comprehensively, plan and implement Contractor Logistic Support (CLS).

BENCHMARKING

The point of departure in benchmarking was to recognise that the main source of information and data was at the waterfront. Accordingly, we set up a joint team comprising representatives from BAE SYSTEMS and the Defence Procurement Agency (DPA) who visited the waterfront and collected data and information from nominated submarines which were then entered on a database. What we were seeking to achieve here was the ability to identify all the costs associated with running a 'Trafalgar' Class submarine with a 'Vanguard' Class nuclear steam raising plant over the eight boat years that we need to support the 'Astute'. Our objective was to establish a baseline and demonstrate to the customer that we could, on the basis of those figures, reduce maintenance costs by at least ten percent and spares usage by at least five percent.

People say that this should be easy to achieve - by determining the baseline and channelling energy in the right direction. It is fine going for a 'Just in Time' approach, but recently we have identified just how vulnerable our industry is in the United Kingdom; for example, a farm tractor parked in front of an oil/petrol refinery, can cause the whole country to virtually grind to a halt. So, where was 'Just in Time' then – and where is it now? The lesson from that experience, and others, is that we must fully understand the risks involved and do everything possible to mitigate any incident. The source of vital information clearly was to be found at the waterfront; we have now completed the Benchmarking Programme and have already established the base line from which we are able to work.

What we found, as a result of collecting the relevant evidence and formulating the database, was a treasure-trove of information. Certainly, we have created a base line; but it has also given us an opportunity to establish the real cost of maintenance. We can now demonstrate that we understand the high cost drivers and can identify during the design phase how they are addressed.

Because we can clearly identify the high cost drivers, we can also identify candidates for Reliability Centred Maintenance (RCM) and focus on those areas that are critical to the continued operation of the submarine, undertake availability modelling and again demonstrate that we can achieve the submarine's availability and reliability targets. Other benchmarking data provides supply support scoping, covering the range and scale of spares.

LIFE-CYCLE COST

We have spent some time developing and populating a life-cycle cost model that fully replicates the life cycle of the 'Astute' submarine. From the model, it is evident that there is a major leap in costs at an early acquisition stage of the three 'Astute' submarine programme. Following through the life cycle model, it becomes clear that the submarine will still require a mid-commission overhaul period and two docking periods. During the creation of the model, we tried a number of ways to identify how we could optimise it, and identify whether or not it was necessary to rely on a mid-commission, long overhaul period (LOP) or, instead, sensibly spread a continuous maintenance approach over the life of the submarine. Rather than stockpile concessions and upgrades for the mid-commission long overhaul period, could we now properly manage maintenance throughout the life of the submarine?

Another challenge was to identify the high cost drivers throughout the life of the submarine. Not surprisingly, in the contract we had to design a submarine for an optimum-sized crew. Significant liquidated damages can be applied if ultimately the customer discovers that more crew are required to operate and maintain the submarine; this really did concentrate the mind. The long overhaul period (LOP) is a second major cost consideration, followed in descending order, by; Docking and Associated Maintenance Periods (DAMPS), spares, Associated Maintenance Periods (AMPs), Docking Periods (DP), and unscheduled docking. Again, these were identified so that we could focus our attention on each.

SUPPLY MANAGEMENT

There is a considerable amount of work in spares range scoping that has to be accomplished if we are to fully understand the range of components and spares that are currently used on 'Trafalgar' and 'Vanguard' Class submarines. More importantly, we need also to identify those parts and spares that have never been used, and to identify those components on which we have 'stubbed our toe' and were found to be in short supply or lacking. Extrapolating from these data, we can identify the range of scale and spares that we must have for the 'Astute' Class submarines.

However, when looked at, cunningly, the best way of providing spare parts for the submarine is to design for line replaceable units, rather than piece-meal parts, and components replacement, rather than rely on narrow band engineering, and a skills base to meet submarine availability targets. We are seeking to achieve easy maintainability using readily available spare parts. What we have already been able to demonstrate, during the 'Astute' design phases, is that we had a base line range of 42,037 spares in 1998. In 1999, this figure for the 'Astute's' spares range projection, based on predicted rationalisations against a two years data set, had been reduced to 38,000. We can confidently predict that by the end of 2001, this figure will have been further reduced to approximately 30,000.

Electronic data management presents a real challenge. We understand the difficulties and complexities associated with it, and we have had the normal amount of e-traffic within the Company that enable us to identify those data bases that will help solve our problems. What we are very anxious to do is to make sure that the system that we fit on 'Astute' will work first time, is 'user-friendly' and is good for the future. We do not wish to be involved in frequent technical up-grades just to keep ahead of software developments. We are now trying to identify the optimum system in the submarines; that they should be user-friendly is absolutely crucial. It is also absolutely essential on a submarine that these systems work first time, every time.

One of our tasks is to accumulate all the data necessary to show that the submarine has been put together in accordance with the 'as-built' datum pack that forms the foundation for any future submarine. However, those data arrive in different formats, so really what we are attempting to do is to come up with a system that can 'hoover-up' that data, whatever the format, and put it into one common data-base. The 'as-built' datum pack would encompass such items of data as: reports; generally word processed documents around the product breakdown structure; safety certificates; maintenance and repair data; live database registers linked directly to configuration management information; electronic 3D model digital drawings and photos; configurations that should be the fundamental basis of the product breakdown structure; quality data made up of archived records; and procedures in word processed form linked to the configuration of the submarine.

By using a Computer Aided Logistic Support (CALS) approach we can create the data once, but use it many times. The biggest worry in data management comes when one is confronted with commissioning and there is a problem for which there are several sources of conflicting information. We are well on top of this, and understand the problem.

We have been to the 'Vanguard' and 'Trafalgar' commissioning teams; we have learned the lessons of the past and have gone into the 'Astute' programme with our eyes wide open. We understand what we are trying to achieve in creating a 'paper-less' submarine. We are working closely with the customer to make sure that the system we provide will operate smoothly and effectively. When one looks at the young submariner of the future, I am sure he would be disappointed if he were to operate the submarine in accordance with a handbook. We are looking towards a 'Star-Trek'-type scenario where he can get information quickly and reliably on a wide screen, use hyper-text, and flip through the different sources of information quickly for both diagnostics and operation. This is where we are heading.

I have already mentioned the need for shared data environments. This is a complex issue, but we already have a wide area network (WAN) running between the Prime Contract Office (PCO) and our colleagues in the Ministry of Defence, the 'Astute' submarine integrated project team (IPT) and the supplier community. The main players are: BAE SYSTEMS Marine at Barrow; Rolls Royce at Derby and Bristol; the Prime Contract Office at Frimley; Strachan and Henshaw at Bristol; the Defence Procurement Agency at Abbeywood; and BAE SYSTEMS at Weymouth. This will extend to the HM Naval Base at Faslane, near Glasgow that will be the eventual home port for the 'Astute' Class submarines.

DESIGN INFLUENCE

As an ex-maintainer, I believe that computer-aided design (CAD) is probably the best submarine maintenance aid that we have ever come up with. With CAD you can look at the maintenance envelopes and removable corridors, and can identify those areas of the submarine that must remain sacrosanct for the purpose of work reduction and moving round the submarine, making sure that maintenance work is accessible and easy. If we achieve nothing else during the ILS programme, we will certainly make sure that the 'Astute' submarines are easy to maintain.

What we are doing, and this is somewhat unique to 'Astute', is to look at other major projects around the world. There is an ILS observation database where we identify the problems associated with support for the submarine. We populate the database, inform and advise the designers; and during design reviews we 'wire-brush' the designs if the designers do not appear to be taking support sufficiently into consideration. That is what we are doing and looking at: continuous improvement to identify and overcome all the problems of the past. As we head towards commissioning, we shall be able to demonstrate to the customer that we are indeed ahead of the game.

Of course, the necessary metrics are available from the observation database. Information can be provided any way it is wanted: pie charts; histograms; or whatever. But what we are really keen to do is demonstrate that we know where we are in the programme during design reviews, and that we have a clear view of what we are achieving.

CONTRACTOR LOGISTIC SUPPORT (CLS)

BAE SYSTYEMS as prime contractor needs first to plan and implement 'In-Service Support' to the three 'Astute' Class submarines over a period of eight years (representing four and a half years' elapsed time) starting after Contractor Sea Trials. We must retain and maintain the design authority, maintenance authority, supply authority and repair authority roles. Regarding design, the PCO must demonstrate the submarine meets the design intent; regarding maintenance, the PCO must plan and control all maintenance periods; as supply authority it must ensure that the right quantity and quality of spares are always available, in the right place at the right time; and finally, as repair authority, it has to make sure that when the submarine is in need of repair, the right procedures are readily available; the work will be undertaken by the RN base staff.

BAE SYSTEMS are obliged to make good any repairs during the Contractor Logistic Support Period (CLSP). The first thing to do, though, is to meet the reliability and availability targets and to get the submarine turned round quickly and back to sea. After this has been achieved, we can then sit down and decide whose problem it was. We therefore need to plan and execute all maintenance periods; this may seem simple, but we already have a submarine use study from the customer that points to a fundamental requirement to ensure that the maintenance that we perform on each submarine can actually be undertaken comfortably during the prescribed maintenance periods. For example, can we get enough numbers of people on the submarine to undertake the planned maintenance at any one time? We also need to achieve the contracted level of vessel readiness, and within the target cost.

The CLS business process model is one of the more complex aspects of the programme. We shall be supporting our 'Astute' submarine within an existing MOD infrastructure so we need therefore to understand how the different Agencies around the United Kingdom operate. To this end, we are working closely with our colleagues in the Clyde Naval Base looking towards the future and 'Astute'.

SUMMARY AND CONCLUSION

So what is new on the 'Astute' submarine? Clearly, we are designing for support and cost reduction. We are looking continually at 'supportability enhancement'. Some of the key areas we are particularly focusing on in this respect are underwater engineering, eliminating corrosion wherever that occurs, and planning for contractor logistic support. Some of the supportability and cost improvement initiatives on 'Astute' are:

- Our colleagues at Rolls Royce have developed a reactor that will last the full operational life of the submarine. This makes a tremendous reduction in cost and obviates the need for a nuclear refit.
- Supply chain management is another initiative. The oil and gas industry has made significant progress in Supply Control Management (SCM) by optimising spares and ensuring that spares are available when required. We are benchmarking what we are doing against what the oil industry has already achieved.
- We have undertaken Reliability Centred Maintenance (RCM) but not as it was done in ILS programmes of the past that carried out RCM on everything. We are using the results of benchmarking exercises to target those areas where we can profitably do the RCM with each candidate item taken from lessons learned from the past.
- Removal corridors and routes, and work-in-way are sacrosanct.
- We shall introduce electronic and technical documentation in a controlled way. The submariners will be trained in plenty of time to be able to use the new technology.
- Underwater engineering will be maximised.
- We do not want any hull cuts; but if a hull cut should prove necessary, we are already designating hull cut areas so that the work-in-way can be kept to an absolute minimum.
- Corrosion management is essential. A submarine in a sea water environment is vulnerable to corrosion and we understand the complications. We know where corrosion is most likely to occur and we are setting out to fix that during the design phase.

In conclusion, on the 'Astute' programme, BAE SYSTEMS is committed to predicting and identifying how we can reduce the cost of ownership. And it will be achieved.

28

New Approaches to Submarine Design and Construction

David Low

INTRODUCTION

The purpose of this chapter is to identify the design and construction challenges presented by the latest Royal Navy submarine programme, the 'Astute' Class. There are three principal factors that have to be addressed to meet this challenge:

1 increased functionality to meet the demands of the Royal Navy;
2 reduced man-hours to design and build the submarines;
3 reduced duration to deliver the overall programme.

This chapter attempts to quantify these factors and assess what their implications really mean for the BAE SYSTEMS Marine yard at Barrow-in-Furness.

STARTING POSITION

In order to 'bound' the challenge, it is necessary to compare the man-hours engaged in the construction of the last 'Trafalgar' Class submarine to be built in the Barrow yard with those sold forward for the 'Astute' Class submarines. The analysis shows that there is a requirement for an overall thirty percent reduction in man-hours for the first of class 'Astute' against the last in the class of five 'Trafalgar' submarines. The challenge is further increased with 'Astute' being a much larger vessel, approximately 25%, to meet the Royal Navy's functional requirements. Furthermore, in terms of the over-all programme, 'Astute' is required to be designed and built in a period that is two years shorter than has ever been achieved before. This is a daunting challenge by any standard.

NEW APPROACHES

What, therefore, are the approaches that we are taking forward to achieve these savings? BAE SYSTEMS Marine has had to look very closely at the build strategy, from which a number of initiatives have been adopted. The Yard cannot deliver the build strategy, however, unless it 'designs-for-build'. It is very important that we move forward with a design concept to support whatever the build strategy demands.

Historically, we have seen programmes where the design has been undertaken separately from the build. The designer has designed the submarine and then says, "here you are, go and build it". That, of course, is a recipe for disaster which will never achieve the same level of efficiency as 'concurrent design'.

To facilitate 'concurrent design', we need a different tool-set. Today, we have within BAE SYSTEMS Marine an integrated data environment that facilitates the delivery of the design information to multiple users across many geographic sites, thus allowing true integration of the build principles.

THE BUILD STRATEGY

We have adopted a number of build principles in order to deliver the submarine on time and to cost. Firstly, it is fairly evident that submarines are products with extremely confined spaces and high equipment packing densities. Because of this, if production work is left to the last possible point within the submarine construction programme, the result is conflicting requirements with competing manufacturing operations being undertaken in a non-optimum environment. We are therefore driving to do the maximum amount of work 'off-boat'. It is very important to try and do as much work in the 'open shop' environment wherever we possibly can; that immediately implies the design needs to embrace greater modularisation. A key factor, therefore, in the 'Astute' progamme is to maximise the amount of modularisation.

The second principle is where we are unable to work on a module; we drive to maximise the open-ended pressure hull out-fit. This means we must delay pressure hull butt closures on construction programmes until the last possible moment. It is significant that we have on 'Astute' developed a build sequence that, through the use of large modules, provides this opportunity.

The third principle – and equally as important – is the testing and commissioning regime employed. Testing commonly is quite a lengthy and labour-intensive process. It is important to make sure that we do not undertake tests unnecessarily through the build cycle, something historically that has tended to happen. One of the key initiatives being developed for 'Astute', therefore, is that we test once and once only. Testing and commissioning, however, is inextricably linked to the acceptance process and therefore the customer will have to underwrite the 'test once' initiative.

PRODUCTION ENABLERS

What are the enablers to deliver these objectives? Firstly, the design must comprehend the build strategy proposed. This is facilitated through the establishment of Integrated Project Teams (IPT's) where production personnel are embedded in the design teams at the start of the programme. A second enabler at Marine is the roll-out of the 'lean manufacturing' programme. 'Lean manufacturing' is about making sure that the flow processes of work through the facilities themselves have been optimised to ensure elimination of any waste and duplication of effort. The third enabler is process improvement. One of the key process improvements adopted for submarine construction is 'dimensional control'. Many problems, historically, have occurred through re-work levels that have been generated through limitations in dimensional control techniques. New techniques using laser technologies now allow as-built dimensions for the structure to be fed back into the Computer Aided Design (CAD) model, thus reducing the potential re-work from technical information.

'ASTUTE': THE DESIGN CHALLENGE

We have to make sure that, when reducing production costs, we do not lose sight of the requirement to enhance capability. We have, therefore, to keep looking forward and focus on the requirement to improve the submarine's fighting capability through up-dated combat systems, enhance stealth with reduced signatures and, most importantly, maintain and improve the vessel's safe operation. The latter issue is something that BAE SYSTEMS Marine is particularly focused on, given the nuclear and ship safety aspects of the product. Therefore, whilst drawing up programmes and identifying cost reduction opportunities, we shall not compromise the safety requirement.

The question of through-life cost reductions has been covered by Harry Wyse in the previous Chapter, so I shall not enlarge on them here. However, minimising design risk is also one of the key factors with which we are very concerned. Whilst always looking for new initiatives, it is imperative that full risk trade-off evaluations are conducted on development activities to ensure that we do not create additional risk which would result in additional costs later in the programme.

WHOLE BOAT DESIGN

The concept of 'whole boat design' incorporates a number of key elements that have been carried forward to help reduce some of the production costs. 'Astute' has a much simpler geometry from previous submarine construction. For example, it has a parallel body hull and common frames within the pressure hull; so, from a manufacturing perspective, these characteristics allow us to set up a manufacturing process that drives the frame manufacturing in a much more efficient and effective way. We are also utilising fully automatic welding on all of our submarine construction processes. All the hull construction is automatically welded, as is the submarine frame construction.

The other thing that is driving 'Astute' is the provision of space within the design to enable the manufacturing process to take place. An example of this is the fact that we are introducing automatic welding of pipe-work in the outfit phase of build. In order to facilitate this, we have to generate, within the boat itself, the space around each of the systems that will allow the automatic welding machines to be installed and operated. We have, therefore, to provide space within the overall design to allow those techniques and technologies to be applied.

CRITICAL MODULES

Furthermore, we obviously have to provide adequate space within the submarine design itself for the installation and mounting of critical modules. Four critical modules have been developed within the 'Astute' programme. First, is the main machinery module. This is a derivative of the 'Trafalgar' Class SSN where all the main turbines, turbo-generators and gearbox are modularised. This module is full power tested 'off-boat' within the Submarine Installation Test Establishment (SMITE) at Barrow prior to being shipped to the submarine. The module is tested against full power requirements prior to installation.

The second, and largest, module is the command deck (weighing over three hundred tonnes) which incorporates all the command and accommodation areas. It will be built 'off-boat', be flexibly mounted and fitted into the submarine hull at the latest possible opportunity. This module is a two-deck construction with separate command and accommodation areas. It will be fully out-fitted and tested to its maximum extent, prior to installation. The combat systems, therefore, will be as fully integrated as far as possible within the constraints imposed by the module itself. All of the equipment will be flexibly mounted within the module.

The manoeuvring room is the third critical module which houses the nuclear reactor control panels. It is an interesting module because it had to be developed with the involvement of principal suppliers within the integrated project team. This module relies on the integration of supplier equipment to form part of the structural design.

The forward engine room is the fourth module that pulls together a number of auxiliary machinery equipment.

DETAILED DESIGN

What has been described above is the big picture: big modules and 'off-boat' construction. We believe we get a productivity improvement of a factor of between two and three by taking work off the boat and doing it in a work / fabrication shop environment. At the next level down, where we get down to a lower level of modularisation and detailed design, the key element is the standardisation of components and parts. Because of space constraints, submarines historically have had every part individually designed and manufactured. BAE SYSTEMS Marine has, quite literally, had thousands and thousands of items within its spare parts and supply systems. All of these parts are individually made and individually supported.

What we have tried to do is to standardise wherever we can. The space / volume of the 'Astute' submarine has allowed us to do that. For instance, when we talk about fittings, fuse panels, etc, we have tried to standardise and reduce the number of different suppliers. A lot of work has gone into reducing the supply base and to reduce the amount of effort that is required to assess individually different system requirements. The simple geometry and spatial design, discussed above, has opened up the opportunity to use orbital welding.

Another key area for improvement is in cable harnessing. Those familiar with pulling cables in ships and submarines will know that it is a major task and takes much time and effort. We have adopted an approach of 'connectorisation' wherever we possibly can. For example, we have developed a number of cable penetrators both for pressure hull and major containment bulkhead applications. We are also looking for cable harnessing where the idea is not to install cables at boat, but to get the cable, and cable harness, manufacturers to do it for us. These harnesses will then be installed as modules.

An illustration of the other standardisation activities is that of breakers versus fuses. We have adopted an approach whereby we have been able to eliminate fuses in the system and replace them with breakers, thus saving considerable build and in-service time and cost by eliminating fuse testing.

We have looked at standardising geometry for items such as vent trunk and lockers. Whilst we already have automatic processes for plate and sheet metal work that are generated though the CAD programme for these items, a reduction in the number of different standard components used will provide significant savings.

THE INTEGRATED DATA ENVIRONMENT

The integrated data environment is driven around the Engineering Data Management (EDM) system coupled to the CADS 5 modelling environment. What we have done at Barrow is to remove the need for plastic models or full-scale mock-

31   The 'O' Class Submarine HMS OSIRIS (S13) (1962)

courtesy BAe Systems

32   HMS DREADNOUGHT (S101) The Navy's first nuclear submarine (SSN) (1960)

courtesy BAe Systems

33   HMS RESOLUTION (S22) The first SSBN Polaris Submarine (1967)

courtesy BAe Systems

34 HMS SPLENDID (S106) In 2000, the first submarine with Tomahawk missiles (1992)

courtesy BAe Systems Marine

35 HMS VANGUARD (S28) The first Trident missile SSBN (1992)

courtesy BAe Systems Marine

36 The 'Upholder' Class Submarine RCS VICTORIA formerly HMS UNSEEN (2000)

courtesy Royal Canadian Navy

ups for 'Astute' or any future ship programmes. We believe that the modelling environment now provides us with the capacity to visualise, through 3D computing capabilities, all the necessary requirements to facilitate operability and maintainability and buildability.

One of the key elements to deliver this is the need to create specific IPTs that immerse the design, production and support people in a concurrent environment. At the present time, for example, we have ten design area IPTs on 'Astute' which have production, integrated logistic support (ILS) and design people in these teams as well as sub-contract managers and suppliers. They are all working hard to drive the product issue right up front so that there is a clear understanding of what the production problems are, something designers do not always either consider or understand. This approach is proving to be very beneficial within the 'Astute' programme where there is absolutely no doubt that significant benefits have been achieved.

I have already mentioned technical production outputs. All of the steelwork is nested and all pipe-work is generated automatically; also, all of our manufacturing outputs are in electronic form. In the production facilities at Barrow, workstation terminals have been installed where output drawings and data from the 3D model are accessed as needed. The manufacturing people are trained to be able to access this information themselves at source. One of the benefits of the CAD / EDM system is its ability to make adjustments through the build. These can be accommodated much more effectively and efficiently whenever there is an issue of tolerancing or when dimensions need to check back through the production process.

Another benefit of the production feed back is that an 'as-built' electronic data model can now be handed to the ILS Team with a much greater degree of accuracy. That team can then use the model for in-service support and spares provisioning.

PROCESS

Some of the process improvements have already been covered above - for example, increased automation. Material control however, is another critically important process. We need to ensure that we have a good handle on material control, particularly as the 'bill of materials' driven from our CAD EDM system requires each item to be individually and uniquely identified to maintain configuration control of the overall product.

I mentioned previously the need to reduce testing. One area where new techniques are being applied to improve the process is the introduction digital ultrasonics. This will enable us to eventually eliminate some of the radiographic techniques which presently place major restrictions in segregating work areas of the boat and the associated down time.

Pipe flushing is another key issue in submarine construction, especially when testing and commissioning. The amount of time spent on flushing systems has historically been long. Improvements in the quality assurance processes, cleanliness levels, and protection regimes should provide opportunities for significant reduction in flushing requirements in the future.

Notwithstanding what has been achieved to date, process improvement continues to be a key plank in BAE SYSTEMS Marine's business development plans.

FUTURE INITIATIVES

It is important to recognise that the initiatives outlined today are not just part of a continuous improvement over previous submarines, but are a step-change in how we undertake our business. If we continued along a path of continuous improvements over the 'Trident' submarines we would not achieve the 'Astute' programme targets. We have to take a step-change and double our efforts to generate the amount of savings we need. We shall probably need another 15% savings beyond a traditional year-on-year improvement programme. This we have set out to achieve.

29

Submarine System Integration

Jeff Owen

INTRODUCTION

As we move into the 21st Century, the UK defence-related industries find themselves having to adapt to new and ever changing commercial, political and technological pressures. In particular, the changing requirements for underwater warfare will potentially make a significant impact on submarine design.[1] The increasing need to operate in littoral waters will inevitably lead to multi-role missions and an increase in the potential types of threats to submarines. This will lead to an increase in the number of, and the demands placed upon, 'Integration Equipment'.

We define Integration Equipment as that equipment which allows the incorporation of typical weapons and/or sensors into the submarine. Strachan & Henshaw have been involved in the development of such equipment for over a quarter of a century. During this period, the company has been placed in almost a unique position of undertaking conceptual designs through to in-service support on a number of submarine and weapon programmes both within the UK and overseas.

In order to meet the changing requirements, Strachan & Henshaw has made significant changes to its organisational structure, design tools and the work environment in order to support an improved process. This paper outlines the approach to the design of such equipment.

INTEGRATION EQUIPMENT – DEFINED

Essentially, 'integration equipment' is equipment which allows the integration of, typically, a weapon and/or sensor into the platform (submarine or surface ship). Such equipment is often characterised by the involvement of logistical movement of material either during a dockside process and/or operationally when at sea.

Frequently such equipment is completely over-shadowed by the more 'glamorous' weapon system or sensor and unfortunately history has shown us that this may lead to unacceptable penalties on the performance of the system, as a whole. In today's 'high tech' world, it is often the 'low tech' issue, such as marine growth, external hydraulics, corrosion, or lack of attention to other integration issues, that often results in major system problems.

The very nature of Integration Equipment tends to involve high integrity components with multi-discipline teams employed in order to derive a cost-effective solution covering such areas as structural integrity under shock, hydrodynamic performance, safety, Integrated Logistic Support (ILS), and human factors.

It is crucial that a good relationship is established between the stakeholders involved, since the interfaces are quite often multi-boundary involving complex physical and performance issues. For example, when reviewing the shock integrity of large equipment, it is often difficult to identify the root cause of high induced stresses; i.e. 'is the tail wagging the dog, or the dog wagging the tail?' This can lead to confusion over the interfaces in the system.

The equipment can often have a profound effect on the design of both the platform and the system being integrated. For example, off-board sensors and towed systems need a clear operating envelope, even when the platform is manoeuvring. Its location inevitably leads to compromises in both the platform design and the effectiveness of the weapon system.

Due to the development cycle of new systems, it is inevitable that existing Integration Equipment has to accommodate new systems or, indeed, that new systems and new Integration Equipment need to interface with existing platforms.

CHANGING THE APPROACH

In order to meet the challenge of 'Smart Procurement' and other initiatives in related industries, the Company needed to review its processes in order to reduce costs and improve delivery times. The task-based approach characterised by different departments and/or groups had served well during the days of poor connectivity with a number of checks and balances in the system. This approach often led to frustration between departments/groups as the design evolved, resulting in re-work as the work done was outdated. Moreover, with pressure on budgets there was little incentive for a group to do extra work above its requirements, even if it would result in an overall budget reduction.

In order to make this change it necessitated the need to alter:

- Organisation
- Tools
- Environment

The organisational change involves multi-discipline teams focused on the delivery of their part of the equipment. The checks and balances with respect to design integrity are provided by the Technical Council, whilst the Programme and Performance Group monitors progress using 'Earned Value' techniques. In order to facilitate communication and collaborative team working, significant changes were made to the work environment. The old environment was characterised by barriers and departmental layouts, in sharp contrast with the new system.

The office is now laid out in a much more open plan fashion, with bold visuals promoting the status of the project to everyone. Although this environment can significantly improve visual and verbal communication, improving the connectivity of design tools can make tremendous improvements to the work rate itself. The concept of the 'Master Model' has been adopted, allowing various disciplines to derive inputs from a single source. Technology limitations force a 'physical view' and a 'system view' which are linked by the Product Data Manager (PDM) system; both views, however, come together using a virtual environment.

CONCURRENT ENGINEERING - WHAT DOES IT MEAN TO US?

Engineering processes are moving away from the old-style 'over the wall'- based schemes where each section or department would complete its task in the design and manufacturing process before passing the project on to the next link in the chain. Concurrent engineering requires a step change in the process, with all parties involved in the design and manufacture of the equipment brought together. Also of vital significance is both customer (procurement authority and end-user) and supplier input, since both have a very important role in the project.

The design process can be divided into a number of distinct phases; these may vary depending on the nature of the project. In general, they can be divided into concept and detail design.

THE CONCEPT PHASE

The objective of initial conceptual studies is to identify feasible cost-effective options for future equipment. One important aspect is to consider whole life issues and costs. Whilst restrictions do need to be taken into account, the generation of the concept, at least in the early stages, needs to be unfettered by such restrictions as far as possible. The aim is to identify the full scope of potential concepts to ensure that the design can be innovative, rather than evolutionary. Such studies take account of emerging technology and the novel application of existing technology/systems not usually associated with the proposed equipment.

However, the objective is not to get 'performance at any price', but to get 'value for money', by balancing the effectiveness gains against cost implications. In these days of restricted procurement programmes and limited budgets, it is essential to have a low risk design and a programme which meets the required time scales. Therefore the equipment design should be:

- *Effective*: - It is paramount that the requirements of the system are identified for comparison with candidate systems; and
- *Balanced* - The seemingly more important performance attributes must be balanced by system engineering aspects (e.g. through-life and Availability, Reliability and Maintainability (ARM)).

To support this work, a number of techniques have been employed including 'Quality Functional Deployment', 'Structured Brainstorming' and the 'Analytical Hierarchy Process' (AHP). In particular, the AHP method has proved an effective decision support tool, by aligning this technique with structured requirement captive/management.

By way of example, the following hypothetical analysis demonstrates how a complex decision can be reduced to a tree of simpler criteria, all of which are seen to have a bearing on the final choice. Viable alternative solutions (options) are compared against one another in pairs (i.e. which is the preferred option, and by how much) with respect to each of the criteria; then, a software tool is used to calculate from this information which is the preferred option overall.

A sample AHP tree for the selection of an undefined, generic submarine integration equipment (IE) system might give three available alternatives as a viable solution, labelled, for example, O1, O2 and O3. The decision is judged to be dependent on three main criteria: the cost impact the integration equipment will have on the platform (labelled CTP); the cost impact the equipment will have on the system being integrated (CTS); and the general effectiveness (E) of the option as a solution.

To give this example greater depth, the effectiveness score has been defined to be the result of a sub-level comparison, consisting of the risk (R) associated with the option, the relative operational performance (P) of the option, and the Through-Life Cost (TLC) of the option. Note that this is still a considerably simplified AHP tree, compared to a real decision tree for this sort of system; but it will serve here to highlight the principles of the technique.

Before the options are compared against one another, it is also possible to weight the decision so that some criteria have more effect on the final decision than others do. In this example, effectiveness is weighted such that it has 40% of the final decision, while CTP and CTS have 30% each. Furthermore, within the Effectiveness Branch, performance is also judged to be a little more important than either risk or Through-Life Cost – again, both of these are given 30% of the Effectiveness 'vote', while whole Performance receives 40%.

With the AHP tree defined in this fashion and, then, entered into the decision support tool, the options are compared against one another for preference, in pairs, and with respect to each of the criteria. A verbal scale is the common method for making this comparison, but preferences can also be defined with a graphical, ambiguous comparison, or maybe by direct percentage weightings. The software then uses this information to calculate the preferred option with respect to the Goal. In the case of the above example, option O3 could emerge as the preferred solution overall, even though it might not have scored well in either CTP or CTS.

Where the AHP method really becomes useful, however, is in the subsequent sensitivity analysis output. This gives an indication of the effect of changing the priority weightings on the criteria. If the priority of CTP, for example, is increased by only 2% to 32% of the final decision, O2 might emerge as the preferred option, whereas if CTP were to be reduced to 17%, O1 might take the lead. This approach is useful when highlighting to the design committee the importance of clarifying the criticality of the Cost to Platform.

Similar sensitivity studies would be performed for the Cost-to-System and Effectiveness attributes, with the end result that the subjectivity of the design committee's decision can be reduced to a minimum.

CONCEPT DESIGN ASSESSMENT PHASE

Following the selection of a concept, further refinement is required. Whilst some of the techniques used in the previous phases may be used to assist with further decision-making, additional techniques, such as 'Design for Manufacture' and 'Design for Assembly' are brought into play in order to promote consideration of manufacture and assembly issues at the concept design stage. "80-90% of the life-cycle design costs (including fabrication, construction, energy, maintenance and disposal) are determined in the first 10-20% of the design phase, i.e. the conceptual design".[2] For this reason, it is important that inputs from all these areas are considered from as early on as possible.

With design of integration equipment (IE) that often involves a logistical element, increasing use is being made of process simulation tools. By modelling systems, the complex interaction between entities of the system and/or process can be established. Moreover, the ability to optimise and investigate 'what-if' scenarios provides a valuable input early in the design process.

Such process modelling has been employed as part of safety analysis and to investigate the optimum logistical movement on a platform. By approaching the design from a process centric direction it becomes possible to rapidly assess the effect of changes in layout, the nature of the required equipment and, significantly, the number of personnel involved.

Integrated Logistics Support (ILS) specialists have been brought into the project zones as part of the new process-centric organisation, along with manufacturing, procurement, Health & Safety – essentially any aspect of the entire product development process would be given an input into the work from the outset. This integration of all the necessary skills (i.e. not only from design and analysis) into the project teams, across the business as a whole, means that products are developed and supported in such a way as to achieve the highest quality for minimum cost, throughout the product life-cycle.

In addition to personnel resources, various technological tools have been identified as bringing value to the design process.

The utilisation of three dimensional (3D) CAD systems significantly assists the understanding of all stakeholders as the design evolves, while making the task of integrating components into a specific volume envelope substantially easier. The ability to integrate physics models/simulations into this environment also significantly reduces both the data entry requirements and the configuration control of the design process.

Extensive use is also made of 'Motion Analysis', 'Finite Element Analysis' and 'Computational Fluid Dynamics', allowing early performance evaluation of options and 'what if?' studies to be carried out. The development of a virtual prototype in this fashion allows many problems to be identified and solved *before* manufacture begins. Previously, these problems would probably not arise until the system was well into prototyping and testing.

Physical models do, however, remain an important part of the tool set, whether they are full scale or smaller. This is particularly true if the asset can be linked into a more extensive simulation in a 'hardware-in-the-loop' scenario, thereby providing real feedback performance data to the software. There is a limit to how far a simulation's behaviour can approximate to the real world; almost by definition, it will always be a simplification. In consequence, there will always be a need to validate a simulation's prediction with empirical data.

DOWNSTREAM PROCESSES

CAD transfer from the company to the customer or supplier remains a costly issue throughout the industry. Although standards are emerging, significant problems are still to be overcome. However, the use of CAD viewer technology is potentially offering some hope in this area. Often there is no need for complete native CAD translation in the supply chain, because all that needs to be transferred is an understanding of the physical interfaces. This can be accomplished via a reduced set of CAD definitions, at a correspondingly reduced cost.

As the design moves into manufacture, modern CNC manufacturing techniques offer the potential for direct transmission of a 3D model to the manufacturers. This could potentially have a radical improvement in the quality of products. Provided the manufacturers were involved from the beginning in a concurrent engineering process, a whole link in the supply chain is therefore removed. Without two-dimensional (2D) drawings, and the errors that accumulate from their generation and interpretation, products can be expected to deviate that much less from their idealised virtual prototypes.

Once in service, it is essential that the principles established by the concurrent engineering process are not abandoned. By maintaining a close link between customer and designer, effective feedback can be incorporated into the day-to-day service support. Furthermore, if the design authority has easy access to the 'hands-on' experience of the customer, a more efficient process of upgrade and development can be expected.

CONCLUSIONS

Although Integration Equipment may be considered the less 'glamorous' side of a system, it is vital that such issues are not overlooked. Maximum added value can be gained by involvement at the initial conceptual phase of a project, of all parties who will have an interest in the product (including suppliers and customers). This means a step change from the old 'over the wall' design process.

Modern technological tools are a valuable third leg in the support of a new design process, along with the organisational structure and working environment. Of particular value are decision support tools, process simulations, and 3D design/ virtual prototypes. Feedback from through-life support is a key issue in order to ensure that systems develop in the most effective manner possible.

Changing requirements in submarine warfare have led to an increase in the number and types of weapon/sensor systems that require integration into the platform, and will continue to do so. In order to meet this challenge, improved design processes and techniques have been developed which are supported by organisational change, improvements in the working environment and significant development of the Computer Aided Design (CAD) and Engineering tools.

With a significant proportion of the life cycle cost being determined in the early stages of the design phase the benefits of structured design techniques in this early stage cannot be over emphasised. The utilisation of computer aided engineering techniques allows early evaluation of options, whilst feedback from through-life support is a key issue in order to ensure system development.

NOTES

1   Fuller, G.H; "The Kit of Parts, An Abundance of Choice", *Warship '99, Naval Submarines 6*, RINA 1999.
2   Wood III W.H., & Agogino, A.M. "Case-based conceptual design information server for concurrent engineering", *Computer Aided Design*, 1996 v.28, No. 5, pp.361-369.

30

Submarine Support and Maintenance

Mike Owen

INTRODUCTION

Whilst the title of this paper is submarine support past and present, I aim to discuss mainly the present and the future. I shall give a brief overview of the facilities under construction at Devonport and then give an outline of the upkeep regime of the current flotilla and how this might evolve in future to improve availability and reduce costs. First, let me consider the facility challenge.

NUCLEAR SUPPORT STANDARDS

Devonport has seen much change since William of Orange founded the Yard towards the end of the 17th Century. However, not since the rapid growth of the North Yard at around the beginning of the 20th Century has there been such furious development activity to update the nuclear support facilities to what the Nuclear Industry refers to as 'modern standards'. This means:

- Safety Lead Design
- Deterministic Justification
- Diversity and Separation
- Holistic Probability Safety Assessments, etc.

These are all are terms regularly banded about, but this all adds up to thousands of tons·of concrete and steel, and many millions of pounds.

To go off at a slight tangent, briefly, this development is against a background of submarine availability not being what we want, or would like it, to be. This can be understood by reading the press. I can only conclude that Samuel Pepys would have been as frustrated today as he was back in the 17th Century when he went on a tour of the dockyards to review the state of the Fleet before William of Orange came on the scene.

All this means that people are asking, 'Well, do we really need these things any more? Can we afford them? Are they not a product from the Cold War arms race and is that not now over? I know that all these issues have been widely discussed and I shall not enlarge on them here. But one thing is clear: the Ministry of Defence, the Royal Navy and we at Devonort Management Limited (DML) need to reduce the overall cost of support as far as we are able and to increase submarine and ship availability, thereby reducing the cost of a sea-day, or any other similar measure.

THE DEVONPORT DOCKYARD FACILITIES

The DML facilities near Plymouth contain five basins. One is the Submarine Refit Complex built in the 1970s. It will soon change its appearance when the large crane currently there is removed and low-level refuelling is adopted. Another is what is known as '10 Dock', which is where the docking and revalidation Assistance Maintenance Periods (AMPs) are carried out under a Captain Fleet Logistics/ Devonport Management Limited (CFM/DML) Joint Project Team. This is a successful partnering arrangement that is now entering into its fourth year and which is probably a pointer for the future.

Third, is '9 Dock', the centre of the 'Vanguard' Class support facility where HMS VANGUARD will dock in 2002 for her first Long Overhaul Period (LOP). This facility will be ready towards the end of 2001, which, in itself, is a pretty formidable challenge. The building is the easy bit; it is the production of the safety case that is the real challenge. Production and maintenance of the modern facility and the safety case are a hugely costly overhead and have to be well loaded to maintain a sensible labour rate.

For this reason, and quite rightly, the Company is working on ways to reduce the size of the labour force. The difficulty in this respect is that reductions in maintenance work result in relatively moderate savings unless the overhead can be tackled at the same time. The answer is to get a good view of the forward loading, and manage the overhead accordingly, much of which has two legs and walks in the gate every morning. The downside is that it is difficult to deal with the nasty surprises on a Friday night, or if, suddenly, there is a large, unscheduled, repair.

Before leaving the Devonport Dockyard facilities it should be noted that they are an up-to-date example of modern standards that are designed to meet the one in 10,000 year natural disaster, such as an earthquake, tornado, or major flood.

SUBMARINE UPKEEP

Moving on to the upkeep process itself, the development of nuclear submarine engineering and materials has made huge strides since the early days of the nuclear programme thirty years ago, when the Polaris boats had to be refuelled after about four years. Now a typical overall upkeep cycle is as follows: the submarine comes out of build and typically remains in service for about ten to twelve years. It will probably have docking every year of about two months duration, but recently these have been rolled up into longer four-month upkeep periods every two to three years. Around the mid-point before a major mid-life upgrade, the submarine might have a capability update, during which time the weapons systems on board the submarine are upgraded. The current 'Tomahawk' cruise missile fit into the current UK 'Trafalgar' and 'Swiftsure' Class SSNs is an example. The process is then repeated until the major upkeep and up-date period; that will probably occur after a period of a further ten to twelve years.

The point about all this is that there is ample opportunity to carry out upkeep in these periods, but only if the submarine systems and their equipment are accessible and the material is readily available. Indeed, it might be argued that the submarines are in upkeep for rather longer then they ought to be. It is, however, equally important to build in capability upgrades during these periods; it is our opinion that this is going to become more important as more commercial off-the-shelf (COTS) equipment is fitted.

INTEGRATED LOGISTIC SUPPORT

Integrated Logistic Support (ILS) is carried out during the design period and is, of course, aimed at enabling this support business to be delivered more efficiently. Typical deliverables are:

- Design the boat so that systems and equipment are accessible and can be serviced without massive 'work in wake'. The Logistic Escape Towers in the 'Vanguard' Class are an initial example. Even so, there is often great reliance on the skill of the Band A Dockyard Slinger.
- Provide control such that drawings, parts lists and other software are readily available and accurate against a known configuration;
- Carry out analyses such that the right spares are available at the right time;
- Install the necessary surveillance and performance monitoring systems such that the condition of the equipment can be maintained as really necessary;
- Specify the maintenance requirements carefully such that the design intent and performance is maintained but at the same time keeping revalidation (checks to see why it is still working) to a minimum;
- Finally, ensure that there is sufficient redundancy robustness built into the propulsion plant design so that systems can be released for maintenance whilst complying with the safety case.

The full effects of the early efforts at ILS on platforms entering the operational phase are only just now beginning to be seen. The results, however, are, as yet, mixed. Taking each of the deliverables in turn:

- Design for upkeep and design for build are not totally compatible in these days of building in sections and end loading fitted out decks into the hull. Cutting the boat into slices for upkeep is impractical and we have to rely on coming in from the side or the top;
- Modern data systems are becoming excellent for drawing part lists and including geographical data, but they must be kept up-to-date and used properly;
- We have seen little progress in spares provision. There are delays in getting the spares that are needed and there may well be comparatively large volumes that that do not move. The modern systems and methods are useless without high grade and expensive intellectual engineering input and then regular updating in the light of experience;
- Most submarines have highly sophisticated surveillance systems, but more time & effort is needed to be spent in their analysis;
- A lot of effort is currently being put into maintenance specification after many years of ratchetting requirements up. It is important that they are kept under regular review and experience injected along the lines of the periodic reductions made by the MOD in the in-service upkeep load;
- The shutdown safety case is a new phenomenon and has not yet been fully addressed.

UPKEEP PERIODS

Turning to the upkeep periods themselves, we are starting to reduce costs and the periods in dock by introducing modern processes and systems. Any upkeep period is handled in the same way, but the Long Overhaul Period, or refit, and up-keep cycles have a larger update package. I mentioned above the increasing importance of introducing new technology rapidly into the submarine flotilla; this is precisely what is happening in both the long and short periods.

This is particularly evident in the communications area where inter-operability is now the name of the game and technology is evolving rapidly. No two fits are the same, and are often being developed in parallel with installation. Concurrent engineering and integrated project teams are all vital in meeting these demands and setting capability developed quickly. In the final analysis, all of this can be dealt with; the problem, however, is emergent work that undermines planning and extends maintenance periods if it becomes too great – it is the old basics of corrosion and cracking that cause much of the extended time on maintenance and repair.

There is some correlation between the eventual size of the work-package and the time elapsed after build or Long Overhaul Period (LOP). This result is not surprising, when one of the requirements of undertaking a LOP - to bring the platform and its systems back to design standards - is taken into consideration.

Then, there is the relative intensity of current upkeep regimes. As the upkeep period grows in length, so the work content undertaken increases out of proportion such that, during Long Overhaul Periods, more effort is expended per week than during Capability Upgrades (CUPs), Repair and Associated Maintenance Periods (RAMPs) and Docking and Associated Maintenance Periods (DAMPs).

One argument that could possibly be made is that, based on this information, the LOP is a far more effective use of upkeep time. As such, the upkeep cycle should be modified to reduce the number of smaller upkeep periods and maximise the work scope of the LOP. However, the condition of the platform deteriorates with time from build or LOP, and such an approach would not only exacerbate the effects of 'peaks and troughs' in the repair industry's workload but possibly also have an adverse effect on submarine availability.

For a submarine platform that is fuelled for life, and which (hopefully) will not require any major intrusive work into the NSRP, it will not receive a combat system upgrade on the scale of the current S&T update. The scope of the Long Overhaul Period will be therefore markedly different.

THE LONG OVERHAUL PERIOD

When the current SSN Long Overhaul Period activities are examined, the drivers on the length of the docking period for a future platform (submarine) are contained within system and structural revalidation. For future platform designs, the opportunity exists to challenge seriously such aspects of the upkeep policy by making use of historical information (for example corrosion of the pressure hull) and drawing up a 'better design'. That is, it would be entirely reasonable to expect the design team of the future attack submarine (FASM), say, to encompass 'design for support' and 'design for up-grade principles' into their platform solutions.

This would clearly have a positive effect on the duration of the Long Overhaul Period, as well as the length of time the vessel spends in dry dock. When this is considered, along with:

- The general Industry trend and MOD desire to move to Reliability Centred Maintenance; and,
- The upgrade of major systems through progressive update using COTS equipment (for example, the combat system);

then a more effective upkeep policy could evolve that does not contain the Long Overhaul Period, Upkeep Cycles, and many smaller upkeep periods, but with the emphasis always on maintaining the platform at a higher readiness state than previously seen.

The potential benefits of such an approach could be:-

- Improved readiness and hence platform availability;
- More effective utilisation of Repair Authorities, leading to improved efficiency and closer co-operation;
- Frequent regular updates to the Design Authorities on system and equipment performance, leading to improved understanding, and optimisation of repair and maintenance requirements;
- More efficient use of support infrastructure, allowing flexibility of operation, increasing the ability to react to unscheduled repair requirements.

The question may well be asked, "what about making provision for major Additions and Alterations (A&As) under such a regime?" It should be remembered, however, that large A&As can and are already contained within CUPs

So what does all this mean? Much of what can be achieved during the in-service phase is preordained by the quality of the *design*; and in that, I include the ILS package. Equally important is the *quality of build*, whether it is welds in pipe systems or hull structure coatings. However, given a particular submarine, such as the current 'Trafalgar Class' SSNs, I am uncertain whether we have the optimum up-keep plan for today's boats; that can only be determined by in-depth analysis and modelling. I am therefore certain we can do a lot better for the future ('Astute') classes. Time alone will tell.

31

SSN Propulsion Options

D Hacker

INTRODUCTION

The nuclear powered submarine (SSN) provides a navy with a potent capability. The nuclear power plant is air independent, mission endurance is only limited by the crew and high transit speeds with a large payload are readily achievable. The challenge for the propulsion system designer is to convert the heat energy from a nuclear reaction into shaft work, to drive a propulsion shaft, and into electrical energy to provide ship services. These conversions must be achieved within a tight space envelope and must be reliable, quiet and safe. The propulsion and power generation systems of a submarine, including the reactor compartment, typically occupy 40% of the internal volume and 25% of the cost of the submarine.

Historically, the driving requirements of the SSN propulsion system may have been safety, reliability and performance. Cost has always been a factor, but may have been secondary to the overriding need of powerful naval nations to possess the capability of nuclear submarines. For the nuclear submarine of the future, the emphasis may be slightly different, with navies requiring enhanced capability but at much reduced life cycle cost. The development time-scales of submarines can be long and the world-wide political situation changeable, factors that lead to the requirement for a submarine capable of great flexibility, to cater for the many unknowns.

Social and regulatory pressures increase the need for safety and reliability of the nuclear propulsion system, and its supporting infrastructure. Increasing environmental awareness requires the submarine community to consider disposal and decommissioning. Alongside these challenges, it must be remembered that the submarine is a weapon of war and must be designed to be superior to the threat that it will face in its operating environment. As technology advances, requirements for signature reduction and combat system enhancement also increase. Thus, the main drivers for future nuclear propulsion developments can be summarised as:

- Life Cycle Cost Reduction
- Operational Flexibility
- Safety & Environmental Concerns
- Signature Reduction
- Combat System Demands

EXISTING PROPULSION SYSTEMS

UK submarines have historically used propulsion systems based on geared turbines. Other Western navies have generally done the same, notable exceptions being the USS TULLIBEE, the USS GLENARD P. LIPSCOMB, and the French 'Rubis'/ 'Amethyste' Class using electric propulsion. There have also been experiments with ungeared turbine drives. Traditional geared turbine drives are compact and proven, but require extensive steam and lubricating oil systems that can lead to high life-cycle costs. Noise and vibration problems associated with the gear train have necessitated the development of sophisticated machinery mounting arrangements. The generation of electrical power has been by additional turbo-generators, with generation, distribution and consumption of power all at the same standard due to the constraints of technology at the time. System efficiencies can be low, particularly if they are optimised around a single operating point, usually maximum speed, and do not reflect the actual operating profile of the submarine. The need, in geared systems, to operate several turbines in parallel at low part loads further compounds the low efficiency. Low efficiency in turn leads to a reduction in life of the reactor core, which is increasingly important in the era of whole submarine life cores.

Most SSNs also have an emergency propulsion motor capable of driving the main shaft and an independent secondary propulsion unit. The SSN requires a source of standby power, that has traditionally been a lead acid battery, and a source of electrical power generation, usually in the form of a diesel generator, which is entirely independent of the reactor. These features ensure the safety of the submarine in the event of loss of reactor power.

Requirements of safety and, perhaps, a degree of conservatism within Western navies, have also tended to favour machinery systems that require a large degree of manual control and supervision, resulting in relatively large crew sizes.

FUTURE PROPULSION SYSTEM REQUIREMENTS

A submarine is by its nature a highly integrated platform and the requirements of the propulsion system cannot sensibly be considered independently of the operational requirements of the submarine as a whole. To predict the requirements of future propulsion systems, it is therefore necessary to predict the operational requirements of the future submarine. This in turns requires the ability to predict the future political environment of the world. This is no mean task!

The key role of the SSN is to deploy rapidly and covertly, at short notice, with a package of sensors, stand-off weapons or special forces. They are also likely to have a continuing role in accompanying important task groups through potentially hostile waters. For this, they will need a propulsion system that can perform in the full range of operational environments from under the polar ice cap to the Persian Gulf and the littoral, without compromise. High running speeds at an acceptable level of radiated signature and sonar effectiveness are likely to be required.

Some trends are, however, more predictable. The submarine must be more affordable, harder to detect and yet at the same time more able to detect the opposition. It must be capable of fulfilling a wide range of missions and yet comply with the legislation of the day for safety and environmental protection. The submarine must be capable of deploying a wide range of weapons and will be reliant on complex computer systems, perhaps linked to data sources in other platforms, to process and manage the complex tactical picture. Manoeuvrability and platform control may need to be enhanced to allow the SSN to operate in a wider envelope, and requirements for platform motion control at slower speeds may become more demanding.

FUTURE PROPULSION SYSTEM OPTIONS

There are three main future propulsion system options addressed in this paper:

- Geared mechanical drive.
- Geared mechanical drive with electric cruise.
- Full electric propulsion.

GEARED MECHANICAL DRIVE

A typical geared mechanical propulsion system is shown in Figure 1. The system features main engines driving through clutches to a gearbox, with an emergency propulsion motor connected to the standby power source. Electrical power is provided by separate turbine generators (TGs) via a converter. This arrangement remains the first choice propulsion system in the large SSNs being built today. Many early problems of noise and vibration have been corrected through evolutionary development and advances in machinery mounting and flexible arrangements. Future developments in gearbox technology promise higher turbine input speeds, improved signature performance and more compact gearboxes. For an SSN that requires a high top speed, these features make geared mechanical drive an attractive option. The drawbacks remain the cost of upkeep of complex mechanical systems and the requirement for independent electrical generation with the added complexity that this brings.

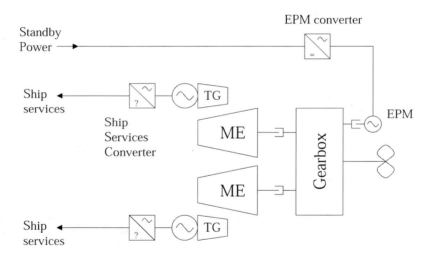

FIGURE 1 - GEARED MECHANICAL PROPULSION SYSTEM

ELECTRIC CRUISE

A typical electric cruise propulsion system is shown in Figure 2. The system is a variation on the theme of geared mechanical propulsion. In this option the mechanical drive mode is complemented by electric motors driving the shaft via the gearbox, providing both cruise and emergency propulsion drive. The power for the motors is provided from the TGs and allows the submarine to operate in a geared electric mode at slower speeds, bringing benefits in both signature reduction and efficiency, as the TGs can be more optimally loaded. The sizing of the cruise motors is dependent upon the cruise speed required, the capacity of the TGs, emergency power, and crash stop requirements. Full power cannot be applied to the shaft when in cruise mode. Cruise motors may also be used to provide a reversing capability, thus simplifying the main engines.

Electric cruise offers improvements in efficiency over geared mechanical with little technology development risk but retains the traditional gear train and any operational and support problems associated with that. Again the drawbacks are the cost of upkeep of complex mechanical systems and the requirement for independent TGs, as well as the constraint of not being able to apply full power to the shaft when in cruise mode.

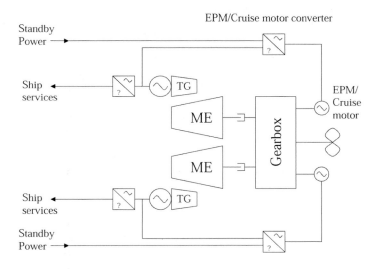

FIGURE 2 - ELECTRIC CRUISE PROPULSION SYSTEM

FULL ELECTRIC PROPULSION

A typical full electric propulsion system is shown in Figure 3. The system features common power generation for both propulsion and ship's services, with a shaft speed motor powered via a redundant converter system. Suitable redundancy for an emergency operation mode would be provided within the main propulsion motor. Electric propulsion has been implemented successfully on USS GLENARD P. LIPSCOMB and in the small displacement USS TULLIBEE and 'Rubis' Class, but has yet to gain general acceptance in large SSNs.

The electric ship concept is gaining in popularity in surface ships, including the Merchant Navy, because it offers a reduced number of prime movers, improved efficiency and ease of automation. These attributes are valuable to the SSN also, but electric propulsion has previously been limited by its size and weight, which exceed that of a geared mechanical arrangement. Advances in power electronics, high speed TGs, and the development of power dense permanent magnet motors that can operate at the shaft speed and power of an SSN, make electric propulsion a viable and attractive option for future classes. Electric propulsion in a submarine provides the added benefits of deletion of the main engines, gearbox, clutches, emergency propulsion motor and reduction of steam and lubricating oil systems.

Submarine operations often require a lot of time to be spent at low speeds and the high part load efficiency of permanent magnet motors will provide a real benefit in core life. Power electronics provide the freedom to generate and distribute electricity at a different standard to that at which it is consumed, with the power conversion local to the consumer. This freedom allows use of high speed TGs that are smaller, lighter, and more efficient than machines generating synchronously. Full electric propulsion requires further development, but offers a significant reduction in the cost of ownership for the SSN of the future. It also has the potential to deliver increased flexibility of power generation and reduction in signatures.

The US Navy is considering an electric propulsion variant of its 'Virginia' Class SSN, convinced that the need for enhanced stealth, expanded energy requirements and new missions will require it. The ability to apportion power throughout the submarine is expected to be increasingly important in the future when autonomous and unmanned underwater vehicles make greater demands on a power system.

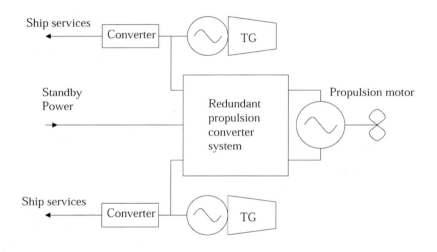

FIGURE 3 – FULL ELECTRIC PROPULSION SYSTEM

STANDBY POWER SYSTEMS

All nuclear submarines have auxiliary diesel generators (DGs) and usually a lead acid battery, which is kept fully charged. The battery provides the necessary electrical load whilst recovering from loss of reactor power whilst submerged; DGs provide long term non-nuclear support whilst snorting or on the surface. The functional requirement for a standby power, which is available instantaneously (e.g. a battery), and a power generation source independent of the reactor, (e.g. a DG) will remain the same for future classes but the technology available to provide this capability may alter significantly.

Closed cycle diesels are under development in the UK, promising extended air independent endurance. Advanced battery technologies, such as ZEBRA, offer increased storage capacity and battery life compared with lead acid. Fuel cell technology has been utilised by the German Navy and Stirling engines by the Swedish Navy. Future SSNs will have a wider choice of standby power sources with greater air independent endurance than their predecessors. This may allow some reduction in the requirements for redundancy within the nuclear plant and increase reliance on long-endurance AIP standby power sources. The requirements for standby power sources must be considered in conjunction with the propulsion system as a whole.

PROPULSORS AND PROPELLERS

The majority of modern SSNs have opted for a single propeller, or propulsor, despite the redundancy arguments against it. The primary drive for a single shaft is related to acoustic signature and hull form considerations. In order to produce the required level of thrust without cavitation or vibration, a large diameter propeller or propulsor rotating at a slow speed is superior to twin shafts with smaller diameter and higher speed propellers. For further improvement in efficiency, and consequent reduction in noise, the pump jet propulsor is generally preferred over the propeller, although it is more expensive, heavier and harder to maintain throughout the life of a submarine due to the accessibility constraints imposed by a duct.

PLATFORM INTEGRATION

The UK 'Astute' Class, in keeping with other modern navies, has sought a high degree of modularity in submarine build to reduce costs. In keeping with the concept of modularity, a reduction in the number of systems crossing the boundaries of the module is sought.

Propulsion systems will need to support this concept as part of the overall drive for cost reduction. The existing geared mechanical systems provide a compact module of turbines, condensers, TGs and gearbox, but are traditionally supplied with cooling water, lubricating oil, hydraulic, and electric system connections. In the future, a reduction in the diversity of systems will be required, and novel concepts, such as vertical modules, may be considered.

The UK Industry Affordability Team has recommended a concept of this nature, with full electric propulsion as the most affordable solution. Division of the submarine into functional vertical modules can allow greater competition for modules and more work on module production to be done outside of the shipyard, with a consequent reduction in cost.

In keeping with trends in surface ships and the Merchant Navy, a higher degree of automation and remote monitoring will be required for future SSNs. The propulsion system will be controlled by a ship-wide Platform Management System (PMS) which will also provide vital support functions such as trending, condition monitoring, and onboard training. This could allow the machinery spaces to be normally unmanned and the Engineering Control Centre (ECC) to be positioned forward of the Reactor Compartment (RC), provided remote surveillance systems can provide adequate detection of hazards such as fire, flood and steam leaks.

The efficiency of platform and propulsion systems will need to be maximised in the era of whole submarine life cores. This process requires an understanding of all of the consumption demands from propulsion, ship services and combat systems, and the effect of those demands on the reactor plant. Efficiency can be modelled using bespoke simulation tools that can predict the implications to core life of any adjustment to equipment or system efficiency. A simplified system efficiency model for Full Electric Propulsion is shown at Figure 4.

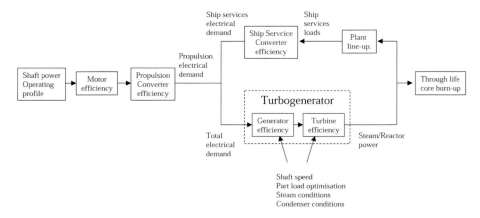

FIGURE 4 – FEP EFFICIENCY MODEL

LINKS TO SURFACE SHIP DEVELOPMENTS

The UK and the US, amongst others, have been developing and demonstrating electric ship technologies that could benefit future SSNs. In addition to the permanent magnet motors and power electronics mentioned previously, advanced induction motors have been developed by ALSTOM. These are larger and heavier than permanent magnet motors, but are claimed to offer a cost benefit for surface ships. The UK Electric Ship Technology Demonstrator (ESTD) programme is also addressing AC and DC distribution system technologies at higher voltages than traditionally used. The use of a DC distribution system in an SSN may offer superior efficiency and flexibility in power conversion, although the future development of compact AC/DC conversion technology, such as Matrix Converters, would provide an interesting option.

With electric propulsion systems selected for the replacement Landing Platform Dock (LPD), Auxiliary Oiler (AO) and Type 45 Destroyer, and likely for the future carrier CV(F), the trend in surface ship propulsion is clear.

COST EFFECTIVENESS

The nuclear cost of ownership is a major commitment for any Navy and an ageing fleet of nuclear submarines can be expensive to maintain. It is the duty of the designer to consider the legacy that he will leave for future generations and to design for reduced life cycle cost.

One of the main cost drivers is the cost of the crew and support staff required to keep a nuclear submarine in a serviceable condition. Future SSNs will need to be designed for both reduced maintenance and higher availability than has been achieved previously. Long maintenance periods and refits may be replaced with more cost-effective running maintenance periods and future propulsion systems will need to be capable of lasting the lifetime of the submarine without major intrusive maintenance.

Review of historical maintenance costs by the UK Industry Affordability Team has indicated that mechanical systems are a major cost driver through life. Investment Appraisals have consistently indicated that electric propulsion provides a significant reduction in operation and support costs. Provided that the necessary development programmes are completed successfully, it is clear that a 'lean-manned' SSN with electric propulsion and a high degree of automation will be the most cost-effective submarine of the future.

CONCLUSIONS

The SSN of the future is faced with a wider range of propulsion options than ever before. Developments in electric ship technologies, especially power electronics and power dense motors, now make electric propulsion a real option for the SSN, and developments in standby power sources provide much greater flexibility in the implementation of redundancy in the propulsion system. The drive for reduced costs is likely to lead to much greater use of automation and a reduction in crew sizes, with the unmanned aft end becoming standard.

32

Submarine Propulsion versus Capability

A.J. Donaldson

INTRODUCTION

The large and powerful fleet nuclear submarine (SSN) is very well suited to the task of sea control in the open ocean and is able to transit at high speed to a distant patrol area, or to escort surface shipping. Mobility, weapons payload, stealth, endurance and round-the-clock readiness are the characteristics that enable an SSN to dominate the area which it patrols.

The relatively small SSK (conventional submarine) is suitable for the littoral, sea denial, role because of its low acoustic, magnetic, thermal and wake signatures, and its low observability from the air. However, it is vulnerable to detection and attack when 'snorting' to recharge batteries.

A large SSK can achieve a transit speed of about 10 knots (surfaced or snorting), and would normally have lower mission endurance than an SSN. Even the largest SSKs would not normally be deployed over a range greater than 4,000 nautical miles. Mobility may be of low significance when a submarine is operating in the littoral, but it must first get there. The submarines best suited to a distant environment may be quite unsuitable for long range operations.

During the Cold War era, naval strategy emphasised objectives for which nuclear power was essential. The operational requirements of today demand incompatible attributes: the stealth and modest size of an SSK, but without the need to snort; and the transit speed of an SSN, but without jeopardy to the asset value of an SSN. These incompatible demands do not allow any easy compromises. However, this paper presents an assessment of the contributions that can be made by Air-Independent Propulsion (AIP) and by advanced batteries.

THE OPERATIONAL VALUE OF AIP

Non-nuclear AIP adds little to the value of a submarine in open water. In this environment of low ASW threat, the elimination of routine 'snorting' is not essential. Additional rechargeable battery capacity would be of greater benefit than the single-use AIP reserves.

AIP is of maximum benefit in the littoral, where elimination of the obligation to snort may be crucial to the feasibility of submarine operations. For medium and long-range missions, AIP re-supply constraints may detract from cost-effectiveness by reducing the ratio of time on station to transit time. A big battery may be more appropriate, with the submarine retreating a short distance from the patrol area, when snorting is necessary.

THE LEADING AIP OPTIONS

The only AIP system in service is the Stirling engine system of the Royal Swedish Navy (although it will soon be joined by the fuel cell system of the German Navy). The Stirling AIP system is seen to perform very well, but it requires a base of very sophisticated engineering technology and it incurs high maintenance costs.

The Hydride/Fuel Cell system will soon be entering service, and its operational characteristics are expected to be very good. However, it requires a technological base of fuel cells, power electronics and powder metallurgy. This is an expensive AIP option, although commercial electric vehicle developments may reduce the cost of such systems. The metal hydride system for hydrogen storage is very heavy, and system integration requires that weight should be saved, wherever possible, in the rest of the submarine.

The Argon Cycle Diesel has been demonstrated in the submarine U1, in the Baltic Sea. This is the lowest cost AIP system, based on commercial engines. There have been previous concepts of Closed-Cycle Diesel, but the Argon Cycle achieves much better performance and operating life.

The MESMA alcohol-fuelled steam turbine AIP system is being developed in France. In terms of system compactness and efficiency, it is inferior to the three systems listed above. The level of technology required is not so great as for the Stirling or fuel cell systems, and MESMA may claim particular suitability for tropical waters.

The combination of fuel cells with a methanol reformer is an AIP option which does not exist yet, but which may eventually be fitted to Canada's 'Victoria' Class (formerly 'Upholder' Class). The Reformer/Fuel Cell system is less compact than the Hydride/Fuel Cell system, but is the best solution when the rest of the submarine cannot provide enough buoyancy to support the weight of hydride cylinders for the endurance target.

ADVANCED RECHARGEABLE BATTERIES

Sodium/Nickel Chloride (ZEBRA) batteries, developed for the electric vehicle market, are becoming commercially available for terrestrial and marine purposes.[1] A commercial-scale factory is under construction, and production is due to begin in 2001. Technology demonstration and proving for the electric car application seems to have met all the major requirements for naval application.

With appropriate mounting and thermal management arrangements, in a typical submarine battery compartment, ZEBRA offers either a 55% weight saving (for the same energy storage) or the combination of 35% extra energy storage and a 40% weight saving (compared with lead-acid batteries). The operational value is greater than 35% extra endurance, in a conventional submarine. This is because normal operation would be intended to maintain some emergency reserve, say 30% of the lead-acid battery capacity, and the top 10-20% of lead-acid battery capacity may not be available because of the low charging rates allowed for completion of charge. A ZEBRA main battery, of nominally 35% extra capacity, could nearly double the energy available for planned use in low-speed patrolling or during snorting transit. The recharging times would be determined by Diesel-generator performance, not by battery limitations. High battery efficiency will also give some enhancement of performance during snorting transit.

In a nuclear submarine, the benefits offered are the safety value of the increased emergency reserves, and the elimination of routine battery maintenance. Operational effectiveness is not changed. In AIP submarines, reduced battery weight is a valuable offset against the weight of hydride storage systems for fuel cells. This opportunity for submarine integrated design may be crucial to the competitiveness of hydride/ fuel cell systems for high endurance requirements.

THE FUTURE OF NUCLEAR PROPULSION

Re-optimisation for tomorrow's operational requirements may take SSN evolution towards larger, higher performance submarines, to emphasise the long-range, rapid-response capability of individual submarines in a numerically reduced fleet. However, this is contrary to the popular expectation that cost constraints will apply to individual vessels, especially in navies that have numerically small fleets.

The large, general purpose SSN has evolved as a cost-effective application of nuclear propulsion for open water. The mission profiles which call for nuclear propulsion also determine the size of the submarine by demanding a large, mixed weapons load, highly capable sensors, integrated control systems, sophisticated communications and high levels of manpower for continual readiness. The nuclear propulsion system represents about a quarter of the total cost. This share of cost is reasonable, in view of the contribution which propulsion makes towards achievement of operational requirements.

THE IMPACT OF NEW TECHNOLOGIES

AIP offers increased capability to navies that have relatively short transit distances from a re-supply point to the patrol area. In relative terms, this is to the detriment of navies requiring longer range and open-water operation.

Advanced batteries are of significant benefit to SSK capability, at much lower cost than AIP. For non-nuclear navies with long-range and open-water requirements, this is more appropriate than AIP. Increased battery performance helps to maintain competitiveness against fleets that adopt AIP.

COST-EFFECTIVENESS AND THE MISSION

The operational envelope of submarine missions defines the submarine size and performance requirements. For example:

- The base-to-patrol transit distance defines both the transit speed and mission endurance requirements;
- The patrol objectives and the patrol area determine the speed required in submerged patrolling;
- The patrol environment determines the submerged endurance required. Under-ice operation does not permit snorting, and airborne surveillance greatly discourages snorting; and,
- The payload requirement is largely determined by the combination of transit distance, mission endurance, patrol objectives, patrol environment and anticipated opposition.

Most of the performance and size targets can be correlated with transit range and patrol area hazard. The patrol area hazard can be regarded as a continuous variable: very low in mid-ocean with minimal opposing presence; very high in confined shallow waters with hostile air cover; and higher still for under-ice patrols.

THE MISSION ENVELOPE DIAGRAM

If patrol area hazard and transit range are used as the axes of a graph, the mission envelope can be represented as an area on the hazard/range plot.[2] Such a plot shows small SSKs as appropriate for short-range patrols in medium threat waters. The largest SSKs are cost-effective over oceanic ranges (less effective than nuclear, but also less costly), and have improved suitability for open water.

Extended installations of advanced batteries offer enhanced ability to enter high-risk areas of hostile water, while slightly improving transit and open water performance. AIP allows a submarine to remain much longer in hostile water, but reduces cost-effectiveness for long-range and open-water patrols, because the AIP system is expensive baggage, when not in use.

The SSn concept represents an extreme downsizing of nuclear submarines, sacrificing speed to minimise cost, but retaining very long dived endurance. It appears good for short-range under-ice patrols, but would have to compete with lower-cost, non-nuclear options in all its other potential roles. Large nuclear submarines are cost-effective for long-range and under-ice patrols, and the new technologies have little impact on their roles.

COMPARISONS WITH REALITY

In my view, the Royal Navy has long-range and under-ice operational requirements that can only be met by a nuclear submarine fleet. Within the context of a nuclear fleet, the new technologies offer greater reserves of emergency power and perhaps cleaner alternatives to Diesels (for in-port power).

In contrast, consider the case of a nation with its naval interests concentrated on the Baltic and the North Sea. Sweden's 'Gotland' Class and Germany's Type-212 submarines are both in the category of AIP submarine, which seems ideal.

Canada and Australia are nations of very great geographical extent, both with interests in two or three oceans. In each case, there is a requirement for submarines of long range, but not necessarily global range. The Canadian requirement is dominated by Canada's Arctic territories where under-ice operation is obviously important. This is consistent with Canadian development of fuel cell AIP and also with previous Canadian interest in nuclear submarine options (both SSN and SSn). The operational effectiveness of the 'Victoria' Class would clearly be enhanced by either advanced batteries or AIP, and the combination of both is most attractive. It is noted that the weight saved by adoption of advanced batteries might facilitate adoption of a Hydride/Fuel Cell AIP system at lower cost than the presently favoured Methanol Reformer/Fuel Cell system.

In contrast, Australia has decided against AIP, and this study supports the view that AIP would not be cost-effective because of the long transit distances. Rather, it should be recognised that good transit performance and good battery endurance in low-speed patrol were major considerations, when the 'Collins' Class was chosen. Refitting with ZEBRA batteries would maximise the advantages for which the class was selected.

CONCLUSIONS

Changing world politics have reduced the number of nuclear submarines required for their principal operational role. At the same time, new battery and non-nuclear AIP technologies have emerged. These offer affordable operational capabilities which non-nuclear submarines have not possessed before.

It is a finding of this study that the new option of an AIP submarine has very little application to the present role of nuclear submarines. The AIP submarine has a distinct role of its own and is not a simple answer to the conflicting attributes required for rapid deployment and for operation in the littoral.

Advanced batteries will maintain the effectiveness of conventional submarines (without AIP). In some cases, the advanced batteries will facilitate integration of AIP (especially hydride/fuel cell AIP) into the submarine propulsion system. For nuclear submarines, the benefits of advanced batteries will be increased reserves of emergency power, increased electrical distribution integrity, and elimination of routine battery testing.

The operational benefits of nuclear, AIP and Diesel-electric options have been assessed against the requirements of different navies in general, and have been compared with the decisions of some identified navies. It is concluded that existing nuclear navies will continue to require nuclear submarines, although in reduced numbers. The non-nuclear AIP submarines are proving attractive to navies with short-range operational requirements, but are less suitable for medium and long-range operations. Non-AIP diesel-electric submarines will continue to have a role, and their competitiveness will be increased by advanced batteries.

NOTES

1   R C Galloway, S Haslam. "The ZEBRA Electric Vehicle Battery: Power and Energy Improvements". *Journal of Power Sources* 80, 1999. pp 164-170.
2   A J Donaldson. "Submarine Propulsion and Operational Effectiveness". *Warship '99, Naval Submarines 6*, RINA, paper 16.

PART VI

FUTURE SUBMARINE & UNDERWATER TECHNOLOGIES

33

US Submarine Joint Strategic Concepts for the 21st Century: Future Undersea Technology

Charles Young

INTRODUCTION

I would like to start by introducing the US Navy's Vision for the Submarine Force which is called the 'Submarine Joint Strategic Concepts for the 21st Century'. Before doing so, I shall begin by explaining what 'Submarine Joint Strategic Concepts' really means to the United States Navy's submarine forces. This will be followed with a few words about the US Submarine Future Studies Group and what it predicts will be the tasking order for submarines by the year 2020.

The US Navy has accomplished a few things in the past few years which are on track with our vision for the future; but it is a vision that is being charted with a well-thought plan. That is the Submarine Forces' 'roadmap'.

SUBMARINE JOINT STRATEGIC CONCEPTS

The US Navy's submarine force has defined its path to the future, the goal being defined in terms of the following four concepts:

- Gain and sustain access for the battleforce;
- Develop and share knowledge;
- Project power with surprise from close-in;
- Deter and counter Weapons of Mass Destruction.

First of all, it is important to understand that submarines have *access*. Most believe that there will be access challenges in the future. Many realise that there are access challenges today. Submarines can get into the area of interest - whether it is militarily or politically denied - and set the stage - prepare the battlespace - for follow-on forces. It can sustain a presence there and be part of the team to protect other US forces. Once there, it can collect the information necessary to develop and share *knowledge*, the second concept. Knowledge is a critical enabler for all military operations and crucial to the nation's peacetime efforts. Should the situation develop, US submarines can *project power*: missiles, torpedoes, special forces, offensive information warfare, bring a unique ability to get close to shore and attack with surprise. Finally, the most challenging and insidious threat that all states face is the use of Weapons of Mass Destruction. With the submarine's inherent access capability, and through specialised applications of developing knowledge and projecting power, submarines can be a key contributor in solving this growing threat.

THE SUBMARINE FUTURE STUDIES GROUP (FSG)

The Submarine Future Studies Group was chartered in 1998 by N87, then Vice Admiral Giambastiani. Its charter was to develop future concepts with the emphasis on revolutionary capability. It was designed to provide needed focus to industry, DARPA, ONR, and government laboratories to enable them to invest in the technologies that will provide military capability from under the sea and which will be needed in the 21st Century. The strength in the FSG lies in its small size, its access closeness to the Submarine Force leadership, and the ability to communicate their thoughts and ideas.

There have been three significant efforts that the FSG has undertaken. First, the FSG has developed concept statements of which the first two are focused on Intelligence, Surveillance, Renaissance (ISR) and Payloads. Second, is an effort to engage junior officers (JO) and get their innovative ideas on where the Submarine Force should be in the future. These JO innovation efforts are important as they generate tremendous ideas for both the near term and far term. This is an important effort. The US Navy's vision of the future will challenge the innovation, dedication, and proficiency of sailors in new and exciting ways. Finally, the third effort in the FSG has been the Submarine Force Vision, namely the formulation of the Submarine Joint Strategic Concepts on which the remainder of this paper is focused.

The FSG holds Junior Officer innovation seminars that receive new ideas from a new generation. These JOs are telling the Navy FSG what they are interested in:

- Quality of work: the better matching of the machines and systems to the knowledge and skill of future operators;
- New weapons: lethal, non-lethal, and their effectiveness against what are perceived to be the future threats. There is a feeling that the current weapons development program is stagnant;
- Thinking Machines: significant decision support improvements are required throughout the ship. Current control panels and displays are not intuitive and, in the case of combat systems, they are user-hostile;
- Information Management: grocery stores have used laser bar code scanners and local area networks for almost two decades, while submariners struggle to embrace these systems.

Paperwork reduction should be a rigorous goal to force and measure improvements. Similarly, individual communications capabilities are essential, allowing instant communications between 'watchstanders'. The USN needs to follow the commercial model.

THE FSG CONCEPT STATEMENTS

As noted above, the first area where the FSG has applied considerable effort is in concept statements, two in particular:

- Payloads – which is the follow-up to the Defence Science Board Task Force on the Submarine of the Future with a focus on payload flexibility capacity;
- ISR – a revolutionary new sensing capability with evolution of technology, especially with offboard vehicles and sensors.

An extension of these FSG Concept Statements is the Submarine Joint Strategic Concepts. Here, the original work was conducted for the DARPA Submarine

Payloads and Sensors Program and was aimed at providing a strategic focus for a 2020 time frame. The Submarine Force leadership has endorsed the Submarine Joint Strategic Concepts. These programmes are central to the submarine force vision for the future. Serendipitously enough, year 2000 being the US Submarine Service's centennial year only adds emphasis to the value of establishing a new baseline focus.

THE PATH TO THE FUTURE

The goal of the USN Submarine Force's efforts is to map out an investment strategy to position the US as a relevant element of the joint force for an uncertain future. The future is considered to be the 2020 time frame, which is very much consistent with many of the Navy and Joint Staff's long-term plans. However, to develop an investment strategy for the long term it is necessary first to define what capabilities are needed for the 2020 time frame. To define these capabilities it must be understood what submarines will do in the 2020 time frame, and, to do that, there must be a strategic vision for future submarine operations. That is where the Submarine Joint Strategic Concepts come into play; they set the framework for the future of which all US Navy submarine efforts are based. The ultimate goal of this 'process' is to define the technology 'roadmap' that will provide the Submarine Force with the capabilities they will need in 2020.

The way the problem was approached was through an Alternative Future World Study, which is a credible methodology. A study 'team' was established that consisted of senior submariners with significant operational experience and non-submariners who would provide a broad view of naval operations, as well as other independent reviewers. A top-down, capabilities-based approach was used. The 'Alternative Worlds' are broad in context but were chosen to circumscribe the vector of an uncertain future and were consistent with those used by the National Defence Panel.

In this process it was found that the common challenges of the alternative worlds that will probably be faced in the 2020 time frame have five basic characteristics:

- There will be a proliferation of weapons of mass destruction;
- Access challenges will exist;
- Quiet, long endurance coastal submarines will be the adversary's primary opponent;
- Competition for information advantage in cyberspace will proliferate; and
- Littoral operations will dominate the area in which we US submarines will operate.

The Alternative Futures Process started by defining a set of candidate submarine tasks that were examined across these future worlds. These candidate submarine tasks were based on history, from evolving strategy and a review of forward-looking assessments of defence needs. It is important to note that submarine tasks were formulated by the efforts of experienced submariners and other military officers who had significant current and past knowledge of submarine and naval operations.

Using the four alternative future worlds discussed above, three matrices were built, all with respect to these alternative worlds. The first matrix examined common world characteristics, such as economic, transnational challenges, WMD proliferation, ethnic rivalries, US influence, and the level of challenge they presented to the US The second matrix examined the importance of the elements of national strategy, the elements and rules of engagement, homeland defence, countering asymmetric threats, and regional conflicts. And the third matrix examined the importance of the elements of the naval maritime concept that supports US military strategy, such as forward presence, knowledge superiority, battlespace knowledge, and battlespace attack, control, and sustainment.

Based on the information from each of the matrices, the relative importance of candidate submarine tasks in each world were evaluated, both in a naval as well as a national context. The relative importance of each of the candidate tasks was then determined, using an evaluation across the worlds. This provided a representative set of tasks that took into account future uncertainty.

It is important to realise that the alternative future worlds analysis was conducted within a national and joint context and submarine contributions were assumed to both the joint and naval operations. The evaluation was then taken one step further – the 'list' of the highest priority submarine tasks for the future was reviewed and the common operational themes identified. These common operational themes are the Submarine Joint Strategic Concepts.

SUBMARINE JOINT STRATEGIC CONCEPTS

As mentioned earlier, these strategic concepts set the vision for the future. The Submarine Joint Strategic Concepts are:

- Gain and Sustain Battleforce Access for Joint and Naval battleforces;
- Develop and Share Knowledge netted with Joint and Naval Forces;
- Project Power with Surprise from Close-in complementing fires from other forces;
- Deter and Counter Weapons of Mass Destruction as an element of Joint Forces.

Vice Admiral Cebrowski wrote a very interesting article in the November 1999 issue of the *United States Naval Institute Proceedings*. In it, the Admiral articulated the need to rebalance the Navy after next, and to be assured there are adequate forces for access, as well as power projection. He stated that access and power projection defined relevance for future operations. Within the context of US strategic concepts, access, knowledge, and power projection define relevance for the Submarine Force of the future. The submarine's ability to gain access enables it to gain and share knowledge, gain access for the battleforce, project power, and impact the efforts against weapons of mass destruction as a unique and complementary element of the US Navy's joint and naval forces. Finally, these concepts apply across the spectrum of operations and not just during conflict.

That sets the context for the future, as defined by the Submarine Joint Strategic Concepts. During that process, representative submarine tasks were defined. The FSG started with approximately 50 candidate submarine tasks for the alternative futures analysis. The assessment and analysis of those tasks resulted in 25 representative submarine tasks for the year 2020. This was not a prescriptive list, but a representative list. The next step was to operationalise the list, so the war fighters became involved and contributed their input to this list of submarine tasks for 2020. As part of the Strategic Concepts Working Groups, the TYCOMS reviewed the analysis and looked at the tasks in an operational context. The result was a list of 23 submarine tasks for 2020.

HIGH PRIORITY TASKS FOR 2020

The highest priority submarine tasks for 2020 are as follows:

- Clandestine ISRT
- SOF Operations
- Mine Reconnaissance
- Underwater Mapping
- Littoral ASUW
- Theater ASW
- Attack Against Hard or Deeply Buried Targets
- Rapid Attack against Time Critical Targets
- Strategic Deterrence
- Forward Presence
- Information Operations
- Forward Engagement
- Suppression of Enemy Coastal Defenses
- Theater Nuclear Deterrence
- Tactical Reconnaissance and Targeting
- Combat Situational Awareness
- Attack against Nodal targets (with high volume, if required)
- Interdiction Operations
- Theater Network Reconstitution
- Covert Neutralization of Mines
- Theater Ballistic Missile Defense
- Arctic Operations
- Extended Mobility Operations

These build upon the existing capabilities of today's US Submarine Force, and represent the tasks where submarines can provide a compelling contribution to joint and naval forces across the spectrum of operations and within the context of the Joint Strategic Concepts. Significant war fighter involvement was used in the development of this list.

WHY SUBMARINES?

The question then is why do submarines need to do those tasks? In other words, what is the compelling reason for submarines to have the capabilities to execute these tasks? The answer to that question is, first of all, *unalerted* presence. Submarines exploit surprise. For example, it allows SOF employment for maximum effect; it also defeats the adversaries' denial and deception tactics; opponents know when satellite coverage is not available but the submarine can defeat this today and it can defeat it in the future.

Second, the submarine is *"First in and last out"*; stealth enables access and staying power. Not only do submarines have access, but they also can enable access for the battleforce and help sustain access. Submarine collection contributes to determining adversary operating patterns and intent and creates uncertainty in the mind of the enemy.

Third, *24/7 coverage*: this is the submarine's long dwell time. Combined with vast sensor reach, it will provide the capability to stay on station 24-hours a day, 7-days a week, independent of the weather. And fourth, the submarine permits *close in, on scene operations*. Being close enables US forces to be responsive and to manoeuvre the deployed sensor net, which are called expeditionary sensors. It also enables quick response or pre-emptive fires with surprise, thereby producing maximum effect. The ability to be close in provides the opportunity to collect information that is not available using other sources. With these attributes, submarines provide the Joint Force commander with a range of options.

FUTURE CAPABILITIES

The next step in the Path to the Future is to define the desired 2020 capabilities. A TYCOM Working Group conducted a representative set of end-to-end assessments of the submarine tasks, which resulted in a long list of desired capabilities.

This extensive list of capabilities and their associated tasks can be rolled up and three overarching 'capability themes' identified. First, extended reach through offboard vehicles and distributed sensors; second, being 'fully netted' to national and theatre of command networks is absolutely crucial and something that the type commander working group insisted is a prerequisite to operations in the future; and third, greater adaptability through modularity. That is a theme that will be explored in more detail below.

The US Navy now has its strategic vision embodied in the Submarine Force strategic concepts and has an idea how submarines will execute that vision, the submarine tasks for the 2020, and the desired capabilities to execute those tasks.

TECHNOLOGY ROADMAP

Next it is necessary to look hard at the technologies that will be needed to execute this vision and to define the investment plan in preparation for the future. Only recently, the Navy reorganised the submarine technology management system to take advantage of this particular construct. The goal of the submarine technology (SUBTECH) management system is to develop technology roadmaps and an investment strategy that will achieve the required 2020 capabilities.

This is a revolutionary approach and the US Navy and its Future Submarine Studies Group is proposing to do things quite differently from what it does today. We see five major areas of technology that are important in this revolution. The first one, and one of the most important, is the whole idea of *getting off board*. This involves getting sensors in the water, on the bottom, on the sea, on the surface, on the land, but away from the submarine. Why do we want to do this? Because it gives us more coverage of an order of magnitude in the Intelligence, Surveillance, Reconnaissance, and Targeting (ISRT) arena. It allows us to use sensors that are quite different from today.

Today, we talk about signals intelligence (SIGINT) and visual sensors, but for the future we also talk about acoustics, vibration sensors, and perhaps chemical and biological sensors for weapons of mass destruction (WMD). The idea of this sensor network is that it is covert - it defeats enemy efforts of denial and deception against our satellites and against today's other assets that they can see and avoid. We believe that in the future this sensor capability will lend itself to targeting. The whole idea is that this sensor network can be used not only to provide information about what is going on, but also to provide localisation information for follow-on targeting, either from follow-on forces or ourselves.

The next revolution is *off-board vehicles* - the way we buy extended reach with the sensors is to put them on vehicles that swim, that fly, and that walk on the ground to get them off and away from the submarine. Doing this covertly with a wide range of payloads enhances the stealth of the submarine. Submarines do not have to operate close to shore and at periscope depth in order to make these things possible. When there is need of a man in the loop for high priority missions such as when someone is needed on the ground, there is the Advanced SEAL Delivery System and the SOF forces.

The third area needed to make all this work, is the need for dramatic *improvements in processing* back on the submarine. The submarine has to be able to monitor the networks that have been deployed; it needs to react to the information that comes from them; it needs to move the sensors around when necessary to cover the right areas; and it needs to do this in near real-time. It is typical today that submarine commanders do not see the results of ISR for months after the fact. In this vision submarines will have to react in seconds, and minutes, and provide the information back to follow-on forces. Not all the processing will be done onboard, but there should be enough to send the relevant nuggets back to the follow-on forces. All of these things are also available to the follow-on forces when they arrive, particularly the ground sensor network.

The fourth area is *connectivity*. As Rear Admiral John Padgett is fond of saying, "submarines don't have a connectivity problem...they have a stealth problem". The issue is how to get high data rate connectivity while maintaining stealth for a long period of time. Concepts such as a high bandwidth fibre optic cable link with a remote surface buoy that can communicate at high data rates back to the joint forces are potential solutions to this problem.

In addition to communicating with other forces, submarines have to communicate with the sensor network. The combination of advanced microcomputer technology, wide bandwidth, and low-power-hard-to-detect RF communications systems, and then, perhaps, connecting fibre optic networks under the sea provide a potential solution to this conundrum.

The final area is *payload* – submarines need more volume, and more flexibility in that payload. Not everything is going to be sent out of a 21-inch tube. Miniaturisation is going to help expand the capacity of the payload and a big piece of this is *adaptability*.

The submarine itself is going to be adaptable with payloads installed in a matter of hours or days using the modularity concepts. Of more significance, the whole force will be extremely adaptable at the theatre level to do the missions that it is tasked to do. The weapons carried can be of a much wider variety than is talked about today: for example with potential to neutralise mines, not just to detect them but be able to counter them; to attack swarms of small surface craft with small weapons; and to take out coastal defences.

All these things that are being talked about are challenges and are clearly revolutionary capabilities and technologies. However, what impressed the FSG when it looked at this list is that all of these things build on the strengths that already exist in the Submarine Force or that American commercial technology is already developing. Small, powerful computers, miniaturisation, electronics, communications ... all these things are heading in that direction, which is the right direction to go.

THE HUMAN RESOURCES REVOLUTION

The future lies not just in technology. A corresponding revolution in the way the US Navy's human resources onboard are used. The strategic concepts, by their nature, are demanding increasing levels of effort onboard the submarine, controlling all these off-board vehicles, monitoring and placing all these sensors, and managing significantly increased data throughput back into the hull. This has to be accomplished without arbitrarily increasing the number of people carried onboard and, more importantly, not overloading the sailors already there. Some of this is technological, and computers and automation will be of help.

More importantly, the US Navy needs to take to heart the kinds of things that Secretary Danzig is saying and aggressively remove barriers to improve the quality of work. It is not a "nice to have" matter but one that is essential to meet the missions in the future. One source of leverage here is the traditions of the Submarine Force: the technical proficiency of its people, their ability to innovate, and their personal initiative. These qualities are going to be critical in the future.

STRATEGIC CONCEPTS WORKING GROUPS

Having outlined a vision, it would be great if the Groups' proposals could be submitted to the POM and get funded. This of course will not work. So, the question is; how can this long-range vision be moulded back into budget submits, to acquisition plans, etc. The FSG is now starting to do just that... the Future Studies Group delegated the task to four strategic concepts working groups.

- The first group comprised of fleet representatives that looked at submarine tasks and capabilities;
- a second group looked at the submarine platform;
- a third group looked at the off-board concept - sensors, vehicles, and communications;
- and a last working group assessed submarine effects (weapons).

These reviews are being conducted over the short-term, in parallel with the DARPA-Navy Payloads and Sensors Program. The Payload and Sensors program efforts are at a time when most of what they working on is proprietary. The FSG is trying to set the umbrella in place now to be able to pick up what emerged from those efforts. These groups are small groups staffed by members of industry, industry, government and the Fleet. The Fleet's involvement here has been critically important to the process. The four groups have been validating what has been done to date with the strategic concepts and submarine tasks and will then validate their technological feasibility.

The intention was not to set up a new process; these groups were disbanded after several months and turned over their results to the Navy's existing Submarine Technology process. Supporting this, the entire SUBTECH process has been realigned to match the strategic concepts, and the DARPA-Navy consortia has been asked to become part of that SUBTECH planning process. The objective is to meld together the things that are going on within the processes today.

In the first group, that of submarine tasks, there was a heavy involvement from the Fleet, from both SUBLANT and SUBPAC. They reviewed, in detail, the strategic concepts and the submarine task list. They validated these, modified them slightly, and produced an extensive list of the desired capabilities for 2020 that the Fleet has identified as needed for the future to execute the strategic concepts and submarine tasks. A critical element identified by the TYCOMS is *adaptability*. The concept of adaptability through modularity is very important.

This adaptability concept is enabled by modularity on the submarine. The platform group has looked at this and there are two areas where they have focused. One, is what is called 'payload modules'. This is just an example and has not been through an extensive design effort. The idea is that fairly large payloads can be of different types and rapidly deployable. The vision is that these modules can be installed and removed from a submarine, while forward deployed, to completely reconfigure its payload. The intention is that the modules would be extremely flexible in their interface with the ocean and that they might be interchangeable with other forces, such as surface ships.

The group also identified 'platform modularity' as an important aspect of the future. The idea here is that the submarine itself would be made up of modules. When major changes to one of these modules was required, instead of laying the ship up in a major overhaul for years, a section of the boat could be cut out and replaced, perhaps, in a matter of months. This is thought to be a key for where US Navy Submarines might go in the future and such concepts as an all-electric ship will be an important enabler that will allow this to be done.

So what does the modular submarine have to offer? No longer would every submarine have to be able to do every mission all the time; instead, there would be the capability to change individual modules as part of an overall strategy for how we outfit the force to meet the missions at that particular time.

The group looking at off-board sensors looked at whether or not these concepts are really feasible. For example, in terms of off-board sensors, the expectation is that in 15-20 years submarines could deploy with something the size of a cell phone, with a sensor capability, a communications capability, and a lifetime duration in the order of months.

They then looked at an on-going unmanned aerial vehicle (UAV) program and in particular a DARPA LOCAS vehicle. This costs about $50,000 to build and with its current design it could deploy about 40 of these types of sensors. While the vehicle duration is a relatively short one, the duration of the sensors is very long and aligns with the concepts that are under discussion.

Next they considered communications. This group looked at the feasibility of whether or not a submarine can carry and lay small fibre optic cables to establish links back to the joint forces: buoys to talk to the land based sensors; underwater connectivity to these links; and RF links in the air. The group concluded that these are feasible with the types of technology that are coming out today. Again, it was concluded that near-term technologies are supportive of the long-term vision.

The weapons, or effects, group looked at how submarine-carried weapons can contribute to joint operations. A key driver for submarine 'fires' is what is called 'non-provocative dwell'. The idea is that weapons are brought to augment - not supplant - joint forces that the enemy does not see and therefore does not react to. Submarines can fire from close in and with great surprise.

This group has conducted some first order analysis through war gaming. What they see is the US having the potential to blunt the enemy early as they start to conduct operations and that this could effectively shorten any war. They have concluded that submarines would be significant players in joint fires with this capability. The group also looked at weapons to defend against swarms of small craft and at possible weapons to neutralise mines covertly. They have also begun to look at what can be done to counter weapons of mass destruction.

CONCLUSION

The first notion I want to conclude with is that off-board vehicles and sensors are the key. They are at the heart of the strategic concepts to extend the reach of submarines. Connectivity is critical. It is not just important; it is absolutely required for both connectivity back to the joint forces as well as to the Navy's networks. And finally, modularity is also really crucial in the platform in order to provide the adaptability needed across the force. The FSG believes that this is feasible and sees no showstoppers from on-going technology work today.

THE ROADMAP TO THE FUTURE

The US Navy Submarine Service has been developing the SUBTECH process for a number of few years. It is very pleased with that process and how it has been working, particularly in its interaction with the R&D and the S&T communities. But it has been primarily focused on the POM today.

The vision for the future has been set by the FSG and endorsed by Submarine Force leadership for the 2020 time frame. The challenge is how to tie those two things together. The Group is looking at, and having some success in coupling across from, the POM to the vision for 2020. In the Future Naval Capabilities process it has been successful in getting funding for unmanned underwater vehicles (UUVs) and also in securing funding from the ASN Chief Technology Officer to provide demonstrations of technologies such as hull and towed arrays, which we think are going to be critical in the future.

The buoyant cable antenna work with DARPA and the DARPA-Navy payloads and sensors program are all also critical. As mentioned above, the SUBTECH process has been realigned and now encompasses, and is reflective of, the joint strategic concepts. DARPA, ONR and the consortia are going to be members of that team in future.

SUBMARINE JOINT STRATEGIC CONCEPTS ... FOR THE 21ST CENTURY

The bottom line is...the US Submarine Force is excited about the future. Rest assured that the road to 2020 will be an interesting one. Thank you for inviting me to contribute to this volume, and congratulations to the Royal Navy's submarine forces - a century of progress and co-operation. The United States Navy salutes you.

Notes on Contributors

Capitaine de Vaisseau Jean-Pierre Barbier joined the French Submarine Service in 1974. Since August 1999, he has commanded the French nuclear attack Flotilla and is Chief of Staff to the Admiral commanding the French Submarine Forces and the Strategic Oceanic Force.

Sir Michael Boyce, GCB, OBE was promoted First Sea Lord in 1998. A submariner since 1965, he has commanded both conventional, nuclear attack submarines and surface ASW frigate. He was knighted in 1994, the year he assumed command of the NATO ASW strike force. In 1997, he was CinC Fleet, a command that combined with that of CinC Eastern Atlantic and Commander Allied Forces Northwestern Europe. From February 2001, he will assume the post of Chief of Defence Staff.

Commander Richard Compton-Hall RN (Retd) was Director of the Royal Navy's Submarine Museum from 1975-1994. He is author of numerous books on submarines, the most recent being *The Underwater Pioneers*.

Tony Donaldson joined the Rolls-Royce Group as a mathematician in 1970. After many years' experience working in nuclear engineering and steam system dynamics, he joined a team assessing alternative power technologies. His current interests include *inter alia* propulsion systems integration and university-based research on direct-methanol fuel cells.

Professor Martin Edmonds, PhD, is Director of the Centre for Defence and International Security Studies at Lancaster University and Editor-in-Chief of the international journal, *Defense Analysis*. A former MoD Lecturer in Higher Defence Studies, his research and numerous publications have concentrated on civil-military relations, UK defence and naval policy, and defence management.

Dr Norman Friedman is a consultant on technology and policy, and is based in New York City. A former Deputy Director Defence Studies at the Hudson Institute, he has acted as consultant to the Secretary of the Navy for ten years. He has written over 21 books, the vast majority of which are on naval matters.

Jock Gardner retired from the Royal Navy in 1994 after twenty year's service whereupon he joined the MoD Naval Historical Branch. Since 1988 he has devoted his time to research and publication, and authored *Anti-submarine Warfare*, a book in the Brassey's Sea Power series, published in 1996.

Dr Eric Grove is one of Britain's leading naval historians. Formerly Acting Director of the Centre for Security Studies at Hull University, he is now Senior Research Fellow at the MoD Naval Historical Branch. His numerous publications on naval subjects include *Vanguard to Trident: British Naval Policy since 1945* and, with Capt Peter Hore, *The Dimensions of Sea Power*.

Derek Hacker is the Future Attack Submarine Manager at Rolls-Royce Marine where he is responsible for the development of submarine propulsion systems and technologies for future classes of submarine. He joined Rolls-Royce in 1997, having previously worked in the MoD where he worked on both the 'Vanguard' and 'Astute' programmes.

Commander Nick Harrap, OBE, RN joined the Royal Navy in 1976, becoming a submariner in 1979. He qualified as a submarine commander in 1989 and subsequently commanded the diesel-electric submarine HMS UPHOLDER and after a spell at the Joint Services' Staff College, the nuclear attack submarine, HMS SPARTAN. Since 1999, he has been on the staff of FOSM at Northwood as Staff Warfare Officer, a post that also carries with it UK Operational Co-ordinator of Submarine Rescue forces.

Professor Keith Hartley PhD, with Martin Edmonds, is Co-Director of the Lancaster and York Defence Research Institute. He is also Director of the York University Centre for Defence Economics and Editor of *Defence and Peace Economics*. He has a long publishing record that includes *The Economics of Defence*, and *the Political Economy of NATO*. He was advisor to the House of Commons Defence Committee 1985-97 and works frequently with the European Commission, the MoD and the DTI.

Commander Peter T. Haydon, RCN (Retd) edits *Maritime Affairs* and is Senior Research Fellow at the Centre for Foreign Policy Studies at Dalhousie University, Nova Scotia. A former career officer in the Canadian Navy, where he served on both submarines and destroyers, he lectures and writes on Canadian defence policy, his most recent book being *The 1962 Cuban Missile Crisis: Canadian Involvement Reconsidered.*

Captain Peter Hore RN (Retd) retired from the Royal Navy in January 2000, his last appointment being that of Head of Defence Studies. Whilst in that post he founded the Navy's Maritime Strategic Studies Institute. He has published widely on naval matters, both policy-related and historical. Among his recent publications is *Maritime Aviation* (with T Hirschfeld) and *Dimensions of Sea Power* (With Eric Grove)

Rear Admiral Anthony N. Howell graduated from the South African Naval Academy in 1968 and became communications officer on the country's first submarine, SAS MARIA VAN RIEBEEK, a boat he later commanded as his last sea-going appointment. From 1986, he was involved in Naval Training subsequently being promoted Chief of Naval Plans and, later, Director Naval Acquisition. He is currently Chief Director, Maritime Warfare.

Captain 1st Rank Igor Kosyr (Retd) is Doctor of Technical Science in Applied Oceanography. From a naval (submariner) family, he graduated from the Soviet Naval College in 1974 and then the Naval Academy in 1984. Specialising in electronic warfare, he took part in eight patrols with the Russian Submarine Service. Most of his shore-based work was in the Navigation and Hydrography Institute. He is currently Liaison Officer of the Submariners Club in St Petersburg and Secretary of the Arctic Allied Convoy Veterans' Association.

Commander Solveig Krey has the unique distinction of becoming the world's first ever woman submarine commander. She graduated in electronics from the Norwegian Navy's Officer Training School in 1985 and joined the Submarine Service in 1989. On completing her 'Perisher' course in 1995, she has since commanded two submarines. She is currently on the Naval Staff in the HQ, Defence Command.

Terry Lindell has been researching torpedoes and fire control for the past eleven years, an interest that has focused on international developments in mechanical analogue computing. An active volunteer in the historic ships community, he has been involved in the restoration of the USS PAMPATINO (SS-383) to operating condition. He currently owns a computer engineering firm, along with two other companies.

Lt Cdr Malcolm Llewellyn-Jones, MBE, RN (Retd) served in the Royal Navy for 27 years where he commanded a front-line anti-submarine helicopter squadron. He retired in 1996 to take up an academic career. He has since completed a Masters degree in War Studies at King's College, London, and is currently researching for a doctorate into Royal Navy anti-submarine warfare.

David Lowe is currently Project Manager, at BAE SYSTEMS Marine Ltd. for the 'Astute' Class submarine programme, the latest addition to the UK's submarine fleet. His career started as a student apprentice with Vickers Shipbuilding and Engineering Limited in 1977. During the past 23 years he has been involved in the design and build activities of all the major submarine programmes in the UK which have included 'Trafalgar', 'Upholder' and 'Vanguard' Class vessels.

Commodore Martin MacPherson, RN (Retd) joined the Submarine Service in 1965, serving initially in 'A' Class submarines. After 'Perisher', he commanded both diesel and nuclear powered submarines. As Commander, he was appointed 'Teacher' for the 'Perisher' course prior to commanding the first of Class, HMS TRAFALGAR. His last naval job was as Director Naval Operations. He is now MD of Landair International, a military computer modelling and simulation company.

Rear Admiral Raja Menon, (Retd) was a pioneer of submarines in the Indian Navy for which he was trained by and worked with the Royal Navy. He was directly involved with the acquisition of the Soviet 'Foxtrot' submarines for the Indian Navy and subsequently, as Head of the Technology Transfer Group, was responsible for the construction of the German designed submarines in India. He is Senior Research Fellow at the Institute for Defence Studies and Analysis and has authored *Maritime Strategy and Continental War* (1998) and *A Nuclear Strategy for India* (2000).

Captain Guillermo Montenegro, (Retd) left the Argentinean Navy in 1985, after 30 years' service. After qualifying as a submariner, he commanded two submarines and held several staff posts, including that of Chief of Staff of the Argentinean Submarine Group. He is currently a professor at the Naval College and at the University of Belgrano and has twice been visiting Professor at the US Naval War College.

Professor Bill Oliver works for BAE SYSTEMS Marine at Barrow and is the shipyard's Programme Director for the 'Astute' Submarine. He has been with the programme since the days of the Batch Two 'Trafalgar' Class bid. Prior to this, he spent twenty years in offshore engineering. Since 1993, he has been visiting Professor in Newcastle University's Department of Marine Technology. A Chartered Engineer, he is also a Fellow of the British Institute of Naval Architects.

Dr Declan O'Reilly's principal interests are in European economic development before 1945, with particular emphasis on Germany. He has researched extensively on technology transfer in the German chemical industry that formed the basis of his books, *Seize and Squander: General Aniline and Film Corporation and Americanising IG Farben in the USA*. He currently works in the Wellcome Unit at the University of East Anglia.

Jeff Owen is Head of Engineering with Strachan and Henshaw. He holds a degree in Maritime Technology, specialising in naval architecture, offshore engineering and environmental factors. As Head of Engineering, his responsibilities are, *inter alia*, the technical requirement of a number of concept studies, the propulsion design for torpedoes, the hydrodynamics design for underwater vehicles and feasibility of controlled deep mechanical sweeping.

Michael Owen started his engineering career with Jaguar cars before joining the Royal Navy Engineers' Service. He attended the RNC at Manadon and also the nuclear course at the RNC Greenwich. In the MoD, he has worked on both the Polaris and Trident programmes before finally becoming the Director responsible for 'Astute' submarine procurement. He joined Devonport Management Ltd in 1997 and is Director responsible for the Company's submarine business.

Antony Preston was Research Assistant at the Maritime Museum, Greenwich from 1966 until 1973. From 1973 until 1983, he was the first Editor of the journal *Defence*, whereupon he became the first Naval Editor of *Jane's Defence Weekly*. From 1989 until 1994, he edited the *Journal of Naval Forces*. Today, he is the Editor of *Warship*, a technical history annual. Broadcaster and lecturer, he contributes widely to overseas naval journals and is author of numerous books and articles on naval topics.

Captain Steve Ramm RN joined the Navy in 1972 and volunteered to be a submariner in 1976. Having served on five nuclear powered and conventional submarines, he completed his 'Perisher' course in 1985. He subsequently served on three more submarines, two as Commanding Officer. After a period as Staff Officer to the Commander Naval Staff in Washington DC, he joined the central staff in the MoD. He currently is Assistant Director responsible for equipment capability in the Underwater Battlespace.

Captain Bo Rask joined the Swedish Navy in 1971, transferring to the Submarine service in 1975. He served on three submarines prior to attending the Staff and War College in 1981-2. In 1983, he was on an exchange programme with the Royal Navy, serving on HMS OTUS. Two more submarine appointments followed before his first command in 1988. Staff work followed until his current appointment as Commanding Officer of the Swedish First Submarine Flotilla. Captain Rask is a member of the Royal Swedish Society of Naval Sciences.

Rear Admiral Rob Stevens became Flag Officer Submarines in 1998. Concurrent with the appointment are those of Chief of Staff (Operations) to CinC Fleet, Commander Submarine Forces East Atlantic, and Commander Submarine Force North. He joined the Navy in 1966 and has served on five submarines (two as

Captain) one aircraft carrier, and one minesweeper. In 1992, he then commanded a frigate as Captain 7th frigate squadron. Other appointments include that of 'Teacher' and as Head of the Royal Navy Presentation Team. In 1995, he was made Director Joint Warfare in the MoD responsible for joint planning, military elements of joint doctrine, information warfare and NBC defence.

Commander Jeff Tall, RN (Retd) is the Director of the Royal Navy Submarine Museum in Gosport, a post he has held since 1994. A submariner for 28 years, he has become something of a legend in the Submarine Service. He passed 'Perisher' in 1974 and over the next twenty years commanded four submarines, two diesel and two nuclear-powered. In the Falklands War he served as Admiral Woodward's submarine staff officer. An author, he has published (with Peter Kemp) *HM Submarines in Camera* and *The Snapping Turtle Guide to Submarines.*

Dr Lee Willett currently works at the Royal United Services Institute responsible for organising its lecture and conference programme. From 1997-2000, he was Leverhulme Research Fellow at the Hull University Centre for Security Studies. During this time he was seconded as Research Fellow on the RN's Defence Studies Staff, researching the future of the Navy's Submarine Service. His most recent publication is "The most important type of warship in the world: the RN Submarine Service and the Strategic Defence Review" in *Submarine Review*, Jan 2000

Harry Wyse joined the 'Astute' project as Integrated Logistic Support Director on the award of the contract in 1997. His responsibility was to establish a team and create the strategy and plans to ensure that 'design for support' principles applied consistently throughout the supply chain. Prior to this appointment, he had spent almost thirty years with Rolls-Royce Marine in submarine support, though admits also to having worked on world-wide leading cost reduction contracts in the oil and gas industry.

Rear Admiral Charles Young, USN is Deputy Commander for Undersea Technology at the US Naval Systems Command, Washington DC, and Commander, Naval Undersea Warfare Centre. He graduated from the Naval Academy, Annapolis, in 1970 and received his Master of Science degree from the University of Delaware. He has had six ship assignments two as Commanding Officer. Shore appointments have included a tour as Director of the Advanced Submarine Technology at DARPA.